SAFE HANDLING

of Chemical Carcinogens, Mutagens, Teratogens and Highly Toxic Substances

VOLUME 1

SAFE HANDLING
of Chemical Carcinogens, Mutagens, Teratogens and Highly Toxic Substances
VOLUME 1

edited by
DOUGLAS B. WALTERS
Technical Programs Manager/Chemistry Branch
National Institute of Environmental Health Sciences (USDHEW)
Research Triangle Park, North Carolina

ANN ARBOR SCIENCE
THE BUTTERWORTH GROUP

Second Printing, 1980
Third Printing, 1982

Library of Congress Catalog Card No. 79-88922
ISBN 0-250-40303-X

Butterworths, Ltd., Borough Green, Sevenoaks,
Kent TN15 8PH, England

PREFACE

The handling of chemicals associated with potential human health hazards is a complex and controversial problem. Various government agencies and private organizations are becoming increasingly concerned with the use of known and potential chemical carcinogens, mutagens, teratogens and highly toxic substances. A review of the regulations enacted or proposed during the last few years and the increasing numbers of chemicals found to be biologically harmful to humans indicate a trend toward tighter future control of these substances. It is imperative that future policies controlling potential carcinogens, mutagens and teratogens recognize the chemical significance of the problem and its relationship to environmental health concerns (i.e., use and discharge).

The assumption made in preparing this work is that these hazardous agents are first chemicals whose use requires interface with chemists to produce timely and effective solutions to usage problems. This necessitates a chemical understanding of all the hazardous agents used—those for which information is available and those about which little or nothing is known. Interaction of the chemists with life scientists, industrial hygienists and safety and health personnel, and engineering professionals is also necessary.

Effective control of potential carcinogens, mutagens and teratogens is difficult, if not impossible, by blanket regulations which cover research, industrial (manufacturing and processing), and academic (teaching) situations. Separate procedures are required for each instance. The emphasis of this book is on the control and use of hazardous agents in a research organization. Problems are often encountered by broad policies written to include all situations likely to occur in particular settings (e.g., private research laboratories). Control over the hazardous agents described herein requires facilities and procedures rigid enough for specific research demands, yet flexible enough to accommodate other research programs in the same discipline and be capable of meeting anticipated future needs with minimal restructuring. A chemical approach to this problem using a protocol system or similar method in conjunction with appropriately designed facilities for laboratories and disposal accomplishes this. Coupled with the necessary informational and personnel requirements a structured approach with flexibility for change is achieved. Although designed for research laboratories this approach could, with modification, be adapted for industrial and academic laboratories.

This book has its origin in the Hazardous Chemical Agent Use Protocol concept used for control of known and potentially known carcinogens, mutagens, teratogens and highly toxic substances at the National Institute of Environmental Health Sciences. This concept uses the information found in the six sections of these two volumes. The format is consistent with the logical sequence of events which should precede any planned experiment including potentially hazardous materials.

Section I concerns appropriate laboratory design, handling and management procedures for hazardous compounds. Packaging and transportation of these materials is also covered. The emphasis of this section is on use of the principles of containment and engineering controls for workers, laboratories and environmental protection. An overview of several representative facilities and programs, each with similar but differing needs, is presented.

A monitoring program is needed after designing a laboratory for hazardous chemicals and developing implementation controls and procedures. Section II deals with methods for chemical monitoring within the laboratory and in the environment external to the laboratory as well as personnel monitoring methodology. A medical surveillance program is also an important part of worker protection. Current medical monitoring often falls short of its intended goals. Close interaction of medical personnel with research and safety personnel is needed. Often serious damage is done by occupational exposure to hazardous agents before the effects of exposure are medically observed. Chemical detection of the causative agent or its metabolite is often impossible or very difficult. Several new medical techniques are presented which may have important future use.

Data on known hazardous agents often overlaps scientific discipline and is scarce and difficult to find. Several chapters in Section III deal with this topic. For experimental compounds about which little or nothing is known, an understanding of their chemical basis for biological activity is important. Some chapters in this section on classification illustrate organizational grouping procedures for categorizing chemicals by functionality, reaction and structure. Chemical classification usually takes place before structure-activity considerations begin.

Section IV leads from chemical classification to the use of structure activity for toxicity prediction. Although currently of limited specific potential, structure-activity predictions help indicate properties, mechanisms of interaction, reactions, hazards, and handling requirements which can be planned for in advance. It is often these physical-chemical properties which are determinants of chemical reactivity and stability which are so important in containing and disposing of chemicals.

The structure-activity approach to toxicity prediction has significant potential for future use. A powerful method which may be instrumental in solving many difficult chemical safety problems will be eliminated if this area is ignored.

Spill control, degradation, detoxification and deactivation are covered in Section V. A large void exists in the chemistry literature for safe and efficient methods for destroying or deactivating the hazardous compounds described here. This approach is difficult but must be considered in the future if we are to gain control over the proper disposal of research chemical wastes.

Section VI discusses disposal methods for hazardous chemicals. The emphasis is on incineration since this method currently has the best potential for solving the problem. Landfill is not considered a permanent solution. The need for appropriate monitoring of incinerator stack effluents for detection of hazardous chemicals from a specific chemical analysis viewpoint rather than general emission criteria is also discussed.

The chapters in this work were contributed by many authors and represent an extensive cross section of knowledge on the safe handling of chemical carcinogens, mutagens, teratogens and highly toxic substances. A few years ago a work of this nature would have been very difficult to write because of the scant knowledge available and lack of concern toward safe chemistry. Current research trends are indicating a change which should greatly increase our knowledge in this area in the next five or ten years.

With the exception of chapters 4, 5 and 24, the material herein was derived from the symposium program "Safe Handling of Chemical Carcinogens, Mutagens and Teratogens—The Chemist's Viewpoint" at the American Chemical Society/Chemical Society of Japan Chemical Congress, Honolulu, Hawaii, in April 1979.

Hopefully, this work will encourage chemists to be more responsive in informing the general scientific community and the public about aspects of their work which bear directly on safe handling of chemicals. The chemist has an excellent opportunity now to make important and long-lasting contributions in this area which can extend a great deal beyond the research laboratory setting.

I wish to thank Dr. James D. McKinney, Chief, Environmental Chemistry Branch, National Institute of Environmental Health Sciences, for the helpful advice, valued criticism and suggestions he provided. I am deeply appreciative to my wife, Carole Lowe Walters, for her time, assistance and patience in bringing this task to fruition.

Douglas B. Walters

Douglas B. Walters, a research chemist at the National Institute of Environmental Health Sciences (USDHEW) in Research Triangle Park, North Carolina, is the former chief of the NIEHS Safety Office and is the Technical Programs Manager of the Chemistry Branch. He received his PhD from the University of Georgia specializing in analytical-organic chemistry of metal complex interactions using NMR spectroscopy and organophosphorus synthesis. He was an active researcher in the USDA's Tobacco and Health Program on the fractionation, characterization and bioassay of cigarette smoke until 1977.

Since joining the NIEHS, he has assumed responsibility for the chemical handling, analytical and safety aspects of the Environmental Mutagenesis Test Development Program. He has assisted in the development of HEW's newly formed National Toxicology Program (NTP) and is a program leader for the NTP's chemistry support and repository functions. He has been involved at various levels in the health problems and concerned with chemical control of environmental quality and safety.

Dr. Walters is the Secretary and Chairman of the Program Committee of the Division of Chemical Health and Safety of the American Chemical Society and interdivisional liaison officer for that division and the Division of Environmental Chemistry. He is the past Chairman of the Northeast Georgia Section of the ACS and was appointed by the National ACS headquarters from 1973-1978 as ACS science advisor to U.S. Senator Herman Talmadge and U.S. Congressmen Robert G. Stephens and Doug Barnard, all of Georgia. He has lectured throughout the United States and is the author or co-author of more than 25 publications.

To

Bertha Beckroge,

Carole Lowe

and

Patricia Jean . . .

the women in my life

CONTENTS

VOLUME 1

SECTION I. LABORATORY DESIGN, HANDLING AND MANAGEMENT

VOLUME 2

SECTION IV. STRUCTURE-ACTIVITY AND TOXICITY PREDICTION

SECTION V. SPILL CONTROL, DEGRADATION AND DEACTIVATION

SECTION VI. DISPOSAL

SECTION I

LABORATORY DESIGN, HANDLING AND MANAGEMENT

CHAPTER 1

CONTROL OF POTENTIAL CARCINOGENIC, MUTAGENIC AND TOXIC CHEMICALS VIA A PROTOCOL REVIEW CONCEPT AND A CHEMISTRY CONTAINMENT LABORATORY

Douglas B. Walters, James D. McKinney
Ake Norstrom and Nathan DeWitt

National Institutes of Health
National Institute of Environmental
Health Sciences
Research Triangle Park, North Carolina

INTRODUCTION

Control of potential carcinogenic, mutagenic and highly toxic chemicals in a multidisciplinary research organization such as the National Institute of Environmental Health Sciences (NIEHS) presents special problems of management and program implementation. Research efforts at NIEHS include genetics, mutagenesis, pharmacology, pharmacokinetics, biophysics, comparative medicine, epidemiology, various toxicology programs and environmental chemistry. In all of these programs chemicals are used that possess varying degrees of hazardous properties. The internal Hazardous Chemical Agent Use Protocol Review System, requiring clearance prior to beginning a research project, in association with a special containment laboratory, has helped achieve control of these problems. Information required in the protocol includes training and experience of personnel involved, chemical properties (e.g., volatility and reactivity), biological effects, proposed experimental procedures, safety considerations for decontamination and disposal of equipment and chemicals, and emergency procedures. This system includes consideration of chemical classification, reactivity and structure correlations; it focuses the available information which is provided so that a workable decision on the safe use of hazardous chemicals can be made. The foundation for this decision-making process is the use of chemicals based on their controllable physical-chemical properties with consideration for their potentially hazardous biological effects. Control of chemicals solely on the basis of biological activity is incorrect and disregards the real issue—these substances are chemicals that can be controlled only through an understanding of their chemistry. Implementation of control procedures is best accomplished by close cooperation among physical scientists, life scientists, industrial hygienists and engineering professionals.

NIEHS SAFETY PROGRAM

The basis of the NIEHS safety program is the Safety and Health Manual [1] containing the policies, regulations, procedures and guidelines of the NIEHS Safety Plan. A similar Radiation Safety Guide [2] is also used to complement the general manual. The manuals are in loose-leaf form and are updated yearly with three-year revisions. As shown in Table I, the Safety and Health Manual is divided into 14 tabbed chapters which present comprehensive information on pertinent subjects. Included are various forms required by the safety office and properly completed illustrative examples. These forms include various hazardous agent use protocols (i.e., chemical, radioisotope and biological), waste disposal and new employee checklists. The manual is indexed and includes a section for additional safety information and updates. A current listing of available references is subdivided by category. Safety at NIEHS is an integral part of the research programs, and the significant need for chemistry input is reflected in the Safety and Health Manual.

Figure 1 shows the general organizational structure used to implement the manual and the safety program. The Office of Safety, under the authority of the deputy director, develops safety rules and procedures, implements safety programs, plans and enforces institute safety policies. The general safety and radiation safety committees advise the NIEHS and its safety office and review, evaluate and recommend adoption of policies and procedures. Branch and laboratory chiefs, through their respective safety coordinators, are responsible for aiding the implementation of safety policies and dissemination of safety information. Principal investigators are responsible for safe control in their use of hazardous agents; they must conform to institute policies and procedures and adequately inform and train laboratory workers and support personnel under their jurisdiction. A description of the duties and responsibilities of these individuals is given elsewhere [1, 3].

Table I. NIEHS Safety and Health Manual

I.	General Policies and Responsibilities
II.	Emergency Procedures
III.	Personnel Protection
IV.	General Safety and Laboratory Policies
V.	Hazardous Chemical and Flammable Solvents
VI.	Hazardous Waste Disposal
VII.	Biohazard Safety
VIII.	Animal Handling
IX.	Radiation Safety
X.	Shop Safety
XI.	Miscellaneous Safety Policies
XII.	Reference Material
XIII.	Index
XIV.	Additional Safety Information

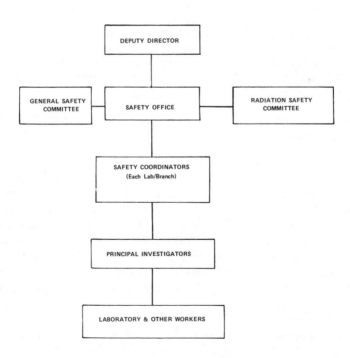

Figure 1. NIEHS Safety organization.

GENERAL PROTOCOL CONCEPTS

Definitions

Control of hazardous chemicals at NIEHS is accomplished through the concept of hazardous chemical agent use protocols. The current working definition at NIEHS of hazardous chemical agents is given below.

1. Agents known to have undesirable biological effects, either acute or chronic are considered hazardous. Reasonable regard is given to size of dose, duration and type of exposure, and physical state of the compound required to produce such effects. (Although certain terms, i.e., undesirable and reasonable regard, are nonspecific, this definition represents the best currently possible for use at NIEHS.)
2. Agents for which toxicity information is not available can be considered hazardous if they are highly suspect for reasons of similarity in chemical structure or function to known toxic agents.
3. Explosive or violently reactive agents are hazardous.
4. Combustible, flammable or easily ignitable agents, or those that burn or serve as fuel for fire are considered hazardous—specifically liquids having a flash point below $140^{\circ}F$ ($60^{\circ}C$) and a vapor pressure not exceeding 40 psia at $100^{\circ}F$ ($38^{\circ}C$).
5. Strong acids or bases which may burn or damage skin or other tissues are deemed hazardous. Consideration must also be given to corrosion of equipment.

Protocols are required for chemicals in categories 1, 2 and 3 but not generally for categories 4 and 5.

Purpose

Scientists are urged to consider safety in initial experimental design and to submit protocols when hazardous chemicals are ordered. This is required, easily monitored and enforced for regulated, radiolabeled compounds. For nonlabeled compounds, the Safety Office utilizes every opportunity to communicate to the scientists the purpose of and the need for a protocol system. For example, the protocol helps determine the degree of hazard and type of containment needed (e.g., hood, high hazard laboratory), personnel protection necessary, extent and frequency of medical surveillance required. Protocols also instruct and inform laboratory and support personnel of hazards (e.g., animal husbandry supervisor, warehouse, facilities maintenance, security and janitorial personnel). For animal studies protocols must be approved before animals are ordered or work begins. Additionally, principal investigators must inform the animal husbandry supervisor when animal waste products may contain hazardous chemicals. Notations on purchase orders alert warehouse personnel to special handling requirements. Special training courses are designed for all support personnel to increase their safety awareness. The protocol describes when special storage conditions are required, and the principal investigator ensures that such facilities exist. When repairs are necessary in laboratories and/or their personnel are vacated or relocated, information in the protocol aids decontamination. These functions are coordinated with the principal investigator and facilities maintenance personnel through the safety office. The protocol system also serves to develop appropriate waste disposal technology and to prepare personnel for possible emergency situations.

NIEHS is considering a new system for hazardous chemical control and inventory. On purchase order requests submitted by scientists all chemicals are classified as carcinogenic, mutagenic, teratogenic, highly toxic or generally safe (c, m, t, htx, OK). Suspect or presumed hazardous agents are included. Other substances that require special handling (e.g., corrosives or explosives) are generally labeled with appropriate warnings according to Department of Transportation regulations. A purchase order for chemicals must be approved by the safety officer before the order is placed. No time delay is expected in this procedure. A scientist who orders a chemical that does not have an approved or pending protocol will receive a notification requesting a protocol within two weeks. Chemicals designated OK are scanned to ensure that protocols are not necessary. When hazardous chemicals arrive at the warehouse, specially trained individuals open shipments in a hood with a properly filtered (e.g., HEPA, charcoal) exhaust vented to the outside. The safety office will deliver hazardous agents that have undergone protocol approval; otherwise, the scientist is requested to submit a protocol immediately, and the shipment is released when the protocol is approved. It is anticipated that this system will help maintain a computerized inventory, enforce the protocol procedure and aid in medical surveillance. Previously ordered chemicals will require manual inventory, screening and classification by the safety office and its safety committee.

Review System

The protocol review system is outlined in Table II. The principal investigator initiates the protocol; the laboratory or branch chief reviews and/or institutes revisions and is usually responsible for approval. Either of these individuals can consult with their safety coordinators or the safety officer. When the safety officer receives the protocol, it is reviewed by three people, usually members of the safety committee and/or individuals familiar with the hazardous agents. When NIEHS occupies its new facility, currently under construction, a medical officer (occupational physician) will be responsible

Table II. Protocol Review Process

Initiation	Principal Investigator	Completes protocol form, send to L/B Chief,
	Laboratory/Branch Chief	Reviews, revises, approves, send to S.O.
Focus	Safety Officer	Initiates review process; performs site visit, if necessary.
Review	Medical Officer	Reviews, decides, approves/disapproves on medical grounds, returns to S.O. in 5 working days.
	Protocol Review Committee	Reviews and returns protocol to S.O. in 5 working days.
Decision	Safety Officer	Issues approval/disapproval and conditions required, in writing.
Begin Work or Appeal	Principal Investigator	Begins work, corrects or amends protocol to S. O. satisfaction, appeals decision to protocol review committee

Note: Time required for review—10 working days.

for review of the protocol and coordination of medical surveillance and other health factors. Presently, if the protocol is approved by the reviewers, the safety officer issues official approval allowing the research to begin. The entire review process usually is completed within ten working days. If approval is not given, the protocol can be revised, corrected or amended according to the reviewers' suggestions. The principal investigator can also appeal the decision to the protocol review committee.

With respect to the protocol concept, the safety officer consults with researchers, arranges for medical surveillance, coordinates the review process, inspects facilities and equipment, determines the adequacy of safety measures, maintains a protocol file and reviews approvals yearly.

Checks and Balances

The checks and balances system is important to the protocol system. Scientists are instructed to order adequate quantities of hazardous chemicals and to avoid over-ordering. Purchase orders for chemicals are screened by the safety coordinators at the laboratory and branch levels and by the safety officer through the procurement office. Safety coordinators have informed the safety office of instances involving on-going research where protocol statements were necessary. Attempts are made to keep inventories of hazardous agents for each laboratory or room. Quarterly, unannounced safety inspections spot unreported hazardous agents or improper use of these materials. Yearly updates are made when existing protocols are revised and new chemicals and employees are identified. This process also identifies new foreign workers who require special training or special language considerations (Table III). Protocols no longer applicable are invalidated. Waste disposal pickup forms are also required and occasionally uncover unauthorized use of hazardous agents. These checks and balances spot incorrect uses of hazardous chemicals. Misuse is usually a matter of simple oversight— for example, a new chemical, such as a free product, that is obtained via a mechanism outside the purchasing procedure, or a chemical used for special work by a new scientist who is unfamiliar with the system. Intentional negligence is rare; it usually requires more time for coverup than for submission of a protocol.

NIEHS PROTOCOL FOR
HAZARDOUS CHEMICALS

When the protocol is evaluated, the reviewer judges the adequacy of six factors: experience and training of personnel; containment facilities; personnel protection measures; deactivation procedures; waste disposal; and emergency procedures. Additional space is provided for specific comments and approval or disapproval.

The NIEHS Protocol for Hazardous Chemical Use is shown in Appendix A. Section I of the protocol requests background information on personnel involved in the work and the location and duration of the experiment. It is essential to include all workers and support personnel and to routinely update information to account for personnel and location changes.

Section II provides data on physical-chemical and toxicological properties of experimental chemicals. Inclusion of correct chemical names and, particularly, structures as well as their physical states and properties is exceedingly important. The chemical structure is often the only information on which to base decision when other data are not available in the literature.

Questions often arise as to where information requested in the protocol can be obtained. Several papers discuss methods of acquiring this information [4-7]. As stated earlier an extensive up-to-date list of references is provided in the Safety and Health Manual. These sources are available in the library, which is prepared to initiate computer searches using a large number of available data bases. The expertise of the safety office, environmental chemistry branch and other institute groups is available for assistance when necessary.

This information is useless, however, unless the scientist reads and applies the information to answer protocol questions in an appropriate manner. Protocol information is needed since different substances, states and reactivities require different experimental conditions, engineering controls, personnel protection, decontamination and disposal procedures. Without this

Table III. NIEHS New Employee Safety Checklist

Employee Name _____ Date _____

Item	Date	Personnel or Supervisor Initials	Employee Initials	Safety Officer Initials
Personnel. Occupation accident/illness benefits, etc., explained				
Supervisor. (1) Safety and health provisions (a) Protective clothing				
(b) Head, foot, ear, etc., protection				
(c) Safety glasses				
(d) Baseline medical exams				
(e) Acquisition of pertinent licenses				
(f) Other (Indicate)				
(2) Safety manual sections to be read (List)				
(3) Designation of standard safety features, equipment and use				
(4) Explanation of pertinent NIEHS safety policies.				
(5) Explanation of special equipment/ facilities to be used (list)				
(6) Special training required (list)				
Foreign Visitors. Specify native language				

basic chemical information, the decision to work with a compound cannot and should not be made. If the principal investigators cannot supply adequate information, it can only be assumed that they do not understand the chemical and should not be allowed to work with it.

Often, with experimental research chemicals, little beyond the name and structure is known; however, it is often possible to predict, at least in part, the properties, mechanisms of interaction, reactions, hazards and handling requirements. Chemical classification techniques [7-10] can sometimes be useful in this task; however, care must be taken in extrapolation and interpolation of chemical data to similar compounds, even within homologous series, since deviations of anticipated behavior usually occur at unexpected times. Structure activity predictions can also be of help. Occasionally, they are useful [7, 8, 11-13] and, hopefully, future structural correlates will be of considerable value in this work [7, 13-15].

A description of the laboratory facilities to be used is given in Section III. Guidelines have been proposed for safe laboratory handling of chemical carcinogens, mutagens and teratogens [3, 16-29]. In addition, descriptions of facilities currently being used for these specific purposes are also in the literature [3, 27, 30-33]. Design of such facilities should be flexible to permit adaptation for future needs, but must also suit current specific needs. Two containment laboratories are available at NIEHS: one for life-scientists [3] and one designed for chemists. The containment laboratory for chemists will be fully described later in this chapter. The purpose of Section IV is to focus the experimenters' attention on the adequacy of available containment facilities and to familiarize them with the basic functioning of this equipment. An added benefit of this section is that malfunctions in equipment or delays in inspection schedules are quickly reported.

A detailed description of the experimental procedures is given in Section IV. Basic information on the amount of materials used is requested as is a brief statement describing the reasons for the experiment. This statement has been found to provide safety personnel with a better understanding of the nature of and motivation for the work.

Three parts of this section merit special comments. First, if animals are used in the study, route and duration of chemical administration (e.g., feed, water, lavage, injection and skin-painting) should be ascertained [34, 35] as well as the possible hazardous nature of the waste products. The physical state, volatility, solubility and the toxic effects are major factors which should be used in determining location for conducting animal studies and the risk to workers and experimental animals.

Second, the outline of procedures and safety precautions should include detailed information on the experimental techniques used. Attention should focus on key statements indicating: closed weighing techniques; chemical transfers done in hoods and glove boxes [36, 37] ; adequacy of place of experiment (e.g., hood) [38] ; concentrations of stock and standard solutions; location and use of experimental instruments; solvents and reagents possessing hazardous properties (e.g., perchloric acid, ethers, benzene, chlorinated aromatics and DMSO); and suitability of protective clothing and equipment. Recent articles [39-42] have described penetration of certain hazardous substances through various types of gloves. Therefore, double gloving using one set of disposable gloves is often required, particularly when glove boxes are used. Respirators and other protective devices must be reviewed to ensure proper protection [43,44] against experimental hazards and to prevent development of a false sense of security and poor laboratory techniques. Emphasis and reliance must always be on containment and engineering controls—not on protective equipment and clothing. Continued surveillance is necessary to ensure that these controls always function within design specifications.

Third, the statement regarding safety training and experience should be evaluated with concern for chemical safety. Included should be the highest academic degree obtained, a description of academic training in a specific applicable area, and specific relevant work experience. Course titles, dates, locations, compounds used and their hazards should be listed.

Input on the safety procedures for decontamination of equipment and disposal of hazardous chemicals is given in Section V. Procedures must be developed for decontamination of experimental equipment and work areas. Often this can be accomplished by washing with an appropriate solvent (and safely disposing of all washings). Procedures should be developed for monitoring to determine that hazardous residues do not remain. It is best to design these techniques so that an appropriate low level of detection is feasible and results are conclusive. Methods should be fast, reliable and easy to perform. When possible, one should design techniques around the problem; for example, when radiolabeled compounds are used, appropriate detection devices offer adequate methods of monitoring. Often, standard qualitative organic analysis spot tests [45] can be used. For special compounds there are recently developed spot tests [46-47]. Where these techniques do not suffice, more involved procedures [48] may be necessary. These include thin-layer, gas, and high-pressure liquid chromatography, and combined gas chromatography/mass spectometry, continuous automated methods or specifically designed procedures [32, 49].

Periodic environmental monitoring of the general laboratory work place [50] and its water and air effluents [51] as well as personal monitoring [52] should also take place. The analytical chemists involved in developing specific monitoring schemes, the safety officer, and the occupational physician performing the baseline [53] and followup physical examinations should periodically meet and coordinate their efforts to effect a meaningful medical surveillance program [54-57].

When considering disposal of the chemical waste products, every attempt should be made to convert these materials safely and efficiently to nontoxic substances [58-64]. Caution must be exercised to ensure that the end products of deactivation are not hazardous—a problem shown to exist even with generally accepted methods of deactivation [64, 65]. If chemical deactivation, detoxification and disposal are not feasible, incineration or equivalent methods of distruction [60, 63, 66-69] are the preferred disposal methods. All materials for disposal must be packaged and labeled to minimize personnel exposure. The method of disposal must be monitored to ensure that even the most refractory materials (e.g., chlorinated hydrocarbons) are broken down so that biologically hazardous materials (i.e. carcinogens, mutagens and toxins) are not being generated by the process [70, 71]. If waste materials must be buried, approved landfill sites must be located, and the materials properly packaged and transported. Organizations using contract services must determine that all aspects of disposal conform to current local, state and federal regulations.

The last section of the protocol describes emergency procedures to be followed in the event of a spill or fire. If a spill occurs, the investigator applies the protocol information based on the physical-chemical properties of the chemical(s) involved. Development of general emergency plans and description of appropriate protective clothing and equipment are requested. For example, should an impermeable (e.g., acid king) suit with self-contained breathing apparatus be used in the cleanup operation, will a less elaborate respirator suffice? What type of filters or cartridges will be necessary when the emergency is over? What decontamination and monitoring methods should be used?

The protocol concept at NIEHS has been an effective part of the safety program when used in conjunction with the high hazard laboratory for life scientists (3) and the chemistry containment laboratory described below.

NIEHS CHEMISTRY CONTAINMENT LABORATORY

A diagram of the design of the chemistry containment laboratory is shown in Figure 2. Use of the room is under the control of the chief and safety coordinator of the environmental chemistry branch. The room is designed for three specific purposes:

1. organic synthesis of hazardous chemicals;
2. analysis by gas chromatography (GC) and high-pressure liquid chromatography (HPLC) of hazardous reaction mixtures and products; and
3. routine weighings of hazardous materials.

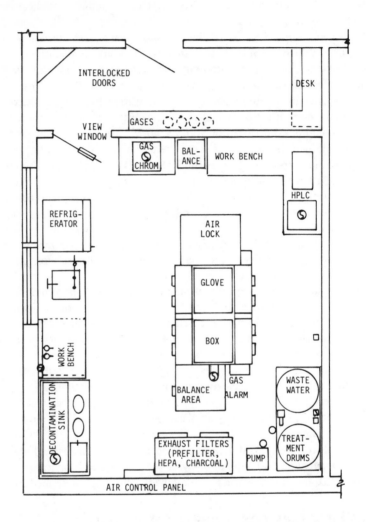

Figure 2. Present hazardous chemistry containment laboratory.

Because of the size of the room (15 by 23 ft) and its equipment, it is difficult for two people to work efficiently at the same time; generally, they can do so only for a short duration. One of these individuals is a chemist specially trained and experienced in high hazard synthesis. The other person normally does weighing or analyses that require use of the facilities for a short time. All users are given a thorough training session, the procedures for use of the room, a baseline physical and periodic medical examinations.

The room is posted as the "High Hazard Chemistry Laboratory—Authorized Personnel Only." An interlocked door system is used so that both doors cannot be opened simultaneously. A log-in sheet is provided for each scientist's identity, date, time and compounds used that day. The outer room (approximately 15 x 6 ft) provides an area for donning clothes; storage for disposable clothes and supplies; access for service personnel to the compressed gases piped into the laboratory; and space for data work-up. Because all hazardous materials work is done in the negative pressure glove box designed for containment, scientists wear disposable lab coats over street clothes, gloves, shoe covers and safety glasses. This clothing is discarded for pickup by the safety officer upon leaving the room.

Room features include monolithic vinyl floor covering with welded seams; a viewing window in the door; large blowout windows on the wall; heat and smoke alarms; impervious, stainless steel bench tops; epoxy-sealed utility conduits; sealed vapor- and waterproof lighting; eye wash in open sink area; deluge shower adjacent to door; explosion-safe refrigerator; push-button intercom phone that can be used without handling the receiver; and backup emergency electrical power. Entrance to the laboratory requires a key; exit does not. An antistatic floor mat such as those used in hospital operating rooms is used on the floor in front of the laboratory door to retain dust particles on shoe covers.

Special room features include a stainless steel glove box (Figure 3) custom-made by the Illinois Institute of Technology Research Institute (IITRI) in Chicago. The box has eight sets of gloves at two different levels, two air locks, a spearate weighing area with glove, separate internal storage areas, an inside coat of strippable epoxy paint, piped in utilities including compressed gases, and a gas alarm for buildup of combustible vapors. Blowout panels for pressure venting are located on top of the glove box to better protect the worker from shattered glass hazards in case of an explosion. The glove box is under negative pressure (approximately 0.25 in.) with respect to the surrounding laboratory space. The negative static pressure of the spaces decreases in steps from the laboratory to the corridor to ensure air flow from the corridor toward the laboratory. A magnehelic pressure gauge is mounted on the box front to indicate proper functioning before use. All exhaust laboratory air passes through a prefilter and a Flanders bag-in bag-out high-efficiency particulate air filter (HEPA) and charcoal filter (Figure 3, top right). Air from the following areas also passes through the Flanders system before being exhausted to the outside environment: the glove box and the custom-designed plexiglass covers surrounding

Figure 3. Custom-made stainless steel glove box.

the Varian 2400 gas chromatograph and the analytical balance outside the glove box (Figure 4); Waters model 500 preparative high-performance liquid chromatograph (Figure 5); and the decontamination sink (Figure 6. Potentially hazardous GC effluents and vapors from the HPLC system, where leaks are likely to develop, are contained and filtered before being exhausted. A control panel (Figure 3, middle left) monitors air flows, air volumes and pressure differentials across the HEPA and the charcoal filter to alert users of pressure buildups due to filter loading. It provides audible and visual alarms in case of malfunctions. When a failure is detected, the air monitoring and control system secures the ventilation system by use of the normally closed mode, i. e., supply exhaust and glove box dampers close when space volumes vary outside adjustable limits. Current technology does not enable reliable predictions for the replacement of charcoal filters; therefore, a tap is provided after the charcoal filter for access to the exhaust duct for chemical monitoring purposes. A redundant series of charcoal filters separated by a monitoring tap would be an even better system. A six-month filter replacement schedule is used based on the amounts of materials and their physical-chemical properites, which indicate whether they are very difficult to dislodge or replace from charcoal. Because of space limitations,

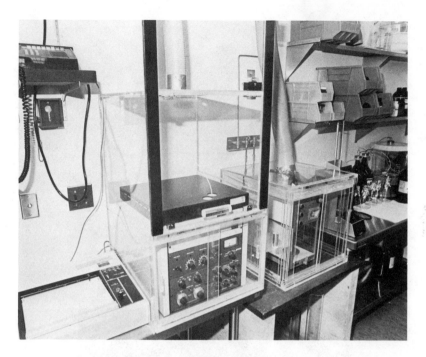

Figure 4. Plexiglass cover for gas chromatograph and analytical balance.

a hood could not be included in this area; however, this eliminates the temptation to work with borderline or less hazardous materials outside the glove box. A slot hood is provided for the small workbench area next to the sink for removal of vapors which may occur during preparatory work with nonhazardous materials before using the glove box.

Figures 6 and 7 show the decontamination sink and accompanying waste-water charcoal filter system. Both units were built by IITRI. Primary decontamination of contaminated glassware is done inside the glove box. The effluent is contained and deactivated, and then given to the safety officer for proper disposal. Glassware is bagged and transferred to the decontamination sink for final decontamination and washing. Wash water is pumped to a holding tank and then passed through a charcoal filter system. A tap is provided between the two tanks shown in Figure 7 for monitoring the waste effluent to ensure its decontamination before discharge into the sewage treatment plant. Holding tank vapors are vented into the HEPA charcoal filter system. Monitoring procedures and frequencies for air, water and surfaces are being perfected; they have been simplified since the room is used almost exclusively for aromatic halide compounds such as 2,3,7,8-tetrachlorodibenzo-p-dioxin (TCDD) and similar compounds.

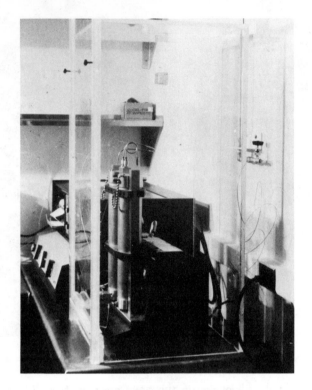

Figure 5. Plexiglass cover for HPLC.

Figure 6. Decontamination sink.

Figure 7. Wastewater treatment tanks for decontamination sink.

Figure 8 shows a schematic of the chemistry containment facility planned for the new NIEHS complex. The basic concept of containment remains, but in an expanded sense. A locker room is provided for changing, if necessary. A lower-level hazard area is designed for work which can be done safely in HEPA and charcoal-filtered hoods and which can also be used for radioisotope work. A vented chemical storage room is available. The high-level hazard laboratory is equipped with two glove boxes and two floor-to-ceiling filtered hoods. A separate decontamination facility with a decontamination sink and a shower-out room is provided. The laboratories are similar in construction to the interim facility described above, with additional provisions for radioisotope usage. Special waste treatment charcoal filter systems are located in the service area in the interstitial space between floors. All compressed gases are piped in.

CONCLUSIONS

The symposium on which this book is based has its origin in the increasing interest of many varied groups dealing with chemical carcinogens, mutagens and teratogens. Many people both within and outside the

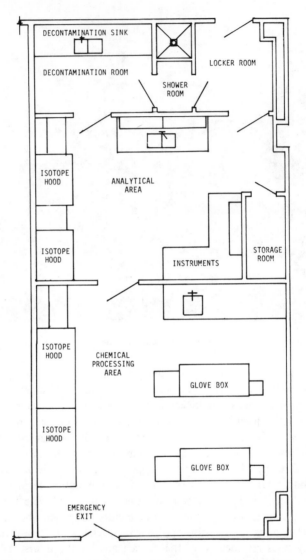

Figure 8. Planned hazardous chemistry containment laboratory.

scientific community are concerned about current, pending and possible upcoming regulations in the use of chemical carcinogens and related substances [72-74]. Even more government agencies can be expected to be involved with their future control. The fact that these substances have carcinogenic, mutagenic or teratogenic hazards is of unquestionable importance. However, it must be emphasized that these materials are chemicals first and that their behavior is a result of their physical-chemical properties.

Many scientists have expressed concern over the possibility of blanket regulations which would control all aspects of use of these compounds. It would seem apparent from a scientific standpoint that there is a need for separate regulations depending on whether these compounds will be used in industrial laboratories involved in manufacturing or processing, in research labs (industrial, government or academic), or in academic teaching laboratories. Naturally, some overlap will be present in regulations to determine the controls required, and interaction among several disciplines is necessary. This volume presents the chemist's viewpoint on safe handling of these substances. The NIEHS safety program, safety manual, and hazardous chemical agent use protocol system described in this chapter, when used in conjunction with properly designed containment laboratories, has been a satisfactory yet nonrestrictive approach to the safe handling of hazardous chemicals.

Chemists working in this area should be encouraged to inform the scientific community and the public about aspects of their work which bear on safe handling. An excellent opportunity now exists to make important, long-lasting contributions that extend beyond the research laboratory setting.

DISCLAIMER

Mention of commercial products and trade names is for informational purposes only and does not imply endorsement by the U.S. Department of Health, Education and Welfare or the National Institute of Environmental Health Sciences.

REFERENCES

1. Walters, D. B., Ed. "NIEHS Safety and Health Manual," DHEW (NIH)-79-1848 (1979).
2. Hamrick, P. E., Ed. "NIEHS Radiation Safety Guide," December, 1978.
3. Hunt, C. L., Jr., D. B. Walters and E. Zeiger. "Approaches for Safe Handling Procedures and Design of a High Hazard Laboratory for Life Scientists," Chapter 2, this volume.
4. Wassom, J. S. "Mutagenesis, Carcinogenesis and Teratogenesis Information Systems," Chapter 16, this volume.
5. Meines, A. F. "Preparation of Carcinogen Monographs," Chapter 15, this volume.
6. Gammage, R. B., and J. E. Turner. "Synthetic Fuel Technologies: Health Problems and Intersociety Cooperation," Chapter 17, this vol.

7. Bracken, M. C. " Information Systems for Predicting Chemical Hazards," *J. Environ. Path. Toxicol.* 2:133-140 (1978).

8. McKinney, J. D., P. Singh, L. Levy and M. Walker. "High Toxicity and Cocarcinogenic Potential of Certain Halogenated Aromatic Hydrocarbons. Some Structure-Activity Aspects," Chapter 22, this volume.

9. Hopfinger, A. J., R. Potenzone, Jr., R. Pearlstein, O. K. Kikuchi, M. Shapiro, G. W. A. Milne and S. R. Heller. "Structure-Activity Analysis in the Classification of Toxic Chemicals," Chapter 20, this volume.

10. Fishbein, L. "Potential Industrial Carcinogenic and Mutagenic Alkylating Agents," Chapter 18, this volume.

11. Harvey, R. G. "Carcinogenic Hydrocarbons: Metabolic Activation and the Mechanism of Cancer Induction," Chapter 23, this volume.

12. Van Duuren, B. L. "Structure Activity Studies of Tumor-Promoters and Cocarcinogens," presented at the American Chemical Society/ Chemical Society of Japan Chemical Congress, Honolulu, April, 1979.

13. Asher, I. M., and C. Zervos, Eds. "Structural Correlates of Carcinogenesis and Mutagenesis," *Proceedings* of the Second FDA Office of Science Summer Symposium, U. S. Naval Academy, August 1977, DHEW(FDA) 78-1046.

14. Chu, K. C. "Quantitative Structure-Activity Relationships in Chemical Carcinogenesis," Chapter 25, this volume.

15. Craig, P. N. "Application of Structure-Activity Studies to Develop Models for Estimating Toxicity," Chapter 21, this volume.

16. "Guidelines for the Laboratory Use of Chemical Substances Posing a Potential Occupational Carcinogenic Risk," Laboratory Chemical Carcinogen Safety Standards Subcommittee of the DHEW Committee to Coordinate Toxicology and Related Programs, revised draft, May 1979.

17. Ehrenberg, L., and C. A. Wachtmeister. "Safety Precautions in Work with Mutagenic and Carcinogenic Chemicals," in *The Handbook of Mutagenicity Test Procedures*, B. J. Kibey, M. S. Legator and W. W. Nichols, Eds. (Holland: Elsvier, 1977), pp. 401-410.

18. Ehrenberg, L., and C. A. Wachtmeister. "Handling of Mutagenic Chemicals: Experimental Safety," in *The Handbook of Mutagenicity Test Procedures*, B. J. Kilbey, M. S. Legator and W. W. Nichols, Eds. (Holland: Elsvier, 1977), pp. 411-418.

19. *Manual on Mutation Breeding*, 2nd Edition, Technical Report Series No. 119, International Atomic Energy Agency, Vienna, 1977.

20. "Carcinogens Regulation and Control: A Management Guide to Carcinogens," DHEW (NIOSH) 77-205 (1977).

21. "Carcinogens—Regulation and Control: Working with Carcinogens: A Guide to Good Health Practices," DHEW (NIOSH) 77-206 (1977).

22. Cater, D. B., and E. Hartree. "Carcinogens, Mutagens and Teratogens," *Biochem. Soc. Spec. Public.* 5:47-54 (1977).

23. "National Cancer Institutes Safety Standards for Research Involving Chemical Carcinogens," DHEW (NIH) 77-900 (1975).

24. "A Manual on the Safety of Handling Carcinogens in the Laboratory," International Agency for Research on Cancer (in press).
25. Ward, J. T., C. H. Williams, Jr., C. D. Wolbach, L. H. Keith and D. B. Walters. "Transportation of Materials from Radian's Hazardous Materials Laboratory," Chapter 5, this volume.
26. Johnson, J. S. "Safe Handling of Chemical Carcinogens in the Research Laboratory," Chapter 7, this volume.
27. Longfellow, D. G. and A. R. Patel. "Preparation, Packaging and Perversity of Chemical Carcinogens—A Repository Viewpoint," Chapter 3, this volume.
28. Sansone, E. B., and M. W. Slein. "Application of the Microbiological Safety Experience to Work with Chemical Carcinogens," *Am. Ind. Hyg. Assoc. J.* 37:711-720 (1976).
29. Rappaport, S. W., and E. E. Campbell. "The Interpretation and Application of OSHA Carcinogen Standards for Laboratory Operations," *Am. Ind. Hyg. Assoc. J.* 37:690-696 (1976).
30. Keith, J. N. "How to Design a Building Safe Against Hazards," *Occup. Health Safety* 4:46-48 (1977).
31. Harless, J., K. E. Baxter, L. H. Keith and D. B. Walters. "Design and Operation of a Hazardous Materials Laboratory," Chapter 4, this vol.
32. Simmon, V. F., and M. V. Pierce. "Design, Implementation and Monitoring of Laboratories for Handling Chemical Carcinogens and Mutagens," Chapter 8, this volume.
33. Ettinger, H. J., E. E. Campbell and G. M. Talley. "Management of Carcinogenic and Highly Toxic Chemicals in a Multidisciplinary Research Facility," Chapter 6, this volume.
34. Darlow, H. M., D. J. C. Simmons and F. J. C. Roe. "Hazards from Experimental Skin Painting of Carcinogens," *Arch. Environ. Health* 18:883-893 (1969).
35. Sansone, E. B., A. M. Losikoff and R. A. Pendleton. "Potential Hazards from Feeding Test Chemicals in Carcinogen Bioassay Research," *Tox. Appl. Pharm.* 39:435-450 (1977).
36. Sansone, E. B., and A. M. Losikoff. "A Note on the Chemical Contamination Resulting from the Transfer of Solid and Liquid Materials in Hoods," *Am. Ind. Hyg. Assoc. J.* 38:489-491 (1977).
37. Hill, R. H., Jr., Y. T. Gagnon and A. W. Teass. "Evaluation and Control of Contamination in the Preparation of Analytical Standard Solutions of Hazardous Chemicals," *Am. Ind. Hyg. Assoc. J.* 38:157-160 (1978).
38. Sansone, E. B., H. Wolochow and M. A. Chatigny. "Potential Hazard Associated with Removal of Needles from Septa in Injection Ports of a Gas Chromatograph," *Anal. Chem.* 49:670-671 (1977).
39. Johnson, T. C., and W. D. Merciez. "Permeation of Halogenated Solvents through Drybox Gloves," U. S. Atomic Energy Commission, RFP-1608 (1971).
40. Sansone, E. B., and Y. B. Tewari. "The Permeability of Laboratory Gloves to Selected Solvents," *Am. Ind. Hyg. Assoc. J.* 39:169-173 (1978).

41. Sansone, E. B., and Y. B. Tewari. "The Permeability of Laboratory Gloves to Selected Nitrosamines," in *Environmental Aspects of N-Nitroso Compounds*, E. A. Walker, M. Costegnaro, L. Griciute and R. E. Lyle, Eds. (Lyon: International Agency for Cancer Research, 1978).

42. Nelson, G. O., G. C. Cardenas and J. S. Johnson. "Glove Permeation by Organic Solvents," presented at the American Industrial Hygiene Conference, Chicago, May 1979.

43. Hyatt, E. C. "Respirator Protection Factors," Los Alamos Scientific Laboratory, LA-6084-MS, 1976.

44. "NIOSH Certified Equipment List as of July 1, 1978," DHEW (NIOSH) 79-107 (1978).

45. Shriner, R. L., R. C. Fuson and D. Y. Curtin. *The Systematic Identification of Organic Compounds*, 6th Edition, (New York: John Wiley and Sons, Inc., 1979).

46. Weeks, R. W., Jr., B. J. Dean and S. K. Yasuda. "Detection Limits of Chemical Spot Tests Toward Certain Carcinogens on Metal, Painted and Concrete Surfaces," *Anal. Chem.* 48:2227-2233 (1976).

47. Weeks, R. W., Jr., and B. J. Dean. "Decontamination of Aromatic Amine Cancer-Suspect Agents on Concrete, Metal, or Painted Surfaces," *Am. Ind. Hyg. Assoc. J.* 39:758-762 (1978).

48. Fishbein, L. "Analysis of Carcinogenic and Mutagenic Aromatic Amines," Chapter 12, this volume.

49. Peirce, M. V., T. M. Distler, S. L. Eckford and V. F. Simmons. "Use of the Ames Salmonella/Microsome Assay to Monitor Laboratory Contamination by Chemical Mutagens," presented at the Environmental Mutagen Society Meeting, New Orleans (March 1979).

50. Melcher, R. G. "Monitoring Trace Amounts of Organic Chemicals in the Laboratory Atmosphere," Chapter 9, this volume.

51. Pellizzari, E. D. "State-of-the-Art Techniques for Monitoring Environmental Carcinogens, Mutagens and Teratogens," Chapter 10, this volume.

52. Segal, A. and G. Leowengart. "Development of a Personal Monitoring Device for the Detection of Direct Acting Alkylating Carcinogens," Chapter 11, this volume.

53. Brandt, R. J. " Medical Surveillance," presented at the Workshop on Cancer Research Safety, Office of Research Safety, National Cancer Institute, NIH, Washington, DC September 1977, pp. 100-111.

54. Shaw, C., Ed. "Prevention of Occupational Cancer," (Cleveland, OH: CRC Press, in press).

55. Joyner, R. E. "Medical Surveillance Problems Under Proposed OSHA Standards," *J. Occup. Med.* 18:690-692 (1976).

56. Kilian, D. J. "Use of Human Biological Monitoring for Risk Assessment of Mutagenesis and Carcinogenic Effect," Chapter 13, this vol.

57. Gross, R. L. et al. "Immunological Assessment of Pulmonary Neoplasia," Chapter 14, this volume.

58. Sansone, E. B., and M. W. Slein. "Degradation of Chemical Carcinogens: An Anotated Bibliography," Chapter 27, this volume.

59. Meiners, A. F., R. P. Reisdorf and H. P. Owens. "Carcinogen Spills, A Challenge to Laboratory Safety Capability," Chapter 26, this volume.
60. Piver, W. T. "Deactivation and Disposal Methods for Small Quantities of Experimental Chemicals," Chapter 29, this volume.
61. Crosby, D. G. "Conquering the Monster—The Photochemical Destruction of Chlorodioxins," in *Disposal and Decontamination of Pesticides*, M. V. Kennedy, Ed., ACS Symposium Series #73 (Washington, DC: American Chemical Society, 1978), pp. 1-12.
62. Kranich, W. L., R. B. LaPierre, L. Guczi and A. H. Weiss. "Catalytic Hydrodechlorination of Polychlorinated Hydrocarbons," in *Disposal and Decontamination of Pesticides*, M. V. Kennedy, Ed., ACS Symposium Series #73 (Washington, DC: American Chemical Society, 1978), pp. 24-34.
63. Hackman, E. E., III. *Toxic Organic Chemicals Destruction and Waste Treatment* (Park Ridge, NJ: Noyes Data Corp., 1978), pp. 29-79.
64. Emmett, G. C., C. J. Michejda, E. B. Sansone and L. K. Keefer. "Photodegradation: Its Limitation in the Decontamination and Disposal of Chemical Carcinogens," Chapter 28, this volume.
65. Chien, P. T., and M. H. Thomas. "Evaluation of Degradation Methods for Nitrosamine Wastes," *J. Environ. Path. Toxicol.* 2:513-516 (1978).
66. Yosim, S. J., K. M. Barclay, R. L. Gay and L. F. Grantham. "Disposal of Laboratory Hazardous Wastes by Molten Salt Combustion," Chapter 32, this volume.
67. DeZearn, M., and D. A. Oberacker. "Detoxification of Materials by Microwave Plasma," Chapter 31, this volume.
68. Wilkinson, T. K., and H. W. Rogers. "Disposal of Chemical Carcinogens, Mutagens and Teratogens from Research Facilities," Chapter 30, this volume.
69. Powers, P. W. "How to Dispose of Toxic Substances and Industrial Wastes," (Park Ridge, NJ: Noyes Data Corp., 1978).
70. O. M. Bjørseth et al., "Monitoring for Polycyclic Aromatic Hydrocarbon (PAH) Content and Mutagenic Activity in Products and Emissions from a Gasifier Demonstration Project," Chapter 33, this volume.
71. Rawls, R. L. "Dow Finds Support, Doubt for Dioxin Ideas," *Chem. Eng. News* (February 1979).
72. "OSHA Proposals Research into the Research Laboratory as Well as the Industrial Workplace," *Anal. Chem.* 50:1326A-1328A (1978).
73. "Laboratory Chemicals May Come Under Costly OSHA Regulations," Science 202:496 (1978).
74. "Chemical Carcinogens: The Scientific Basis for Regulation," Science 201:1200-1205 (1978).

APPENDIX

NIEHS PROTOCOL FOR HAZARDOUS CHEMICAL USE
(Preferably Typed or Legibly Written)

TO: NIEHS Safety Officer   DATE: _____

FROM: _____, Principal Investigator

_____Approval   _____Disapproval   _____Lab/Branch Chief

_____Approval   _____Disapproval   _____Medical Officer

_____Approval   _____Disapproval   _____Safety Officer

To expedite review by the Safety Committee, submit the original and 5 copies.

I. . PERSONNEL INVOLVED IN EXPERIMENTAL PROGRAM

    A. Laboratory or Section Supervisor _____

    B. Room where hazardous chemical will be used _____; stored _____

    C. Other investigators _____

        Technical help _____

    D. These other workers have been made aware of the hazards involved in using this

        chemical by the principal investigator and have received a copy of the protocol:

        _____yes; _____no. If yes, list date _____

        If no, explain: _____

        _____

    E. If animal care facilities are involved in this experimental study, the Supervi-

        sor of this facility has been notified and has received a copy of the protocol:

        _____yes; _____no. If yes, list date _____

        If no, explain _____

    F. Estimate of duration of experimental program (week, month, year). _____

        _____

II. PHYSICAL - CHEMICAL AND TOXICOLOGICAL PROPERTIES OF THE CHEMICAL

    A. Chemical name and structure (also Trade name, if known) _____

        _____

    B. Physical form (solid, liquid, gas) _____

NIEHS PROTOCOL FOR HAZARDOUS CHEMICAL USE (Continued)

II. PHYSICAL - CHEMICAL AND TOXICOLOGICAL PROPERTIES OF THE CHEMICAL (Continued)

C. Vapor pressure or boiling and flask points (if applicable) _____

D. Melting point (if applicable) _____

E. Solubility: water _____; other solvent _____

F. Other properties related to stability and reactivity (e.g., corrosive, heat or

shock sensitive, etc.) _____

G. Major known toxic effects

   1. Acute _____

   _____

   2. Reference _____

   _____

   3. Chronic _____

   _____

   4. Reference _____

   _____

III. DESCRIPTION OF LABORATORY FACILITIES

A. Room number _____

B. Type of containment equipment (hood, glove box, etc.) _____

C. Type of air circulation in the laboratory (recirculating, once through, etc.)

_____

D. Date the operation of hoods and air circulation equipment were last checked

_____

   1. Face velocity of hood _____ f/min

   2. Number of air changes in room _____/hour

E. Approximate date fire extinguisher last inspected _____

F. Distance to nearest emergency shower and/or eye fountains _____

IV. DESCRIPTION OF EXPERIMENTAL PROCEDURE

A. Expected amounts used (approx.) in micrograms, milligrams or grams:

NIH-2404-3 (12-78)

NIEHS PROTOCOL FOR HAZARDOUS CHEMICAL USE (Continued)

IV. <u>DESCRIPTION OF EXPERIMENTAL PROCEDURE</u> (Continued)

Total received _____; amount used per experiment _____

Amount used per month _____

B. Expected place research with chemical will be conducted:

Hood _____; other (specify, i.e., open benchtop, etc.)_____

_____

C. Will live animals be used in the study? _____yes; _____no.

If yes:

1. Kind of animal (rat, rabbit, etc.) _____

2. Approximate number of animals/experiment _____

3. Approximate does or treatment/animal _____

4. Where will animals be housed and for how long _____

_____

5. Are waste products from animals considered hazardous? _____yes; _____no.

If yes, date animal care supervisor was notified _____

D. Training and experience of personnel involved (attach current copy of "Statement of Safety Training and Experience"). _____

_____

_____

E. Give a brief summary of the underlying reasons for the experiment. _____

_____

_____

F. Outline the procedures to be followed and the safety precautions to be taken in this experimental program. Include a description of storing, handling, use of equipment, use of animals, making up and storage of solutions, etc. _____

_____

_____

NIEHS PROTOCOL FOR HAZARDOUS CHEMICAL USE (Continued)

IV. DESCRIPTION OF EXPERIMENTAL PROCEDURE (Continued)

_____

_____

_____

_____

_____

_____

_____

_____

G. Indicate solvent system to be used in analytical determination _____

_____

_____

V. SAFETY PROCEDURES FOR DECONTAMINATION OF EQUIPMENT AND DISPOSAL OF HAZARDOUS CHEMICALS

A. Give procedures for cleaning and assuring decontamination of:

1. Glassware _____

_____

_____

2. Animal cages _____

_____

_____

3. Laboratory benches and hoods _____

_____

_____

B. Give procedures for disposal of wastes (Can the material be chemically converted into innoxious substances; is incineration preferable and if so, how should chemical be packaged to minimize exposure to incinerator personnel; or if neither of these two options are possible, how should waste be packaged for burial in land-

NIEHS PROTOCOL FOR HAZARDOUS CHEMICAL USE (Continued)

V. SAFETY PROCEDURES FOR DECONTAMINATION OF EQUIPMENT AND DISPOSAL OF HAZARDOUS
CHEMICALS (Continued)

fills?) Consider liquid (solutions), solid wastes, wash water, left over unused
chemical, and animals in your description. _____

_____

_____

_____

VI. EMERGENCY PROCEDURES

Describe emergency procedures to be followed in the event of an accidental spill of
fire involving the chemical or other chemicals or solvents that are part of this research program. In addition to the general emergency plan, include with this plan
the following items:

A. What to do with hood airflow and airflow for the laboratory and building. _____

_____

_____

_____

B. A description of the type of protective clothing and type of respirator to be
worn to re-enter laboratory. Where are respirators located? _____

_____

_____

_____

VI. EMERGENCY PROCEDURES (Continued)

C. A description of the decontamination process. _____

_____

_____

_____

_____

_____

_____

CHAPTER 2

APPROACHES FOR SAFE HANDLING
PROCEDURES AND DESIGN OF A
HIGH–HAZARD LABORATORY
FOR LIFE SCIENTISTS

Christopher L. Hunt, Jr.,
Douglas B. Walters and Errol Zieger

National Institutes of Health
National Institute of Environmental
Health Sciences
Research Triangle Park, North Carolina

INTRODUCTION

In 1970 the Occupational Safety and Health Act was enacted to assure safe and healthful working conditions for workers [1]. The standards promulgated by the Occupational Safety and Health Administration (OSHA) have had minimal effects on research laboratories because they are designed for manufacturing concerns and are not readily applicable or adaptable to research institutions. This is evidenced by standards for 14 chemical carcinogens that became effective January 29, 1974 [2]. Laboratory provisions and the standard for 4,4'-methylene *bis*(2-chloroaniline) were repealed by a federal court on December 17, 1974, after a challenge by the Synthetic Organic Chemical Manufacturers Association [3].

A new policy to regulate carcinogenic chemicals is being proposed by OSHA. These regulations will include mechanisms for identifying and classifying known or suspected carcinogens [4]. The categories are summarized in Table I. It is expected that OSHA will include research laboratories in these regulations [5]. Of concern to many institutions is the cost involved in monitoring workplaces and whether the regulations will be so restrictive as to actually hinder research [5-8].

Table I. Proposed OSHA Carcinogen Categories

Category I	Confirmed human carcinogens, Carcinogenicity established in two species of test animals or in one species if results have been duplicated.
Category II	Suspected carcinogenic substances. Positive in only one animal species and not duplicated.
Category III	Substances for which additional information is needed.
Category IV	Reserved for carcinogens not believed to be found in American workplaces.

Other federal agencies are also developing carcinogen standards. Several years ago, the Department of Health, Education and Welfare assigned this task to the Laboratory Chemical Carcinogen Safety Standards Subcommittee of the HEW Committee to Coordinate Toxicology and Related Programs. This chapter will discuss the proposed HEW guidelines, which the authors feel are exceeded by the National Institute of Environmental Health Sciences (NIEHS) protocol system and high-hazard laboratory for life scientists.

Drafts of the proposed guidelines have undergone numerous revisions, indicating the controversial nature of the subject and the problems encountered in writing guidelines around regulations.

NIEHS PHILOSOPHY

NIEHS, part of the National Institutes of Health and a component of HEW, strives to meet whatever regulations or guidelines are issued. NIEHS has a vested interest and an obligation to provide the best possible facilities for ongoing and proposed biomedical research to determine the effects of chemical, biological and physical environmental agents on man's health and well being.

Portions of the NIEHS safety program and protocol system are described elsewhere in this publication [9]. Experimental protocols are effective mechanisms for ascertaining safety and health measures required for any given experiment. The institute safety officer initiates the protocol review process and approves or disapproves proposed research for safety and health reasons. Particular attention is paid to the volatility, reactivity [9-12] and stability of compounds, as well as potential for cross-contamination of samples [13], factors often overlooked by life scientists.

Existing NIEHS laboratories were not adequate for the safe handling of chemical carcinogens and mutagens. It was therefore necessary to identify space which could be utilized effectively for constructing a high-hazard containment laboratory to alleviate this problem. The involved scientific personnel, engineering staff, and safety and health specialists jointly redesigned the area into a maximum containment facility sufficient for research involving carcinogens and mutagens. The facility also exceeds the requirements for P-3 containment level recombinant DNA research [14].

Experiments performed using carcinogens in the NIEHS high-hazard laboratory include in vitro bacterial, yeast, fungal and mammalian cell mutagenesis and toxicity, and in vitro metabolism studies. Additionally, this facility is used for treatment of microorganisms, mammalian cells and fruit flies with mutagens in experiments which are completed in conventional laboratories. Furthermore, all weighing of carcinogens is done in this room, even if the experiment is to be performed outside the area.

Psychologically, there is an advantage to storing, dispensing and using chemicals in such a room because the investigator is constantly reminded of the hazard potential associated with the particular agent and is less likely to become careless in its use.

HEW GUIDELINES

The proposed HEW guidelines provide an approach for protecting laboratory workers and the workplace from chemical carcinogens without impeding research [15]. Some important points of the guidelines are summarized below.

I. Responsibilities

A. Operating agencies must have a specific plan directed toward the safe handling of chemical carcinogens in research settings as part of their general safety and health program.

B. Supervisors are directly responsible for ensuring that their workplace and subordinates are in compliance with the guidelines.

C. A safety officer must be appointed to develop and manage the program, maintain records, inspect work areas, and approve working protocols prepared by principal investigators.

D. Principal investigators have specific responsibilities including:

1. selecting appropriate control practices in consultation with the safety officer;
2. establishing emergency procedures for spills or accidental exposures; and
3. obtaining approval of experimental protocols for planned research, disseminating information to involved personnel and providing required training, such as safe handling techniques.

II. Medical Surveillance

A. Preassignment physical examinations are used to established baseline parameters for monitoring changes in employees; examinations are given to all employees assigned to work with chemical carcinogens before they begin work.

B. Periodic examinations are given to update medical and work histories and can help to determine if occupationally related changes occurred in parameters measured.

Medical surveillance requirements of NIEHS include storage of 5-10 ml of blood serum that can be of use in determining whether specific changes have occurred through work-related exposure. They may also be useful in identifying actual chemicals involved in the exposure. When the employee undergoes the periodic examination, a list of chemicals with which the individual has worked since the last examination is furnished, plus any information of importance to the occupational physicians.

C. Medical records are maintained by the operating agency while the employee is there. Thereafter, records are sent to the Director of Safety, HEW, and are kept for a specified time period.

III. Worker Education

Scientific, janitorial or maintenance staff who may be exposed to chemical carcinogens should receive information regarding: possible sources of exposure, potential health effects, proper methods of protection and work practices, and the medical surveillance program. Protocols will be readily available to all affected employees.

IV. Work Practices and Engineering Controls

An important section of the proposed guidelines concerns work practices and engineering controls. Employees need to exercise caution and avoid becoming overly reliant on personal protective devices or laboratory hoods. A false sense of security can develop which can lead to poor work practices and a resulting covert exposure to hazardous agents. Recent studies indicate that even with above-average work techniques, training and use of hoods, considerable potential for contamination and exposure exists [16-19]. Similarly depending on the type of material, permeation of laboratory solvents through gloves is often greater than expected [20, 21].

V. Personal Practices

A. Protective Clothing. The degree of protective clothing varies with the hazards of a particular chemical. Requirements for the minimum and maximum are given in Table II. Contaminated clothing must be decontaminated prior to being laundered.

Table II. Requirements for Protective Laboratory Clothing

Minimum	Maximum
1. Fully Fastened Laboratory Coat	1. Jump Suit
2. Gloves	2. Gloves
3. Impermeable Apron[a]	3. Impermeable Apron
	4. Shoe Covers
	5. Head Cover
	6. Respirator

[a]Optional at the discretion of the supervisor.

B. Eye and Face Protection. Face and eye protection in the laboratory is of prime importance because of the possibility of a chemical splash or explosion that could cause permanent damage. Safety glasses are required at all times as a minimum in the laboratory. Face shields that protect the face and neck are used when a chance of a violent reaction of explosion exists. Contact lenses are not considered eye protection.

C. Personal Hygiene. There is to be no eating, drinking, smoking, chewing gum or tobacco, application of cosmetics or storage of food in the laboratory. Risk of contamination and subsequent ingestion of the contaminant is too great and cannot be overlooked. Hands are washed after operations where a chemical carcinogen is used. If accidental exposure to a carcinogen has occurred, a shower is required. A shower is also required after the last exit from a high-hazard containment area.

D. Mechanical Pipettes. Mouth pipetting is not permitted. Several commercially available mechanical pipetting aids can be used [22]. It may be necessary to try several before a suitable one is found.

VI. Operational Practices

Areas where chemical carcinogens are used or stored require the following:

A. Entrances to work areas must be posted with permanent signs bearing the legend: Danger—Chemical Carcinogen—Authorized Personnel Only.

B. Flow of traffic is controlled through these identified areas by allowing only authorized personnel to enter. Doors to the area are closed while work is in progress.

C. Easily cleanable work surfaces (e.g., stainless steel, strippable epoxy-type paint) or appropriate covering such as dry, absorbent, plastic-backed paper are required.

D. Glove boxes, laboratory hoods and biological safety cabinets are used as containment devices when volatile carcinogens are used or when there is potential for aerosol formation. The guidelines require that effluent air from primary containment devices be treated by any of several recommended techniques before it is exhausted [23]. Various classes and types of biological safety cabinets and their applicability to research involving carcinogens are listed in Table III.

E. Analytical instruments, such as gas chromatographs, that can release vaporized or aerosolized carcinogenic material must be vented by low-volume, high-velocity exhaust systems [24].

F. Approved respirators are used where there is potential for inhalation of known or suspected chemical carcinogens. Careful selection of the proper device is imperative. The safety officer selects respirators from those appearing on the NIOSH Certified Equipment List [25].

G. A storage area for stock chemicals and maintenance of required inventory records are required. Only needed quantities of a carcinogen, in suitable labeled containers, are allowed in the work area. Secondary containment methods are used when transporting solutions.

H. Good housekeeping practices are in effect. Because of the potential aerosol formation, dry mopping and sweeping are not allowed. Wet mopping techniques or a high-efficiency particulate air filter (HEPA) filtered vacuum cleaner [26] are used. Spills are cleaned up according to procedures outlined for that particular chemical by the principal investigator and approved by the safety officer. The best method is deactivation or neutralization if it can be done safely and efficiently.

I. House vacuum lines are protected to prevent contamination. Separate vacuum pumps equipped with traps and disposable HEPA/activated charcoal filters are recommended [27].

J. If carcinogenic compounds are packaged and shipped, precautions are taken to insure against the chance of breakage or leakage under ordinary conditions [28, 29].

Table III. Applications of Biological Safety Cabinets in Research[a]

Biological Safety Cabinet			Research uses/applications	
Type	Work Opening	Face Velocity (ft/min)	Chemical Carcinogens	Recombinant DNA
Class I	Glove panel not in place	75	No	P1-P3
	Glove panel in place without gloves	150	Yes	P1-P3
	Glove panel in place with gloves	NA	Yes	P1-P3
Class II				
Type A	Fixed height usually 10 inch	75, minimum	No	P1-P3
Type B	Sliding sash provides opening adjustable from 8 to 20 in. for introduction and removal of equipment and materials. To obtain proper face velocity, experimentation should be done with 8-in. opening.	100 at 8-in. sash opening	Yes in low dilution and volatility	P1-P3
Class III	No direct opening. Access is through double-door sterilizer and decontaminant dunk bath.	NA	Yes	P1-Pr

[a]Adapted from "Laboratory Safety Monograph, A supplement to the NIH Guidelines for Recombinant DNA Research," National Institutes of Health (1978).

K. Decontamination of equipment and spills and the eventual disposal of wastes [30, 31] are the most difficult problems confronting research laboratories using chemical carcinogens. Methods used for decontamination and spill control should utilize chemical monitoring to ensure effectiveness. Disposal technology must be applicable to the particular hazardous waste being processed to provide effective destruction.

VII. Facility Requirements

A. Handwashing facilities are required in each work area, and shower facilities are required in the buildings. High-hazard containment laboratories require showers adjacent to the change rooms.

B. Air from containment devices and the general workroom area must be exhausted so that it does not recirculate. Air is treated before exhaust, and the work areas are under negative pressure to provide for the inward movement of air.

Animal Experimentation

Work practices and engineering controls applicable to laboratories apply to animal facilities using chemical carcinogens. Although there is real potential for employee exposure to a chemical carcinogen [17], this area is frequently overlooked. The safety protocol addresses the manner of housing, operational procedures and extent of protective clothing.

Areas requiring particular attention include, but are not limited to, chemical handling, dosage preparation and administration, animal care and housing, sanitation and maintenance, and necropsy/histopathology. Studies have shown these to be potential sources of contamination [16-18, 32].

Inhalation chambers utilized for animal studies are designed to be under negative pressure to the rooms in which they are contained as well as the adjacent corridors and to have sufficient backup systems to prevent positive pressurization and subsequent room contamination even during a total chamber failure. Ventilation systems for the chambers must be independent of the regular room systems.

VIII. Appendices

A. A list of substances regulated by OSHA and those considered for inclusion in the guidelines by the HEW Committee (Table IV) is included.

B. Guidelines for infrequent users of small quantities of chemical carcinogens are included. The authors feel this section is misleading. It suggests some levels of use are safe when there is no definitive evidence to support this. Caution must be exercised when handling hazardous compounds at all times, regardless of the frequency of use.

C. Included are suggestions for work practices and engineering controls beyond those already described. These are designated by HEW on an as-needed basis. Examples include: specialized protective clothing, a completely closed containment system for the handling of highly potent chemical carcinogens, and environmental monitoring of certain laboratory activities.

D. A safety action plan, similar to the protocol used at NIEHS for several years [9, 33], is described. It is designed to help the principal investigator consider safety and health aspects of proposed research and to aid the safety officer in evaluating planned protective and emergency measures.

E. An outline of the rationale for periodic health assessment is included. The need for medical, biological and chemical monitoring of workers and the inherent problems in accomplishing such monitoring are discussed.

Table IV. Substances Posing a Potential Occupational Carcinogenic Risk

Substances Currently Regulated by the Occupational Safety and Health Administration as Carcinogens

Asbestos	Ethylenimine
4-Nitrobiphenyl	*beta*-Propiolactone
α-Naphthylamine	2-Acetylaminofluorene
Methyl chloromethyl ether	4-Dimethylaminoazobenzene
3,3'-Dichlorobenzidine (and its salts)	N-Nitrosodimethylamine
bis-Chloromethyl ether	Vinyl chloride
β-Naphthylamine	Inorganic arsenic
Benzidine	Benzene
4-Aminodiphenyl	Coke oven emissions

Substances Considered Carcinogenic by the HEW Committee to Coordinate Toxicology and Related Programs

Benzo(a)pyrene	7,12-Dimethylbenz(a)anthracene
Benz(a)anthracene	Dibenz(a,h)anthracene
3-Methylcholanthrene	N-Nitrosopiperidine
N-Nitrosodiethylamine	1,4-Dinitrosopiperazine
N-Nitrosodi-*n*-propylamine	N-Nitroso-N-ethylurethane
N-Nitrosodi-*n*-butylamine	N-Methyl-3-nitro-1-nitrosoguanidine
N-Nitroso-N-methylurea	1,1-Dimethylhydrazine
N-Nitroso-N-ehtylurea	1,2-Dimethylhydrazine
N-Nitroso-N-methylurethane	Hydrazine
2-Aminofluorene	Methylhydrazine
N-Hydroxy-2-acetylaminofluorene	Procarbazine
N-Acetoxy-2-acetylaminofluorene	Chlorambucil
Dimethylethylenimine	Uracil mustard
3,3'-Dimethoxybenzidine	Carbon tetrachloride
3,3'-Dimethylbenzidine	Chloroform
4,4'Methylene *bis*-(2-chloroaniline)	1,2-Dibromo-3-chlorpropane
m-Toluenediamine	Ethylene Dibromide
Polychlorinated byphenyls	Propylenimine
Diepoxybutane	4-Nitroquinoline-1-oxide
p-Dioxane	Diazomethane
N-[4-(5-Nitro-2-furyl)-2-thiazolyl]-formamide	
Bromoethyl methanesulfonate	Cycasin
Ethyl methanesulfonate	o-Aminoazobenzene
Methyl methanesulfonate	3'-Methyl-4-aminoazobenzene
Ethionine	Aflatoxins
Urethane	
1,3-Propane sultone	

F. A discussion of the purpose and types of primary containment equipment is included. Selection of laboratory hood, biological safety cabinet or glove box is important [34] and is done in conjunction with the safety officer and the engineering staff. Containment devices are checked regularly for proper operation according to established procedures [35, 36].

NIEHS HIGH-HAZARD LABORATORY FOR LIFE SCIENTISTS

Figure 1 illustrates the floor plan of the NIEHS high-hazard laboratory for life scientists. All attempts were made to make it as safe and functional as possible within the available space.

Architectural Features

Entrance is through a change room with pass-through wall lockers where street clothes are stored and picked up after leaving the exit change room. Shelves are provided for disposable protective clothing that must be worn by anyone entering the area. Entry and exit rooms act as air locks. Doors are electrically interlocked so that two adjacent doors cannot be opened simultaneously; all travel is in one direction.

Surfaces (walls, floor and ceiling) are coated with an epoxy finish for ease of washdown and decontamination when necessary. Shelves and benches in the work area are stainless steel.

Equipment in the room includes: laboratory hood; class II biological safety cabinet; double-door pass-through steam sterilizer; high-speed centrifuge; two ventilated CO_2 incubators (connected via manifolds to CO_2 tanks outside the room); two freezers; refrigerator; analytical balance; water bath on a timer; gyrator shaker; vacuum pump; and a push-button telephone that can be used without picking up the receiver. The freezers, refrigerator and sterilizer can be serviced from outside the room. There is also an alarm button for use in an emergency.

Viewing ports are provided because the room is, by design, isolated. Angled mirrors allow all areas except the entrance and exit to be viewed by an outside observer. Personnel in other areas of the building are requested to glance through the ports occasionally to check on researchers working inside.

Some of these features can be seen in Figures 2 and 3.

Mechanical Features

Two exhaust systems are provided for the facility. One system exhausts the laboratory hood and incubators through a Flanders bag-in/bag-out prefilter,

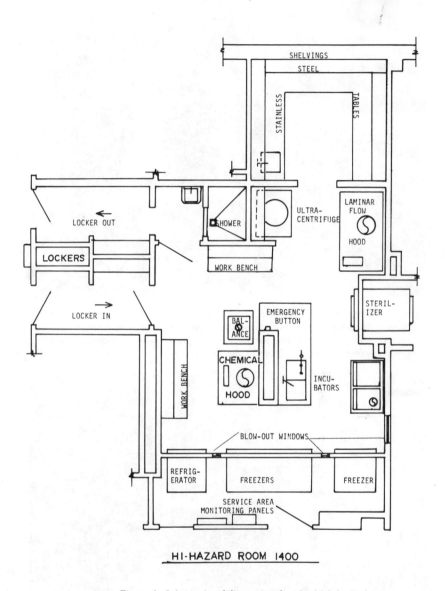

Figure 1. Schematic of floor plan for the high-hazard room.

HEPA filter, charcoal filter assembly. The other system is for the biological safety cabinet; air from it is discharged through a similar filter assembly. Both supply and exhaust air systems are monitored and controlled by a central control system (Air Monitor Corporation, Santa Rosa, CA) that allows the air volumes to remain fairly constant and the room to remain under

Figure 2. Interior view of the room. Shown (left to right) are the biological safety cabinet, double-door pass-through autoclave, two vented CO_2 incubators, two freezers, and some of the stainless steel shelves and benches. A portion of the lighting system is seen at the top of the photograph.

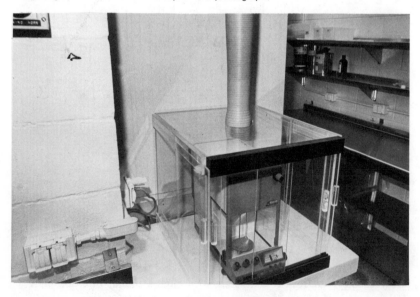

Figure 3. Enclosed analytical balance.

negative pressure to the rest of the building. If the exhaust(s) fail, the controls automatically shut down the supply air and give both audible and visual alarms on indicator panels located at the entrances to the facility and in the work area directly above the exit door. A central control panel (Figure 4) located outside the room allows for checks on pressure drops across the filters and on other measurable parameters within the room. The control panel is checked routinely, and a log is maintained. The safety officer periodically reviews the log to ensure that all systems are operating properly and observations are made punctually.

Figure 4. Control panel for air monitoring system (located outside the high-hazard room.)

Electrical Features

The electrical system has two backup systems: an emergency generator activated automatically if power is lost, and emergency batteries to supply power for a limited time if a total system failure occurs.

Change room lights remain on continuously. The work area has fluorescent lighting for normal operations and red lighting for light-sensitive materials. During nonworking hours, a timer automatically activates an ultraviolet (uv) lighting system. The UV lights are interlocked to the entrance door and are automatically turned off when someone enters the facility. A manual reset button is pushed upon exiting to reactivate the UV lights.

A smoke sensor in the room automatically releases the exit door for speedy egress in case of fire.

Operational Procedures

Access to the high-hazard laboratory is controlled by the NIEHS safety officer. Individuals desiring to work in the area first attend an orientation session describing the features of the room, its limitations, and the institute policy on research in the room. A section of the NIEHS Safety and Health Manual [33] includes this topic. After being designated, authorized researchers must file an approved protocol before starting any experiments. Keys are signed in and out and are maintained by the safety officer who arranges scheduling of the room. The keys, unless specifically authorized, must be returned at the end of the workday. Policies concerning the room are strictly enforced, and violations may be grounds for permanent loss of privileges and/or possible disciplinary action.

SUMMARY

Safe facilities for research involving carcinogenic and mutagenic compounds must exist. Properly designed high-hazard laboratories coupled with a realistic safety and health program for hazardous chemicals are needed. Today's emphasis on safety and health, especially in light of recent studies indicating that chemists have a higher risk for certain types of cancer [37-40], dictates that yesterday's hands-off attitude regarding regulations concerning research laboratories should not continue. Health protection must be a part of all facilities and research planning [41].

The primary factor in the design of the NIEHS high-hazard laboratory is to provide maximum safety with minimum hinderance to the individual researcher. This exemplifies what can be accomplished when scientific personnel, safety and health professionals, and engineering staff combine their talents to create functional, safe and unique laboratory space from areas previously used for different purposes.

DISCLAIMER

Mention of commercial products and trade names is for informational purposes only and does not imply endorsement by the National Institute of Environmental Health Sciences.

REFERENCES

1. U.S. Congress, Public Law 91-596, Occupational Safety and Health Act of 1970, December 29, 1970.
2. *Federal Register* 39(20):3756 (1974).
3. *Federal Register* 41(163):35184 (1976).
4. Crapnell, S. "Battle Lines Forming Over OSHA's New Carcinogen Policy," *Occ. Hazards* 40(5):61-64 (1978).
5. Libby, R. A. "OSHA Proposals Reach into the Research Laboratory as Well as the Industrial Workplace," *Anal. Chem.* 50:1326A-1328A (1978).
6. Smith, R. J. "Laboratory Chemicals May Come Under Costly OSHA Restrictions," *Science* 202:496-499 (1978).
7. Long, J. E. "Tighter Safety Rules Ahead for Academic Labs," *Chem. Eng. News* 53(28):21-22 (1975).
8. Sanders, H. J. "Chemical Lab Safety and the Impact of OSHA," *Chem. Eng. News* 54(21):15-27 (1976).
9. Walters, D. B., J. D. McKinney, A. Norstrom and N. DeWitt. "Control of Potential Carcinogenic, Mutagenic and Toxic Chemicals via a Protocol Review Concept and a Chemistry Containment Laboratory," Chapter 1, this volume.
10. Hopfinger, A. J., R. Potenzone, Jr., G. W. Milne and S. R. Heller. "A Model for Classifying Hazardous Compounds," Chapter 20, this volume.
11. Chu, K. "Quantitative Structure–Activity Relationships in Chemical Carcinogenesis," Chapter 25, this volume.
12. George, W. H. S., and C. E. Searle. "Chemical Carcinogens as Laboratory Hazards," in *Chemical Carcinogens*, C. E. Searle, Ed. (Washington, DC: American Chemical Society, 1976), p. 485.
13. Ehrenberg, L., and C. A. Wachtmeister. "Handling of Mutagenic Chemicals: Experimental Safety," in *Handbook of Mutagenicity Test Procedures*, B. J. Kilbey, M. Legator, W. Nichols and C. Ramel, Eds. (Amsterdam: Elsevier Scientific Publishing Company, 1977), p. 413.
14. "Guidelines for Research Involving Recombinant DNA Molecules," National Institutes of Health (1978).
15. "Guidelines for the Laboratory Use of Chemical Substances Posing a Potential Occupational Carcinogenic Risk," Draft Report, Laboratory Chemical Carcinogen Safety Standards Subcommittee of the DHEW Committee to Coordinate Toxicology and Related Programs (June 5, 1979).
16. Sansone, E. B., J. A. Poiley, R. J. Pienta and W. B. Lebherz, III. "Potential Hazard of Tissue Culture Assays Arising from Carcinogenic Compounds Incompletely Removed by Washing," *Cancer Res.* 36:2455-2458 (1976).

17. Sansone, E. B., A. M. Losikoff and R. A. Pendleton. "Potential Hazards from Feeding Test Chemicals in Carcinogen Bioassay Research," *Toxicol. Appl. Pharmacol.* 39:435-450 (1977).
18. Sansone, E. B., A. M. Losikoff and R. A. Pendleton. "Sources and Dissemination of Contamination in Material Handling Operations," *Am. Ind. Hyg. Assoc. J.* 38:433-442 (1977).
19. Sansone, E. B., and A. M. Losikoff. "A Note on the Chemical Contamination Resulting from the Transfer of Solid and Liquid Materials in Hoods," *Am. Ind. Hyg. Assoc. J.* 38:489-491 (1977).
20. Weeks, R. W., Jr., and B. J. Dean. "Permeation of Methanolic Aromatic Amine Solutions Through Commercially Available Glove Materials," *Am. Ind. Hyg. Assoc. J.* 38:721-725 (1977).
21. Sansone, E. B., and Y. B. Tewari. "The Permeability of Laboratory Gloves to Selected Solvents," *Am. Ind. Hyg. Assoc. J.* 39:169-174 (1978).
22. Halbert, M. M., J. Krober, D. Vesley and N. Vick. *Catalog of Pipetting Aids and Other Safety Devices for the Biomedical Laboratory.* University of Minnesota, School of Public Health (1975).
23. Keith, J. N. "How to Design a Building Safe Against Hazards," *Occup. Health Safety* 46(2):46-48 (1977).
24. Barrett, J. C. "Low Volume, High Velocity Exhaust Systems," *National Safety News* 106(5):60-64 (1972).
25. "NIOSH Certified Equipment List as of July 1, 1978," DHEW (NIOSH) Publication No. 79-107 (1978).
26. Weeks, R. W., Jr., and B. J. Dean. "Decontamination of Aromatic Amine Cancer-Suspect Agents on Concrete, Metal, or Painted Surfaces," *Am. Ind. Hyg. Assoc. J.* 39:758-762 (1978).
27. Rappaport, S. M., and E. E. Campbell. "The Interpretation and Application of OSHA Carcinogen Standards for Laboratory Operations," *Am. Ind. Hyg. Assoc. J.* 37:690-696 (1976).
28. Ward, J. T., C. H. William, Jr., C. D. Wolbach and D. B. Walters. "Transportation of Material From Radian's Hazardous Materials Laboratory," Chapter 5, this volume.
29. Longfellow, D. G., and A. R. Patel. "Preparation, Packaging and Perversity of Chemical Carcinogens—A Repository Viewpoint," Chapter 3, this volume.
30. Weeks, R. W., Jr., B. J. Dean, and S. K. Yasuda. "Tests Monitor Carcinogenic Aromatic Amines, Aid in Work Decontamination," *Occup. Health Safety* 46(2):19-23 (1977).
31. Piver, W. T. "Deactivation and Disposal Methods for Small Quantities of Experimental Chemicals," Chapter 29, this volume.
32. Baldwin. C. L., F. L. Sabel and C. B. Henke. "Bedding Disposal Cabinet for Containment of Aerosols Generated by Animal Cage Cleaning Procedures," *Appl. Environ. Microbiol.* 31:322-324 (1976).
33. "NIEHS Safety and Health Manual," National Institute of Environmental Health Sciences, DHEW (NIH) 79-1848 (1978).

34. "Laboratory Safety Monograph, A Supplement to the NIH Guidelines for Recombinant DNA Research," National Institutes of Health (1979).
35. "National Sanitation Foundation Standard No. 49," National Sanitation Foundation (1976).
36. "SAMA Standard for Laboratory Fume Hoods," Scientific Apparatus Makers Association (1975).
37. Li, F. P., J. F. Fraumeni, Jr., N. Mantel and R. W. Miller. "Cancer Mortality Among Chemists," *J. Nat. Cancer Inst.* 43:1159-1164 (1969).
38. Olin, R. "Leukemia and Hodgkin's Disease Among Swedish Chemistry Graduates," *Lancet* II:916 (1976).
39. Searle, C. E., J. A. H. Waterhouse, B. A. Henman, D. Bartlett and S. McCombie. "Epidemiological Study of the Mortality of British Chemists," *Brit. J. Cancer* 38:192-193 (1978).
40. Olin, G. R. "The Hazards of a Chemical Laboratory Environment— A Study of the Mortality in Two Cohorts of Swedish Chemists," *Am. Ind. Hyg. Assoc. J.* 39:557-562 (1978).
41. Bolton, N. E., C. L. Hunt, T. A. Lincoln and W. E. Porter. "Health Protection Must be Part of Planning," *Occup. Health Safety* 46(2): 30-32,39 (1977).

PREPARATION, PACKAGING AND PERVERSITY
OF CHEMICAL CARCINOGENS –
A REPOSITORY VIEWPOINT

David Godwin Longfellow

>   Chemical and Physical Carcinogenesis
>   Branch
>   National Cancer Institute
>   National Institutes of Health
>   Bethesda, Maryland

A. R. Patel

>   Diet and Nutrition Program,
>   Special Programs Branch
>   Division of Cancer Cause and Prevention
>   National Cancer Institute
>   National Institutes of Health
>   Bethesda, Maryland

INTRODUCTION

Few would argue the importance of placing "safety first" as the cornerstone of any laboratory utilization of chemical carcinogens whether it be in a biological, chemical or teaching laboratory or in an industrial setting. In reality, however, the construction of a coherent, realistic and usable safety protocol for chemical carcinogens in a particular laboratory setting is a difficult task at best.

This difficulty stems in part from the lack of specific information in the literature concerning the safe preparation, handling and disposal of chemical carcinogens. Prior to the last decade, guidance was available primarily from texts and handbooks which focused on safety and accident prevention in the chemical laboratory *per se*, or in toxic substances management. More recently, however, a number of good sources of specific information on safe handling of chemical carcinogens have begun to appear, such as "The IARC Monographs on the Evaluation of the Carcinogenic Risk of Chemicals to Man"[1]. This series has dealt with a wide range of selected chemical groups. Guidelines and safety standards have also been prepared by a number of government laboratories and institutes. These have included: "The NCI Safety Standards for Research Involving Chemical Carcinogens"[2]; "NCTR Carcinogen Standards"[3] from the National Center for Toxicological Research; and, more recently, "The Code of Practice for the Safe Handling of Chemical Carcinogens in Medical Research Council Establishments"[4].

Another source of difficulty is apparent when one attempts to formulate safe handling protocols and standards suitable for universal application in all laboratory settings. Discrepencies and inappropriate responses are soon apparent as one translates from generalities to a specific laboratory condition. For instance, the safe handling of chemical carcinogens in the research or academic laboratory requires different considerations from those applied in the industrial setting or bulk chemical synthesis laboratory. Unlike the industrial operation that tends to use repeatedly large quantities of relatively few chemicals, the academic and research oriented laboratory tends more toward the use of a wide variety of chemicals in small quantities on an infrequent basis. Monitoring effectively for chemicals in the latter condition is difficult, costly and time-consuming. The potential risks found in different laboratory settings and operations vary and so must the methods used to avoid them.

One additional variable which deserves recognition when designing protocols for the handling of chemical carcinogens is the wide diversity of disciplines and degree of training of the personnel who are to be doing the manipulations. The very nature of chemical carcinogenesis has required the involvement of biologists, biochemists, molecular biologists, animal technologists, and many others. We can expect that formal training in good laboratory practice in the chemical laboratory has been minimal for these professionals, not to mention the technical personnel. Moreover, there is an increasing interest in the use of chemical carcinogens as tools to probe basic aspects of metabolism, enzyme induction, DNA repair and genetic abnormalities. Once a carcinogen is considered primarily as a reagent and not foremost as a carcinogen, there is a tendency to let the principle of "safety first" also take a lower order of priority.

The objective of this chapter will be to describe and summarize the facilities used and experience gained in the preparation, packaging and shipping of chemical carcinogens in a program of the Division of Cancer Cause and Prevention of the National Cancer Institute. The Carcinogenesis Program of the DCCP, NCI, established the Repository for Chemical Carcinogen Reference Standards in July 1975. A chemical synthesis and analysis program was also initiated by contract to provide a reliable supply of research materials. The objective of the NCI repository has been to provide a centralized source for the safe storage, packaging and distribution of well-characterized carcinogens and related chemicals to be made available to the worldwide research community as reference standards. By providing chemicals with a high level of purity and uniformity, it is hoped that a major source of variability in research results can be overcome. Furthermore, the safe handling of these dangerous materials can be assured at all steps in their processing from synthesis, storage, repackaging and shipping to the receipt by the user of a package which can be opened with complete confidence.

The repository, operated by the Illinois Institute of Technology Research Institute (IITRI, Chicago), was designed to fulfill the need of the scientific community for analytical amounts of authentic reference standards of chemical carcinogens. Another task of considerable magnitude for which certain parallels and similarities are apparent is that of procuring and characterizing sufficient quantities of environmental chemicals to use as substrates in short-term in vitro tests and long-term animal bioassays for chemical carcinogenesis. The Carcinogenesis Testing Program of the National Cancer Institute has a national mandate to determine the carcinogenic potential of environmental chemicals. Chemicals are selected on the basis of potential for human exposure, chemical structure, and other considerations such as availability and purity. The procurement and characterization of chemicals is one of the essential steps in the success of bioassays. A summary of analytical information, physical properties and handling information collected on chemicals prior to submission for animal bioassays will be included. The information outlined is not only essential for the design and implementation of a successful bioassay, but is important information to have on hand prior to safely employing any chemical carcinogen in substrate quantities in a laboratory setting.

PREPARATION

Description of Program

The chemical repository for unlabelled carcinogens is operated under NCI contract at IITRI. The repository stores, repackages and distributes carcinogens to research laboratories designated by the NCI project officer. Chemicals are provided, together with analytical documentation and safety data sheets. The current inventory of the repository totals more than 425 compounds including 36 N-nitrosamines, 13 polycyclic aromatic hydrocarbons (PAH) and 95 PAH metabolites and analogs. Shipping activity has been at the level of more than 2000 samples per year. Eleven other contracts at eight different institutions provide chemical synthesis and analysis of designated compounds. A list of current contractors is provided in Table I. As part of a PAH metabolite synthesis contract, the Midwest Research Institute (MRI) in Kansas City, Missouri, maintains a repository for radio-labeled chemical carcinogens for the NCI.

Table I. Current Contractors in the NCI Chemical Carcinogen Reference Repository Program

Chemical Repository	IIT Research Institute Chicago, Illinois Contract No. N01-CP-55646 Dr. James Keith
Organic Synthesis of Cold and Tritiated Polycyclic Hydrocarbon Derivatives	University of Chicago Chicago, Illinois Contract No. N01-CP-33385 Dr. Ronald Harvey
	Midwest Research Institute Kansas City, Missouri Contract No. N01-CP-33387 Mr. James Wiley
Synthesis of Hetero-Substituted Polyaromatic Hydrocarbons	SRI International Menlo Park, California Contract No. N01-CP-85612 Dr. Elmer Reist
Synthesis of 2,3,7,8-Tetrachlorodibenzo-p-dioxin and Other Dioxin Cogeners	IIT Research Institute Chicago, Illinois Contract No. N01-CP-85945 Dr. Alan Gray
Basic Ordering Agreements for Organic Synthesis of Specified Chemicals	IIT Research Institute Chicago, Illinois Contract No. N01-CP-85635 Dr. Alan Gray
	Inveresk Research International Edinburgh, Scotland Contract No. N01-CP-85639 Dr. Margaret Henderson
	Midwest Research Institute Kansas City, Missouri Contract No. N01-CP-85636 Dr. Richard Heys
Basic Ordering Agreements for Organic Synthesis of Specified Chemicals	New England Nuclear Corporation Boston, Massachusetts Contract No. N01-CP-85638 Dr. Felix Granchelli

Table I, continued

Research Triangle Institute
Research Triangle Park, North Carolina
Contract No. N01-CP-85634
Dr. John Kepler

Southern Research Institute
Birmingham, Alabama
Contract No. N01-CP-85637
Dr. Y. Fulmer Shealy

SRI International
Menlo Park, California
Contract No. N01-CP-85600
Dr. Elmer Reist

Design

All of the contractors participating in this program have had long established programs in organic synthesis. However, indicative of the serious approach to the hazards involved, a number of the contractors have designed and constructed new and dedicated facilities for carcinogen synthesis. In other cases, major renovations and protocol changes have been implemented. In either approach, it is clear that major rethinking of all aspects of the facility including construction materials, air handling, lighting, personnel access/egress, waste disposal, and maintenance must be taken into consideration and be coordinated.

The IITRI repository facility design is seen in Figure 1. This 625-ft^2 area features independent ventilation; automatically maintained negative air pressure; exhaust filtered by a high-efficiency particulate air filter (HEPA) and charcoal filters; monolithic epoxy and polyurethane floor covering; special glove box design; and vault storage of volatile carcinogens.

Entrance to the repository is permitted only through the locker room door for authorized personnel with keys. Disposable laboratory coats are donned before entering the workroom. In the center of the workroom is a stainless steel glove box with four internal compartments for handling up to four different sample operations at the same time. A 3-ft-wide filtered fume hood is located on the right side of the workroom and is used for all liquid handling, preparation of samples for analysis, and some repackaging procedures.

To the rear of the workroom are two vaults separated by a special decontamination shower area. After cleanup of a seriously contaminated area, operating personnel would enter this shower to decontaminate their

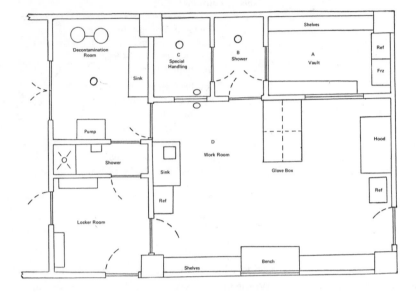

Figure 1. Floor plan diagram of repository at IITRI.

protective clothing. There are ten shower heads, so arranged that it is possible to rinse off an acid suit with little difficulty. The doors to the shower and vault areas are sealed with silicone rubber gaskets and closed by special latch dogs which ensure proper sealing of the gasket.

In the vault area stock containers are stored in sealed cans on metal shelves while less stable or more volatile materials are kept in cans under refrigeration in a safety refrigerator or freezer.

Exit from the workroom area is made only through the decontamination room. A sink to the left of that door permits hand washing prior to exit and between operations. Laboratory coats are removed in the decontamination room. A sump pump and holding tanks located in this room are connected to the floor drain of the emergency shower and eye wash station in the workroom. Contaminated wastewater can be handled by filtration or chemical treatment prior to release into the wastewater system.

Access/Egress

Facilities handling chemical carcinogens must operate on the principle of limited access to authorized personnel only. This is essential not only from a standpoint of containment, but also for perhaps less obvious reasons of security, liability and a heightened awareness of safety on the part of those exposed.

Entrance ways should be clearly marked for the hazards involved and access restricted by locks. Carcinogen synthesis laboratories at MRI have installed push-button combination locks on the main access/egress doors (Figure 2). Other exits from a suite of interconnected laboratories within the hazard containment area are provided for emergency exits but are controlled by breakseals for exit only.

Figure 2. Access/egress doorway to synthesis suites at MRI. Push-button combination lock restricts access, and warning of hazard is clearly posted (radioactive material warning is also posted at entrance but out of field of this view).

Floors, Walls and Work Surfaces

Floor coverings in hazard areas should be of monolithic (seamless) construction. Floors, walls and ceilings in the repository have been sealed with epoxy and then covered with a textured polyurethane finish. Workbenches should be nontextured, nonpermeable and should be kept covered with plastic-backed bench paper for absorbancy and easy cleanup. In general, all surfaces within a hazard containment laboratory should be designed to facilitate cleanup in case of contamination, as well as for maintaining clean working areas. In the workroom of the repository (Figure 3), the plumbing is enclosed in pilasters (next to the refrigerator), and a soffitt (upper right) encloses the intake air duct as well as the exhaust duct and prevents dust buildup on ducts.

Figure 3. Interior view of repository workroom looking left toward locker room. Large, double-pane, safety glass window on the left provides view of repository from hallway.

Hoods and Glove Boxes

A 3-ft wide Kewaunee hood is used for all liquid handling operations in the repository (Figure 4). A makeup air feature permits entrance of additional air from the top of the cabinet as the sash is lowered, thereby reducing the variation in face velocity. A deflector at the front of the hood draws air from the area below the hood bench to reduce the turbulence caused by the presence of the operator's body at the face of the hood.

The repository glove box (Figure 4), was specially fabricated from stainless steel. There are four internal compartments with interconnecting ports which can be opened in order to pass objects between compartments. Nitrogen gas from a single cylinder is valved to each of the compartments through 0.25-in. copper tubing. While performing operations in the box, nitrogen is continuously purged into the compartment at a tank regulator pressure of 5 lb. This is the only source of makeup air to the box. There are no electrical or plumbing services inside the box. Light is obtained through panels on the roof of the box. Kodagraph ultraviolet filter sheets are placed over the panels and the windows to further protect photosensitive compounds.

Figure 4. Interior view of repository workroom looking right toward the glove box and fume hood.

Between each glove port on the box is a bag-out port consisting of an 8-in. diameter opening to which is attached a polyethylene bag for use in packaging operations (described later).

Disposal of Airborne Waste

The repository laboratory and containment equipment are vented independently from all other building exhausts. Negative pressure in the laboratory is automatically controlled. About 3 feet above the locker room door (seen in Figure 3) is pressure sensor tubing leading to controls in the locker room. An alarm sounds when the pressure difference is lost. Exhaust air is expelled through sealed ducts to the roof. Figure 5 diagrammatically illustrates the exhaust system as it exists on the roof of the building. Dual risers serve the repository, and each is connected to a stainless steel filter housing on the roof. Each housing contains four filter stages (prefilter, two HEPA filters, and a charcoal filter) which can be replaced using the same bag-out procedures as those used in glove box transfers (Figure 6). Used filters are transferred directly into a plastic bag, thus avoiding contamination of the maintenance staff. The box above the filter housing contains a

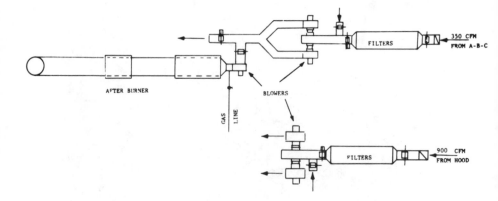

Figure 5. Diagram of the exhaust system on the roof of the repository at IITRI. A, B and C refer to the repository floor plan seen in Figure 1.

Figure 6. Flanders bag-out filter housing on the repository roof. Photohelic gauge is located in the box on the top of the unit.

photohelic gauge used to monitor pressure drop across the filters. Records are maintained concerning filter replacement. One common practice is to replace the primary HEPA filter on a regular basis and to advance the secondary HEPA filter into the primary position. A new HEPA filter is then placed in the secondary slot.

A subject of some concern is how often filters should be changed. Change is of course indicated following a major contamination or when gauge readings indicate an increased pressure differential (change in flowrate). However, short of these positive indicators, most laboratories institute change on a regular cycle such as once every six months—an expensive operation. Contractors at SRI International have fabricated their own bag-out type of filter housing which they locate in the duct directly above the hood (Figure 7). This unit is constructed of plywood reinforced with angle iron and seams which are sealed with caulking. Exhaust air passes first through a HEPA filter that removes particulate material larger than 0.3 μ. The exhaust then passes through two activated charcoal filters set up in series to remove volatile components from the air stream. When the filter unit is scheduled for change, the whole unit is sealed in plastic and incinerated. A new unit is then placed in the duct line.

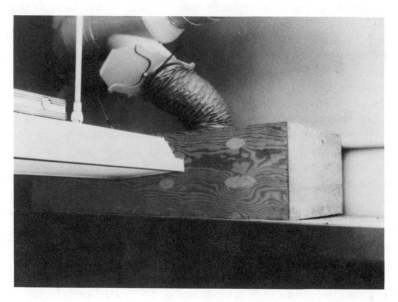

Figure 7. Plywood fabricated filter housing installed above fume hood at SRI International.

This laboratory has also devised a test method for monitoring the efficiency of the hood filter system. Monitoring ports have been installed in front of charcoal filters #1, between charcoal filters #1 and #2, and behind charcoal filter #2 (Figure 8). Periodically, a charge of carbon tetrachloride is released in the hood and a halogen detector is connected to the monitoring ports. A halogen signal at port #1 indicates the presence of the carbon tetrachloride at the entrance to the carbon filters and the proper functioning of the equipment. As long as the monitor connected to the port between the two carbon filters gives no signal, the filters are not saturated and are judged to be working properly. When the monitor at the middle port begins to give a halogen signal, carbon filter #1 is effectively saturated with material and must be replaced. Carbon filter #2 prevents environmental contamination during the brief period that carbon filter #1 is overloaded. The effectiveness of carbon filter #2 is indicated by a negative halogen signal at port #3, which is at the end of the exhaust system.

The exhaust system for the repository diagrammed in Figure 5 includes an emergency incinerator which would provide an additional margin of safety in the case of accidental spillage of volatile compounds which might pass through a charcoal filter (e.g., vinyl chloride or ethylenimine). The system is designed to provide a residence time of 1 sec at 1600°F, at exhaust velocities up to 500 cfm. Under normal operating conditions, the incinerator is bypassed. When needed, the incinerator can be activated by a switch in the workroom (above the sink, Figure 3). Automatic controls divert the exhaust to the incinerator after its operating temperature has been reached (approximately 1.5 min). The location of the filters and incinerator on the roof of IITRI is seen in Figure 9.

Laboratories involved in the synthesis of chemical carcinogens or the handling of large samples should give serious consideration to the provision of auxiliary systems for exhaust air handling. An emergency power generator should be capable of maintaining negative pressure differentials in the laboratory and containment cabinets. Alarm systems should alert personnel to a failure of the negative pressure exhaust system. A system with dual blowers on a single duct provides valuable insurance in the event of worn bearings or a burned-out motor. Blowers should be fitted with belt pulleys carrying multiple belts so that a single belt failure does not close down the entire facility.

The dual exhaust air ducts in the repository laboratory are interconnected by a diverter which can be activated while filters are being changed in one of the filter housings. In this way, the facility can be maintained operational by exhausting all air through one duct temporarily.

Maintenance personnel who must inspect and service the exhaust systems for such operations should be aware of the potential exposure hazards and

Figure 8. Filter monitoring ports and schematic diagram representing their location within the filter housing (SRI International).

should be provided with appropriate protective clothing, such as gloves and respirators.

Storage of Chemical Carcinogens

A comprehensive program for storage of chemical carcinogens should incorporate principles of *safety, stability, security* and *accountability.* The need for the first two elements is easily discernible, albeit not always easy to attain. *Security* is a concept less familiar to the academic research laboratory, although it has long been an important principle in the industrial setting. Security in this discussion is intended not only as a restriction of admission to the laboratory so as to avoid inadvertent exposure to laboratory personnel, but also includes an intentional plan to restrict access to chemical carcinogens so that only authorized personnel administer the

Figure 9. Installation of dual-exhaust air system on the roof of the IITRI Repository, including Flanders filter housings and emergency incinerator.

primary stocks. This caution is not only necessitated by the excessive cost
of many carcinogens today but, more importantly, by the fact that many
carcinogens are highly toxic and there have been documented cases where
they have been used as human poisons. At MRI a surplus fireproof safe
has been utilized as a storage compartment for selected stable carcinogens.

Accountability implies that a storage inventory is established which can
account for what chemical carcinogens are on hand, where and when they
were obtained, and where they are stored. The approximate amount brought
into the laboratory and a log accounting for its disposition should also be
maintained. Inventory control programs similar to those used for radiolabeled
materials are readily adapted for this purpose. This aspect of a storage program is even more important in the case of the laboratory that is an infrequent user of carcinogens.

The NCI repository maintains a detailed inventory system which is computer generated. Chemical names, synonyms, CAS numbers, and Wisswesser
line notation are provided together with quantitative information on the
amount of a chemical on hand, the amount shipped during a given period,
the projected balance for the month, and a 6-month projected balance
based on an average use rate. Information on suppliers, lot number, date
of receipt, physical data, analytical purity, stability and safety data are also
maintained.

Carcinogen stocks in the repository are stored in glass vials under a nitrogen atmosphere with screw caps having a Teflon* liner. Liquid samples are heat-sealed into ampoules. Primary containers are labeled minimally, with an assigned inventory number and the weight contained (in the case of small vials). If size permits, the chemical name and log number are also placed on the primary container. Each primary container is then heat-sealed into an individual polyethylene plastic bag and stored in a fully labeled paint can with a lid. All chemicals are segregated into separate containers for storage. Adjustable metal shelves (Figure 10) in the vault are used for the more unstable, toxic, volatile or corrosive compounds. Less hazardous compounds are stored on shelves in the workroom. An approved laboratory freezer and refrigerator in the vault are available for compounds requiring lower temperature storage.

Protective Clothing

The selection of protective clothing in a carcinogen hazard laboratory is dictated by the type of operation being performed, the nature of the

Figure 10. Repository vault (A) for shelf and refrigerated storage of chemical carcinogens. Refrigerator and freezer are Labline approved cabinets.

*Registered trademark of E. I. du Pont de Nemours and Company, Wilmington, DE.

compound being handled and the philosophy of hazard containment under which the facility is operated.

The NCI repository does not attempt to distinguish, with regard to personnel protection, between substances found carcinogenic in man and those found carcinogenic only in animals. Nor does it distinguish between carcinogens and potentially carcinogenic chemicals, or analogs, but treats all chemicals received as extremely hazardous materials.

Another important principle is that all chemicals are handled in containment cabinets (glove boxes or hoods), and, therefore, protective clothing is for the most part a secondary barrier between the chemical and the handlers.

The style of a particular lab coat or glove does vary from one laboratory to another in the NCI repository program, but the code of dress is essentially uniform. As a more versatile or more durable product line becomes available, changes are made.

Protective clothing is donned in the access/egress or locker room area before entering the workroom proper. The particular elements of dress included at the MRI synthesis facility are seen in Figure 11. These include rubber shoe covers (more durable than polyethylene booties), disposable coveralls (spun-bonded olefin), radiation film badge, safety glasses and gloves. Within the workroom area one pair of disposable gloves is worn at all times. These may be surgical latex or polyvinyl chloride gloves. While working in the fume hood, an outer pair of nitrile rubber gloves is also worn. This material has good solvent penetration resistance (Figure 12).

Workers in the repository at IITRI have been wearing wrap-around gowns which tie at the side in order to have a fully protected front when standing at the fume hood. Since no synthesis operations take place in the repository, these workers have not used the coverall pants as used at MRI.

Additional Considerations

Certain operations in a synthesis laboratory do not lend themselves well to being performed in the standard glove box or hood and yet have a high inherent chance of contaminating personnel. Weighing operations are universal problems for containment. At MRI the balance operations are performed in a specially constructed glove box which has its own connection to the exhaust system and is separated from the exhaust by an absolute filter (HEPA) (Figure 13). An intake filter to the upper right provides makeup air, and a bag port fitted with a plastic bag collects all solid waste. A door to the left permits introduction of containers. Closed ports on the top allow access to the balance for maintenance and adjustment.

Figure 11. Protective clothing worn by MRI personnel in the organic synthesis facility. Proper attire includes safety glasses, radiation film badge, coveralls, shoe covers, and two pairs of gloves (latex inner and nitrile outer).

Some balances are now available which feature a remote sensor head which is attached to the main telectronics of the balance with a cable. This feature permits the main workings of the balance to remain free of exposure to carcinogens. Such a system was recently installed in the repository facility at IITRI.

Another laboratory operation which can be isolated in a similar arrangement is thin-layer chromatography (TLC). A close-up view of the TLC box at MRI is seen in Figure 14. The sample entrance door is on the left. Yellow glass viewing ports filter out UV light. A TLC viewer (featuring long and short UV and white light) is located in the middle of the box. The

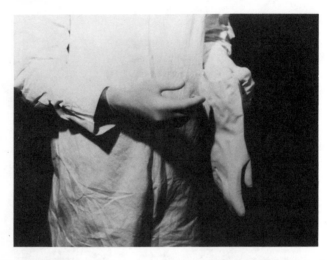

Figure 12. Hand protection includes latex surgical gloves worn at all times in the facility. Nitrile gloves are also worn over the latex pair when working with chemicals.

Figure 13. Analytical balance installed in a containment cabinet at MRI. Solid waste bag-out port is on the left. Air enters through a filter at the upper right. Chemicals enter cabinet through door on left. Exhaust air is HEPA-filtered (conical duct on upper left.

Figure 14. Containment cabinet for TLC operations in general synthesis laboratory at MRI. Access door is on the left front of the cabinet. Makeup air enters through filter on the left side. HEPA filter can be seen above the center section.

box in the duct above the TLC contains the absolute filter; a label indicates the installation date.

Liquids containing carcinogens are also a persistent problem in the synthesis laboratory because of potential for spillage and because of waste handling. The use of sealed floors and diaper-covered counter tops has already been mentioned. The work area inside of the fume hood should ideally feature covered edges and corners to facilitate containment of spills. Stainless steel trays can also serve this purpose.

Liquid waste disposal problems can be greatly minimized by pouring liquids into plastic containers filled with commercially available cat litter. This very absorbent, inexpensive material can reduce all wastes to a solid state for easier disposal. When the plastic jugs are full, they are sealed with tops and placed into 55-gal barrels which are in turn sealed and then removed for burial (by a licensed contractor/hauler). It is recognized that burial of toxic chemical waste is not an ideal solution. However, it is the only realistic solution available to most laboratories at present.

PACKAGING

Subdivision and repackaging of carcinogen stocks is a major function of the chemical carcinogen repository. The primary packaging of liquids and solids is handled by different protocols in order to avoid sample leakage during shipment.

Liquid Sampling

For sampling small volumes of liquid carcinogens it is desirable to use a system which will transfer rapidly and reproducibly a fixed amount of sample with a minimum need for decontamination of equipment. For large volumes, such as several hundred milliliters, the best way is probably to use standard laboratory glassware which must be decontaminated after use. This usually involves multiple rinses with a suitable, compatible solvent, followed by an overnight soaking in a chromic acid bath and conventional glassware washing.

For small volumes, on the order of several milliliters, and especially in the microliter range, it is economical and convenient to use disposable equipment. Disposable glass pipettes are available, but they are generally less convenient to use in a fume hood than the disposable-tip pipetting systems currently available. With these systems the pipette or its plunger never touch the liquid. The sample is drawn into a disposable polypropylene tip. A wide variety and range of single-volume pipettes is available.

Also available are a variety of glass vials that can be heat-sealed by melting the tip of the ampoule with a pencil flame and drawing out the neck in order to fuse the glass into a closure. Many of these ampoules are available "prescored" at a lower constricture on the neck to facilitate opening by the user.

One particularly convenient design for some applications is a "multi-dose vial," which features a conical bottom for complete recovery of liquid, a threaded outer collar and an ampoule neck for heat-sealing. When the contents are to be used, the neck is snapped off and a septum screw cap top is placed on the collar. The sample can then be withdrawn with a needle and syringe as needed.

Solid chemicals are subdivided exclusively in the glove box. Using a remote-sensor balance head, the chemicals are weighed out to the desired amount into pre-tared, dram glass vials. Screw caps are lined with Teflon discs to minimize reactivity with the contents. Various containers used for solids and liquids are seen in Figure 15.

Many chemical carcinogens are extremely electrostatic, a problem of some magnitude for weighing operations. A commercially available static eliminator such as the "ZEROSTAT," familiar to stereo and photography buffs, can be used to reduce or eliminate this problem.

After filling, the primary containers are labeled with identification number and weight (and log number and chemical name if space permits) and

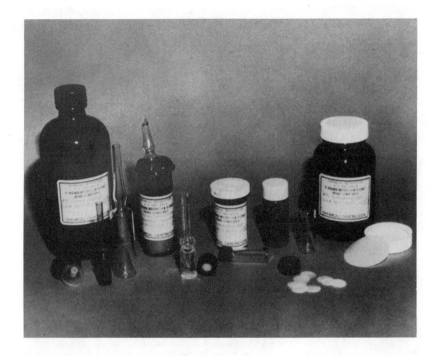

Figure 15. Containers used to subdivide chemical stocks. Liquids are placed in ampoules which are then heat-sealed. Solids are packed in vials with Teflon top liners.

sealed into a polyethylene flat-tube bag. The bag-out operation from the glove box is facilitated by an 8-in. opening between the glove ports. Over this opening lay-flat tubing is attached. The other end of the tubing is heat-sealed at all times. When a vial is ready to be removed from the glove box, it is passed through the bag-out port into the plastic tubing next to the sealed end. An electric impulse heat sealer is used to complete the sealing of the tube into a bag. The sealer is equipped to make a double seal with a 16.5-in. sealing width. The automatically timed heat impulse can be controlled over a range of 0-10 sec, so that a perfect seal can be obtained with any thickness tubing or a variety of types of plastic. Lay-flat, 13-in. polyethylene tubing of 0.002-, 0.004-, and 0.006-inch thickness has been tested on the unit at the repository and was found to produce a leak-tight seal with ease.

The heat sealer is mounted on a small laboratory cart, having raised sides so that it can be wheeled up to the bag-out port of the glove box.

A knife is affixed to the bag sealer so that after a seal is made, the knife can be drawn between the double seals releasing the finished, bagged sample and leaving the tubing sealed. This maintains the integrity of the isolation cabinet. Figure 16 illustrates the bag-out and sealing operation just described. Liquid samples are similarly sealed into plastic bags.

Figure 16. Heat-sealing a bottle into a polyethylene bag as it is removed from the glove box.

Each sample is then placed into an amber-colored plastic pill bottle with a snap top. This container has the complete identification information typed onto an affixed label. These containers are again sealed into bags as complete insurance against leakage (Figure 17). These packages are then rolled into absorbent packing paper and sealed with tape (Figure 18) before placing into paint cans. The sequence of these containers is seen in Figure 19.

A single paint can may then be packed with several chemicals provided they are of a compatible hazard class described by Department of Transportation (DOT) regulations. This would exclude, for instance, a volatile sample being packed together with one classified as a poison. Carcinogens per se are not classified by DOT. After the roles of chemical vials are placed in the can, additional absorbent paper is packed around them and above them to prevent movement. Vermiculite and styrofoam beads should be avoided for

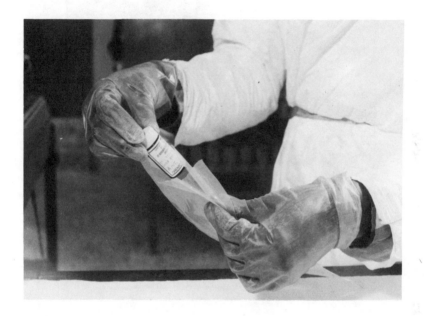

Figure 17. Primary containers sealed in plastic bags are placed into plastic snap-top pill bottles with labels. These are in turn sealed into a second plastic bag.

this purpose because of their electrostatic behavior and tendency to contaminate other areas such as a hood or glove box during unpacking. The paint can is labeled to identify all contents, the shipper's address, recommendation for storage, hazard warning and notification that contents should be opened only by the addressee.

The lid is placed firmly on the can and is further held secure by strips of nylon fiber tape or by can clips which are inserted in the lip of the lid and are pressed into place by a screwdriver blade. This precaution prevents the lid from popping open during air shipment due to a sudden change in pressure.

A shipper's bill of lading is then prepared for each can and its contents. The can then leaves the repository on a cart to be taken to the shipping room at IITRI. Each can is packed into a cardboard carton which is at least 1 ft square. Even if the can itself is small, this practice helps to prevent the loss which occasionally occurs with smaller packages.

Figure 18. Samples which have been double plastic-sealed are rolled into absorbent paper and packed into paint cans. Note labels.

The cardboard box is lined with 1-in.-thick styrofoam sheeting which reinforces it against impact and minimizes severe temperature variations to the contents. The can is surrounded by a firm packing of absorbent paper. An envelope is placed inside the box. Included is a warning that the package contains potentially carcinogenic material; it describes how the contents are packed and warns that the primary container should be opened only in a laboratory hood or glove box. Also included is a control sheet to be returned to the repository. On this sheet the recipient indicates the date received and advises of any deficiencies or damage to the package. Finally, the carton is sealed closed with tape.

The carton is then addressed and labeled to comply with DOT regulations, airline regulations, and those of the surface carrier (Figure 20). No package is sent by the U.S. Postal Service. Commercial carriers have demonstrated an excellent record of timely reliability and accountability, which is of considerable importance to the success of such a repository operation.

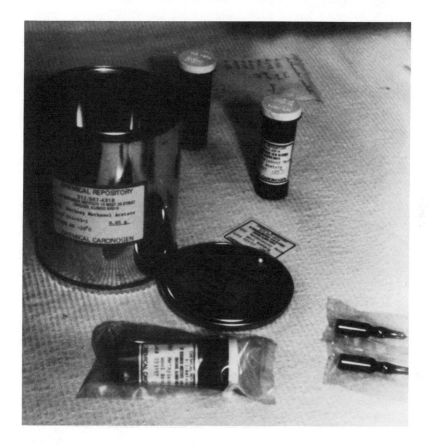

Figure 19. Samples are sequentially packaged: first into a glass ampoule or vial; then sealed into a plastic bag; then into an amber plastic bottle; then rebagged; and finally sealed into a paint can.

Approximately one week before shipping the sample by commercial carrier, a letter is sent to the addressee which advises that his request is being filled and that shipment of specific compounds will take place in about one week. Data sheets are also provided for each chemical including general references for laboratory safety and disposal. Analytical information includes: chemical and common name; chemical structure; molecular weight; lot number; date received at repository; storage requirements; melting point; results of elemental analysis; spectral data (IR, UV); and chromatography (TLC, GC and HPLC, if available). Property data sheets summarize the available information on physical characteristics, handling hazards, classification, recommended storage, special characteristics, decontamination, personal protection, first aid, and references.

Figure 20. Paper labeling of the shipping carton is essential both for compliance with regulations and for timely delivery. Note the DOT classification, radioactivity warning, address and return address label. The shipper's bill of lading is also affixed to another side of the box (not shown).

Every attempt is made to assure the minimal amount of time in transit for a shipment. This includes careful study of the available carriers to the point of destination, well-labeled containers, and avoidance of shipping immediately prior to weekends or holidays. The repository monitors each shipment until receipt of notification by the addressee that the shipment was received in good order and without serious delay.

PARALLELS TO A BIOASSAY PROGRAM
REPOSITORY

The objectives of establishing a repository for the bioassay program include the following responsibilities:

1. the procurement of bulk quantities of selected environmental chemicals;
2. selection of storage conditions and determination or estimation of shelf life;

3. analysis for purity and identification of minor components;
4. gathering and furnishing health hazard information to testing laboratories;
5. handling information;
6. determination of homogeneity and concentration of the chemical in feed, vehicle or inhalation chamber; and
7. determination of chemical stability in the feed or vehicle.

Although the quantities of a chemical needed for an animal bioassay differ from those needed in analytical studies by orders of magnitude, there is, for the most part, little difference in the scope of information on a chemical needed to handle it wisely and safely in the two circumstances. A checklist of data and information that should be obtained on a chemical prior to testing is outlined in Table II.

Table II. Data and Information Checklist

I. Procurement data
   Manufacturer/Supplier
   Amount Obtained
   Lot Number
   Batch Number
   Purity (Label)
   Analytical Data (if available)
   Container/Packing Description
II. Health Hazard Information
   A. Toxicity Data
   B. Route of Exposure
      1. Ingestion
      2. Inhalation
      3. Skin
      4. Eye
   C. Toxicity Symptoms
      1. Acute
      2. Chronic
      3. Emergency and First Aid Procedures
III. Physical Properties and General Information on
     Analytical Grade Chemicals

Chemical Name	Physical State
CAS Number	Appearance/Odor (if available)
Common Name	Boiling Point
Synonyms	Melting Point
Structure	Specific Gravity
Molecular Formula	Vapor Pressure
Molecular Weight	Stability in Storage
Use Pattern	Solubility

Specific Exposure
Rationale for Selection
To Be Purchased
To Be Furnished
Receipt Date
IV. Chemical Handling Information
Laboratory Ventilation Requirements
Analytical Method for Monitoring Laboratory Air
Protective Equipment Needs
Eye
Gloves
Respiratory
Other

Flash Point
Flammable Limits
Extinguishing Method

Handling and Storage Conditions
Degradability
DOT Requirements
Classification
Disposal

V. Bulk Chemical Analysis
  1. Elemental Analysis
  2. Physical Properties
     Physical State
     Appearance/Odor (if available)
     Boiling Point
     Melting Point
     Specific Gravity
     Solubility
  3. Spectral Data
     Infrared
     Ultraviolet
     Nuclear Magnetic Resonance
  4. Vapor-Phase Chromatography
  5. Thin-layer Chromatography
  6. High-Pressure Liquid Chromatography
  7. Electron Impact and Chemical Ionization Mass Spectroscopy
VI. Quality Control of Dosage Regimen or Exposure
  1. Determination of Homogeneity and Concentration of Chemical
     in the Feed, Vehicle or Inhalation Chamber
  2. Stability of Chemical in the Feed or Vehicle
  3. Purity and Stability of Vehicle (e.g., corn oil peroxides)

ACKNOWLEDGMENTS

The authors wish to acknowledge the informative discussions and illustration material provided by Dr. James Keith of IIT Research Institute, Mr. James Wiley and Mr. James Engel of Midwest Research Institute, and Dr. Elmer Reist of SRI International, which helped make this work possible. The expert technical assistance of Mrs. Ann DuLaney in the preparation of this manuscript is also gratefully acknowledged.

REFERENCES

1. "IARC Monographs on the Evaluation of the Carcinogenic Risk of Chemicals to Man–Vol. 1-20," International Agency for Research on Cancer (1972-1979), Lyon, France.
2. "NCI Safety Standards for Research Involving Chemical Carcinogens," DHEW Publication No. (NIH) 76-900 (1975).
3. "NCTR Carcinogen Standards," National Center for Toxicological Research, Jefferson, Arkansas (1975).
4. "Code of Practice for the Safe Handling of Chemical Carcinogens in Medical Research Council Establishments," Medical Research Council, London, England (1978).

CHAPTER 4

DESIGN AND OPERATION OF A
HAZARDOUS MATERIALS LABORATORY

James M. Harless, Kenneth E. Baxter and
Lawrence H. Keith
> Radian Corporation
> Austin, Texas

Douglas B. Walters
> National Institute of Environmental
>   Health Sciences
> Environmental Chemistry Branch
> Research Triangle Park, North Carolina

INTRODUCTION

The area of chemistry dealing with handling hazardous materials has expanded rapidly in recent years. Increasing numbers of industrial and research chemicals have been found to be biologically harmful to humans. Several programs are currently underway or proposed to better define and understand the harmful effects of the hazardous compounds in the modern world. Such programs include the following, which are part of HEW's newly formed National Toxicology Program: U.S. Environmental Protection Agency's priority pollutant program; National Institute of Environmental Health Sciences' environmental mutagenicity test development program, and National Cancer Institute's carcinogenicity testing program. To conduct research involving hazardous chemicals, hazardous materials laboratories are being designed and built so that chemical handling can be performed with a minimum risk of exposure for operating personnel and the surrounding environment.

The scope of current research involving hazardous materials requires facilities which can support a wide range of chemical activities. Some of the activities being performed in these hazardous materials laboratories are:

- chemical repository services,
- synthesis,
- chemical separations and purifications,
- preparation of analytical standards,
- extraction of environmental samples and preparation of extracts
  for analysis, and
- chemical analyses.

Laboratories can be built for one or two of these activities or designed as versatile facilities which meet the requirements of all these functions. Regardless of the type of facility, two requirements exist for proper functioning of a hazardous materials laboratory: to support the chemical activities for which it was designed by providing proper workspaces and equipment, and to provide maximum protection for operating personnel and the environment against contamination by chemicals contained within the laboratory. These requirements can be satisfied through proper design of the facility and implementation of effective operating procedures within the laboratory.

Radian Corporation has designed, built and operates a modern, efficient hazardous materials laboratory (HML). This facility is highly versatile and supports a full range of chemical activities including those listed above. During the designing of the HML physical plant and its operating procedures, very little information concerning HML construction and operation was found in the literature. Information Radian obtained about construction techniques, operational procedures, and governmental regulations for such a facility came from private and governmental regulatory agencies. The major sources of this information were:

- National Institute of Environmental Health Sciences
- Illinois Institute of Technology Research Institute
- University of Texas, M. D. Anderson Tumor Institute at
  Smithville
- Public Health Division, Department of Microbiology, University
  of Texas at Austin
- National Cancer Institute
- Safety Section, National Institute of Health
- National Institute for Occupational Safety and Health
- Occupational Safety and Health Administration
- National Institute for Toxicological Research at Pine Bluff,
  Arkansas
- Argonne National Laboratories

In the following sections, major elements of the Radian HML design and operating procedures will be discussed. It should be remembered, though, that each HML is a unique facility whose design and operation is a function of its intended use, local construction constraints, changing governmental regulations and many other factors. Information presented in the following sections represents one set of solutions to some important problems encountered in design and operation of this facility. They are based on the best available data and the judgments of Radian's design personnel.

DESIGN OF RADIAN CORPORATION'S HAZARDOUS MATERIALS LABORATORY

The principle design philosophy behind Radian's HML was to create a highly versatile facility while ensuring maximum protection against the uncontained exit of contaminating chemicals. This philosophy was translated into a controlled access structure containing workspaces and equipment capable of supporting a full range of chemical operations. The laboratory building and its utilities/mechanical support systems, air handling system and wastewater purification system were designed to assure operational safety and containment of hazardous chemicals.

Structural and Floor Plan Design

Radian's HML was constructed as a new facility rather than as a remodeled existing facility. This appeared to offer the most cost-effective route to a self-contained, first-class facility. By using this approach, all of the interrelated systems and the desired versatility could be designed without prior constraints imposed by an existing structure. A floor plan of the Radian HML is shown in Figure 1. Although built adjacent to an existing building, none of the laboratory walls are common to existing walls; the laboratory space and the existing building are separated by utility areas (G and H in Figure 1) and walkways. This arrangement provides an atmospheric buffer between the HML and the surrounding structures in case of escape of contaminating materials.

The building was designed to easily connect with future additions through existing window openings in the north exterior wall in both the laboratory and dressing areas, C and B, respectively, in Figure 1. It is 1½ stories high; the main floor of the building houses the showers, dressing rooms and laboratory facilities, and the upper half-floor contains most of the utilities and mechanical equipment serving the laboratory. Interior walls are gypsum wallboard covered with three coats of epoxy polymer-based paint. Floors are covered with vinyl sheet flooring, and seams are sealed by thermal welding. The flooring is coved 6 inches onto wall surfaces in the laboratory portions of the building. The facility was constructed at a cost of $\sim \$120/ft^2$, including subambient storage areas, laboratory furniture and mechanical support.

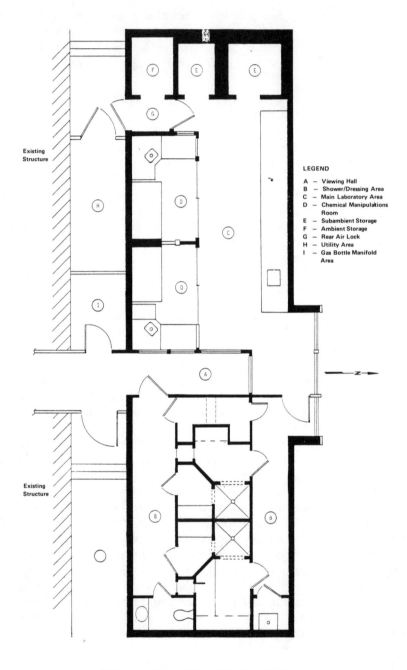

Figure 1. Floor plan of Radian's HML.

LEGEND

A — Viewing Hall
B — Shower/Dressing Area
C — Main Laboratory Area
D — Chemical Manipulations
       Room
E — Subambient Storage
F — Ambient Storage
G — Rear Air Lock
H — Utility Area
I — Gas Bottle Manifold
       Area

Existing
Structure

Existing
Structure

Visual observation of all laboratory workspaces is provided by the viewing hall (area A in Figure 1). Figure 2 is a photograph of the HML taken from the viewing hall. A clear view of the fume hood workrooms (D), main laboratory room (C), subambient storage area (E), and safety shower is available from this hallway. This is an important safety feature for a HML because it allows external visual monitoring of personnel working in the facility and of the safety shower area. In case of an accident inside the laboratory, personnel external to the facility can assess the situation and determine appropriate responses from a safe vantage point. Intercom communication is also provided between the viewing area and the main laboratory area. Also located in this hallway is the master control and monitoring panel for the laboratory mechanical support functions. Control switches, operating monitors and malfunction alarms for the fume hood exhaust and auxiliary air blowers, exhaust air filtering systems, laboratory air conditioning system, lighting and subambient storage areas are located on this panel.

The shower and dressing area (area B in Figure 1) provides personnel access to the laboratory. Facilities are provided for removal and storage of street clothes, dressing into laboratory clothing and showering. Laboratory clothing and respirators are stored in the inner dressing area and in the inner hallway. Hampers for containment of used, washable materials

Figure 2. View of the HML from the viewing hall.

are provided; these are emptied from the exterior hallway. Passage between the dressing areas is accomplished by going through the shower area, although a shower is required only when leaving the facility at the end of a work period. Restroom facilities are provided in the external area of the dressing area to ensure that laboratory personnel go through the proper decontamination procedures prior to using these facilities. Access to the external areas and to other parts of the Radian complex during work periods is provided by a passage located at the west end of the dressing/ shower area. Personnel must remove protective laboratory clothing and wash exposed skin surfaces prior to leaving the laboratory via this passage. Detailed access procedures will be discussed later.

The main laboratory (area C in Figures 1 and 3) contains general workspaces and storage areas. This area is always operated at a negative pressure with respect to both the dressing area and the outside atmosphere. This is to prevent the escape of any chemical material that might be present in the laboratory atmosphere. The negative pressure differential is established by a balance between the air exhausted by the fume hood exhaust fans and air supplied by the air conditioning system. The design of the air handling system will be discussed in detail later in this chapter. Workspace in the main laboratory area is general purpose and is mainly used for equipment preparation, record keeping and dishwashing. The safety shower and

Figure 3. Interior of the HML.

eyewash station are located in this area. Handling of open chemicals in the main laboratory area is done only in a glove box. All other manipulations are performed in the chemical handling rooms.

The chemical handling rooms (area D in Figures 1 and 3) are isolated from the main laboratory area by glass walls and sliding glass doors and are operated at a negative pressure with respect to the main laboratory area. All hazardous materials are handled in these rooms unless a glove box is required. The handling rooms are equipped with stainless steel fume hoods and general laboratory bench space. All air leaving the facility is exhausted through the fume hoods in these rooms and is filtered and decontaminated prior to release to the atmosphere.

Chemical storage areas are located at the west end of the main laboratory and are identified as areas E and F in Figure 1. Two subambient storage areas (E), one at 5°C and the other at -20°C, and an ambient temperature storage area (F) are available.

The airlock (area G in Figure 1) for receiving and exiting of chemicals and equipment is located at the rear of the facility. This area was incorporated into the building design so that materials could be transferred into and out of the laboratory without allowing direct contact between the outside environment and the laboratory atmosphere. This is another method of minimizing the risk of escape of any chemical species which might accidentally be present in the laboratory air. Since the laboratory operates at a negative pressure with respect to the atmosphere, the air flow is inward whenever either door is opened. The airlock is operated such that both doors are never opened at the same time.

The laboratory's electrical control panels, hot water heater, vacuum pump and laundry facilities are located in utility area H. Access to mechanical services located in the chase area above the laboratory and on the roof is provided through this room. Breathing air, argon and nitrogen are supplied to the laboratory from gas bottle manifolds in area I in Figure 1.

Several areas of Radian's HML are not shown in Figure 1. The wastewater treatment area and the emergency auxiliary generator are located outside the west end of the building. A 5-ft high chase space over the entire structure provides access to all plumbing, electrical conduits and relays, refrigeration equipment for the subambient storage rooms, and most of the air handling equipment. Supply and exhaust blowers for the fume hoods, the exhaust air purification system and some of the air conditioning equipment is located on the roof of the laboratory building.

Workspace Design

The versatility and functionality of Radian's HML was achieved mainly through the design of the workspace and storage areas incorporated into the facility. The HML was specifically designed to support the following types of chemical activities:

- chemical repository services,
- syntheses,
- separations and purifications,
- analytical standards preparation, and
- preparation of environmental samples containing hazardous compounds for analysis.

However, it has been found that a facility designed for these operations can support almost any normal chemical operation, including instrumental analysis.

The main laboratory area is designed as a general purpose workspace, although it is not used for handling chemicals. Approximately 20 ft of benchtop work area and undercounter storage are provided. This space is occupied by a controlled-atmosphere glove box, general workspace and a large glassware cleaning area. The glove box is the only place in this laboratory space where chemicals can be handled, and it is usually used for chemicals too hazardous or too unstable to be manipulated in a fume hood. Utilities provided in this area include breathing air, compressed air, argon, nitrogen, natural gas, vacuum, hot and cold water and deionized water.

Space in the main laboratory is also allocated for a large 16-sprayhead safety shower and eyewash station. An emergency alarm button is provided adjacent to the shower for easy access in case of personal injury or contamination. Once activated, the alarm system sounds throughout the Radian office/laboratory complex. A desk for records preparation and maintenance is provided, and a computer terminal containing a keyboard, CRT display, and line printer is located in the east end of the laboratory. This terminal is connected to Radian's central computer system where all inventory, safety and transaction information for chemicals stored in the HML is maintained. The incorporation of a computer terminal in the HML allows Radian to successfully manage repository operations for both the National Institute of Environmental Health Science and the Environmental Protection Agency wherein hundreds of compounds are stored and cataloged, and aliquots are removed and shipped to various laboratories around the world.

The chemical manipulation rooms were designed to house the majority of operations conducted in the HML. Each room is isolated and is operated at a negative pressure with respect to the remainder of the laboratory; therefore, any chemical released in these rooms is isolated. Each room is equipped with a 6-ft stainless steel fume hood and approximately 10 ft of benchtop workspace and undercounter storage. The fume hoods selected for this facility were Kewaunee "Solvent Sweep" auxiliary air hoods. These hoods are especially versatile because they are designed to provide approximately 4 ft of interior vertical clearance, enough to allow the use of tall reflux and distillation columns commonly required for chemical syntheses. A minimum face velocity of 150 ft/min is maintained across the face of each hood with the sash in the fully open position. Utilities supplied to each room include breathing air, vacuum, compressed air, argon, nitrogen, natural gas, hot and cold water and deionized water. An emergency alarm button is located inside each manipulation room for use in personal injury or contamination situations.

The large storage facilities incorporated into Radian's HML are necessary for maintaining chemical repository services. Commercial, walk-in, refrigerated chambers are used to maintain chemicals at $5°C$ and $-20°C$, and a third area is used to store materials at ambient temperatures. A total of 5000 to 6000, 100-g lots of chemicals can be stored in the HML. The storage areas are an integral part of the laboratory and are therefore isolated from the surrounding environment. The refrigeration units for the subambient storage areas are located in the overhead chase space for ease of maintenance. The temperature of each refrigerated area is constantly monitored, and an alarm is activated both inside the HML, on the master control panel, and in the Radian offices if the temperature rises above the normal operating range.

Mechanical/Utilities Design

One of the most difficult tasks in the design and construction of Radian's HML was the selection and integration of utilities and mechanical facilities needed to support the laboratory and allow it to function in the proper manner. This involved determinations of which utilities such as water, electricity, gases, etc., were needed, how they were to be introduced into the secure portion of the facility and what types of backup systems were needed. Also included in this task were design of the very complex air handling and purification system and design of the wastewater treatment system. These systems are described in the following paragraphs.

Utilities serving the HML are as follows: hot and cold water, deionized water, compressed air, natural gas, vacuum, argon, nitrogen, breathing air, and electricity. All pipes and conduits carrying these services were constructed in the overhead chase space whenever possible, and entrance into the laboratory facility was accomplished through the ceiling or walls as required. Whenever an inner wall was traversed, the area around the incoming pipe or conduit was completely sealed, first by polyurethane foam and then by a silicone polymer sealant. This was done to assure maximum isolation of the laboratory atmosphere. All utilities are supplied to the main laboratory area and both chemical manipulation rooms.

The wide variety of gases supplied to the laboratory is necessary to support a full range of chemical activities. Although rarely are all of these gases in use, they were plumbed into the facility at time of construction to provide versatility and to avoid difficulties of adding service after the HML was in operation. Natural gas and compressed air are provided from existing facilities, and breathing air, argon and nitrogen are supplied from compressed gas cylinders connected to manifolds in utility area I, Figure 1. Manifold vacuum is obtained from a large capacity vacuum pump serving the HML. Air removed through the vacuum system is filtered through activated charcoal before reaching the atmosphere.

Hot and cold water and deionized water are all supplied to the laboratory from existing facilities. All water outlets in the HML are fitted with vacuum-breakers to prevent backflow of water into the service lines.

Electricity is normally supplied to the HML through electrical circuit panels in utility room H in Figure 1. However, since hazardous materials are stored at subambient temperatures in the HML, and since the isolation of the facility depends on the maintenance of negative pressure inside, the HML electrical system is equipped with an auxiliary generator. This natural gas-fired, 30-kw generator is designed to automatically begin operation and support critical laboratory functions in the event of a power failure. The fume hood exhaust blowers, the air conditioner fans, the subambient storage refrigeration units, and approximately one-half the laboratory lighting are supplied electricity from the auxiliary generator. After restoration of normal electrical power, the generator turns off, and full operation of all electrical equipment is restored.

The design of the air handling and purification system was the most complex part of Radian's HML development. The components of the system were specified by Radian personnel, but the air conditioning, air moving and flow balancing portions of the design were handled by B-Squared Engineering, Katy, Texas, a group experienced in the design of air moving systems in negative pressure facilities. A schematic of the air movement system in the HML is shown in Figure 4. The system consists basically of three parts: one exhaust section which is the two fume hood exhaust blowers, and two air supply sections, one of which is the air conditioning/heating system and the other the fume hoods' auxiliary air blowers which supply makeup ambient air for the hood exhausts. The total exhausted air is balanced against the total supplied air to create a negative pressure inside the HML dressing area (-0.03 in. static pressure) and main laboratory area (-0.06 in. static pressure) with respect to atmospheric pressure. Negative pressure (-0.1 in. static pressure) is also maintained in the chemical manipulation rooms relative to the main laboratory room.

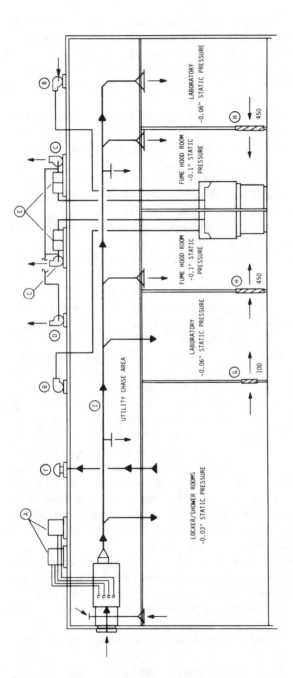

Figure 4. Schematic of the Radian HML Air handling system.

LEGEND

A - AIR CONDITIONING
B - AUXILIARY AIR BLOWERS
C - MAIN EXHAUST BLOWERS
D - AUXILIARY EXHAUST BLOWER
E - EXHAUST AIR FILTERS
F - SHOWER AREA VENTILATOR
G - LABORATORY ENTRANCE BYPASS VENT
H - FUME HOOD ROOM ENTRANCE BYPASS VENT
I - CONDITIONED AIR DISTRIBUTION

The air flows inside the laboratory are governed by the amount of air exhausted through the fume hoods. These exhausts are set to establish ⩾150 ft/min face velocity across the hood openings with the sashes in the fully opened position. Approximately 60% of this exhausted air is supplied by the auxiliary air blowers associated with each hood, and 40% is supplied by the air conditioning system.

Air continually passes into the laboratory area from the dressing/shower area at a rate of 100 ft^3/min through a bypass vent located above the entrance door. When the door is opened, the vent closes, and the air is swept through the door opening. This prevents air inside the laboratory from escaping into the outer areas. A similar flow pattern is established at the entrance to the chemical manipulation rooms. An air flow of 450 ft^3/min is maintained through bypass vents until the doors are opened. The air is then drawn through the door opening to prevent escape of air from the rooms into the main laboratory area.

All air exhausted from each fume hood is drawn through a filtration/purification unit prior to discharge into the atmosphere (see Figures 4 and 5). One Flanders Model E-2 bag-out filtration unit is used for each hood exhaust system and is located just upstream of the exhaust blowers. This system employs a 24 x 24 in. HEPA 0.5-μ prefilter for collecting dusts and mists, a 24 x 24 x 6 in. charcoal adsorbent bed for trapping organic vapors, followed by a second 24 x 24 in. HEPA filter to trap any contaminated carbon dust that might be released from the carbon filter. This system is adequate for the ~1400-ft^3/min exhaust flow from each fume hood. The status of each HEPA filter is continuously monitored on magnahelic gauges located in the main control panel (area A, Figure 1). They indicate the pressure drop (ΔP) across each HEPA filter; when the ΔP across a filter reaches a value approximately three times that registered when the filter was new, the filter is changed. No system for monitoring the activity of the carbon adsorbent has yet been devised; that filter is routinely changed every 6 to 12 months depending on the number of hours the fume hoods are in use and the types of operations performed in them. The decision to change the carbon adsorbent is made by the laboratory supervisor and Radian's safety officer.

Filter changing is performed using the Flanders bag-out system. When the filters are installed, large plastic bags are attached around the filter access opening. When a filter is changed, it is disconnected and pulled into the bag with the bag serving as a barrier between the person changing the filter and the contaminated filter. After removal, the filter is sealed in the bag, and the whole unit is incinerated at high temperature (>2000°F).

As shown in Figure 4, an auxiliary exhaust blower was designed into

Figure 5. View of the HML air handling system showing main blowers, auxiliary blower and filter system.

the fume hood exhaust system. Under normal operating conditions, the two main exhaust blowers are used, one for each fume hood, and the auxiliary blower is inoperative and isolated from the exhaust ducts by dampers. If a main exhaust blower fails for any reason, pressure sensors in the duct sense the resulting pressure change and automatically activate the auxiliary exhaust blower. The appropriate dampers are also actuated to isolate the malfunctioning blower and open the exhaust duct to the auxiliary blower. Simultaneously with the above activity, the pressure sensors also activate the main alarm system in the control panel. A second alarm sounds if the auxiliary blower has not returned the exhaust system to normal operation within 2 to 3 min after failure of the main exhaust blower. Once the main blower is placed back in full operation, the auxiliary blower stops operation, and the dampers return to their normal positions.

The design of the wastewater treatment system for Radian's HML is based on a system reported by Nony, Treglown and Bowman [1]. The system, shown schematically in Figure 6, consists of a holding tank, pump, particulate filters, and activated carbon and nonionic polymeric resin adsorbents arranged in series. The Radian system uses a 500-gal holding tank to receive

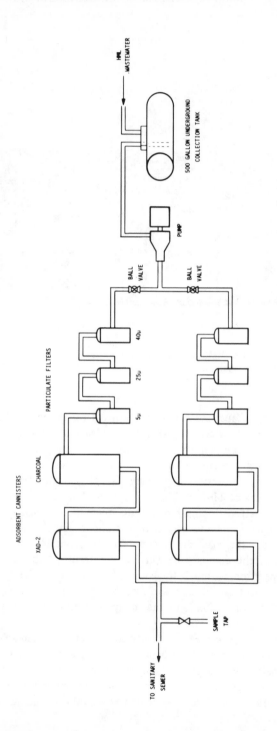

Figure 6. Schematic of the Radian HML wastewater treatment system.

all the wastewater from the main laboratory and chemical manipulations areas of the HML. As the tank fills, a level sensor actuates the pump which draws water from the tank and forces it through the filtering and adsorbing system and then into the city sanitary sewer network. The water flows sequentially through 40-μ, 25-μ and 5-μ particulate filters, ~1.2 ft^3 activated charcoal and ~1.2 ft^3 of Amberlite XAD-2 resin. The system is constructed using two parallel filtering/adsorbing trains so that one train is available for use while the other is being replaced. The particulate filters and adsorbents are replaced yearly unless routine analysis of the effluent reveals that organic materials from the laboratory are present. Disposal of the spent filters and adsorbents is by high-temperature (>2000° F) incineration or burial in an EPA-approved land fill.

Samples of effluent from the HML wastewater purification system are collected and analyzed quarterly. The samples are extracted according to the EPA's priority pollutant protocol, and the extracts are analyzed by gas chromatography using flame ionization and electron capture detectors. The results from successive analyses are compiled and compared to the analyses of blank samples collected from the trains when they are first put into operation. An increase in the number or concentration of organic compounds in the effluent automatically results in a change of filters and adsorbents.

The operation of the wastewater purification system is continually monitored by a level sensing switch located inside the tank. The switch is connected to a time delay relay so that if the pump does not reduce the water level in the tank within 3 min after it is turned on, an alarm is activated on the main control panel.

OPERATION PROCEDURES FOR RADIAN'S HAZARDOUS MATERIALS LABORATORY

The design and implementation of HML operating procedures are equally as important as the design of the physical plant for assuring minimum risk of exposure of operating personnel and the environment to the chemicals housed within the facility. Operating procedures design is a difficult task in the development of a good laboratory because many details must be considered and included. Each laboratory is unique in its design and function, and little guidance is available from published sources. However, some of the goals that must be achieved in order to design effective procedures are:

- maximum personnel safety,
- maximum protection of the environment outside the laboratory,

- isolation and positive control of chemicals,
- applicability to all types of chemical manipulations performed in the laboratory,
- maximum work efficiency and personnel comfort, and
- minimum operating costs.

Of course, all of these goals cannot be fulfilled for each procedure, but they should be considered for each procedure as it is developed.

Operating procedures designed for Radian's HML are summarized in the following paragraphs. They cover the four main areas of laboratory operation: personnel protection, materials handling, waste disposal and decontamination. The procedures were developed for a facility and personnel supporting a wide variety of chemical functions. Only the generalized design along with selected important details of these procedures is presented; however, many individual, detailed procedures are required for the safe and efficient functioning of Radian's HML.

Personnel Protection

Personnel protection procedures are the most important procedures to be developed during the design of a HML. They must be designed to provide maximum protection for personnel working in the facility, and they must minimize the risk of accidental contamination of outside areas by laboratory personnel. The principal personnel protection procedures for the Radian HML include procedures for entrance into the laboratory, protection during normal operations, and exit from the laboratory.

Personnel entering the HML must first remove all street clothing in the exterior dressing room. After passing through the shower area and into the interior dressing room, they don washable, two-piece laboratory scrub suits and tennis shoes. Disposable coveralls and shoe covers made of Tyvek® are then put on over the washable undersuits; Tyvek head covers are also used when working with highly hazardous materials. The Tyvek clothing is impervious to most chemicals and affords good protection from spilled materials. This outer clothing is discarded daily, and the scrub suits and shoes are laundered every 2 to 5 days in the HML laundry facility. Just prior to entering the laboratory, personnel put on two pairs of gloves to prevent contamination of the hands. The first pair are latex surgeon's gloves, and the outer pair are vinyl plastic, neoprene or other materials. Gloves of different materials, hence different permeabilities for chemicals encountered, are used to decrease the chances of a chemical permeating through the gloves to the skin [2-5]. The inner gloves are connected to the sleeves of the Tyvek coveralls with masking tape to prevent exposure of the forearms. The outer gloves are removed and replaced after each operation in the laboratory.

Personnel in Radian's HML are required to wear some type of respiration device whenever they are working with open chemicals (except in the glove box) and when they enter any of the three chemical storage areas. Half-face and full-face respirators (equipped with both particulate and organic vapor cartridges) and airline respirators are provided. Cartridge respirators are used when compounds of low to moderate hazard are being manipulated, and airline respirators are used when working with highly hazardous compounds such as known carcinogens and toxins. The highly hazardous compounds are identified by the laboratory supervisor and/or safety officer from reported toxicity data and chemical intuition. General guidelines for the use of respirators in normal HML activities are as follows:

- entry into storage areas—half-face or full-face respirator with organic vapor cartridges;
- handling of solids not classified highly hazardous (fume hood—half-face or full-face respirator with particulate cartridges;
- handling of liquids not classified highly hazardous (fume hood—half-face or full-face respirator with organic vapor cartridges;
- handling of highly hazardous materials (fume hood)—airline respirator and full body protection; and
- handling of highly hazardous materials (glove box)—no respirator required.

These general procedures are minimum requirements. It is necessary that laboratory personnel be adequately trained in the rationale for use of respiration protection devices and that they use common sense in the selection of these protection devices whenever they are working with specific hazardous chemicals.

The second area of procedures design involving personnel protection is work area selection. In Radian's HML the two work areas for handling chemicals are the fume hoods and the glove box. Compounds determined to be highly hazardous or air-sensitive are handled in the glove box, and all others are handled in the fume hoods. The selection of workspaces for specific compounds is monitored and guided by the laboratory supervisor and the safety officer.

Procedures for exiting the HML have been developed for two situations: leaving the laboratory during regular work periods but remaining inside the Radian complex, and leaving the Radian premises. When leaving for short periods of time, HML personnel are required to remove all Tyvek protective clothing, shoe covers, respirators and gloves, then wash all exposed skin surfaces (face, neck, arms and hands) with soap and water. They may then exit through the passageway at the west end of the dressing area (B in Figure 1) wearing their scrub suits and tennis shoes. Full showers are not required for exit under these circumstances because of practical considerations and employee comfort; the risk of unsuspected contamination from the laboratory underclothing is negligible. When personnel exit the laboratory to leave the Radian complex, they must remove and discard the Tyvek clothing and remove and store all other laboratory apparel. Filter cartridges are removed from respirators, and the respirators are washed with soap and water. Laboratory personnel then shower, being careful to wash their entire bodies and hair with soap. They can then leave the facility.

Materials Handling Procedures

Procedures have been developed for the three material handling operations conducted in the Radian HML: chemicals storage, chemicals manipulation, and transfer of materials out of the laboratory. As with all other procedures developed for the HML, these are guidelines that must be constantly reviewed and evaluated for applicability to each chemical handled in the laboratory. The general philosophies for developing such procedures are safety, versatility and common sense.

Chemicals stored in the HML are packaged in hypovials and steel cans or in screw-cap glass bottles. All materials which are stored as part of repository services are transferred to glass hypovials and sealed with Teflon®-faced septa (Figure 7). They are then labeled, heat-sealed in a plastic bag

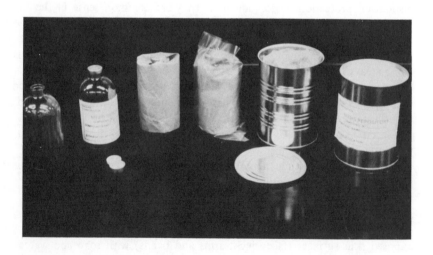

Figure 7. Preparation of sample for storage in NIEHS respository.

and stored in a labeled, friction-sealed can. This system offers maximum isolation and physical protection for the sample. Materials used for syntheses and standards preparation are generally stored in screw-cap glass bottles. Highly hazardous materials are stored as described for repository samples. The selection of storage temperature is based on the stability, volatility and other physical characteristics of the individual compounds.

Selection of workspaces (glove box or fume hood) for chemical manipulations are made as described in the preceding section on personnel protection. Regardless of the workspace, all chemical manipulations are performed on plastic trays covered with absorbent paper to provide initial containment of any spills. Packages of materials received from outside sources are placed on trays and opened in a fume hood. The fume hood sash is closed to a position to assure an air velocity of >200 ft/min across the opening before the packages are opened. Tests have shown that all dusts arising from packing materials are swept into the hood exhaust under those conditions.

Procedures have also been developed for packaging and handling chemicals leaving Radian's HML to go to analytical laboratories in the Radian complex or to be shipped to other laboratories. Materials transported within the Radian facilities are crimp-sealed in hypovials fitted with Teflon-faced septa, and the vials are decontaminated by washing with one or more appropriate solvents. The samples are then labeled, wrapped in absorbent paper, heat-sealed in a plastic bag and packed in a plastic or steel carrying container for transfer. A data sheet containing the compound identification, physical properties and hazards, handling procedures and accountability documentation accompanies each sample.

Materials transported to other laboratories are sealed in hypovials and decontaminated, then labeled, wrapped in absorbent paper, heat-sealed in two plastic bags, wrapped in bubble-pack and mechanically sealed in a labeled steel can. Safe handling and emergency procedures documents accompany each sample. These procedures were developed for use in a repository services program sponsored by the National Institute of Environmental Health Sciences and are discussed in more detail in another section of this book [6].

Waste Disposal Procedures

Major nonaqueous wastes generated from Radian's HML include the discarded expendable laboratory materials and waste chemicals. These wastes are divided into burnable and nonburnable materials inside the laboratory and are disposed of accordingly. Burnable materials, including most chemicals, laboratory clothing and packing materials, are incinerated at >2000°F in a commercial natural gas-fired incinerator. Discarded glassware is also fired under the same conditions, but is removed after the incinerator has cooled and is then discarded. Chemicals such as chlorinated hydrocarbon solvents which could damage the incineration equipment and noncombustible packing material such as vermiculite are buried at an EPA-approved, commercial chemical disposal site. All waste materials leaving the HML are double-bagged in heavy polyethylene bags and labeled as hazardous materials.

Contamination Monitoring and Decontamination Procedures

The Radian HML is periodically monitored for buildup of chemical contamination in the air and on laboratory surfaces. Routine decontamination of laboratory work surfaces is performed, and when indicated by monitoring procedures or a chemical spill, additional decontamination procedures are initiated.

Routine air monitoring in the HML is performed at least quarterly using NIOSH charcoal tube sampling procedures. Laboratory air is drawn through the tube for an 8-hr period, and the charcoal adsorbent is extracted with carbon disulfide or other suitable solvent. The extract is analyzed by gas chromatography using flame ionization and electron capture detectors, and chromatograms from each sample are compared to those from blank samples collected prior to initiation of HML operation. The presence of new compounds or higher concentrations of pre-existing compounds indicates that a contamination problem exists.

Laboratory surface samples are also collected and analyzed at least quarterly to monitor contamination levels. Cotton swabs saturated with acetone are used to collect samples from six 100-cm^2 surface areas in the laboratory. These areas are on walls in the main laboratory area, each manipulation room and each storage area. The swabs are extracted with acetone and analyzed by methods analogous to the charcoal extracts above.

Routine decontamination of the HML consists of weekly washings of the floor and all horizontal surfaces where chemical deposits might build up. Decontamination is done using strong detergent solutions. If air or swab samples indicate that a contamination problem exists, the entire laboratory area is thoroughly washed with a strong detergent solution. Solvent washes are used if the contamination persists. Sponges and mops used for laboratory cleaning are discarded after each use.

Decontamination procedures used for chemical spills are divided into two methods, one for liquids and one for solids. Liquid spills are generally handled by collecting the material onto absorbent paper followed by washing of the area with strong detergent. Absorbent paper saturated with an appropriate solvent is then used for a final wash of the area. Solids spilled in the laboratory are first collected on dampened absorbent paper, and the area is cleaned as above. All laboratory clothing worn during decontamination procedures is immediately removed and replaced with new clothing. All contaminated materials are double-bagged in polyethylene bags and incinerated. Self-contained, acid-resistant suits are used to remove spills of highly hazardous materials which would pose a threat to personnel in normal laboratory attire. These suits are located outside of the HML to prevent them from being contaminated and to prevent decontamination teams from being exposed to hazardous chemicals before they are fully protected. Spill cleanup procedures are the same as described earlier. In order to assure that no residual contamination remains, air and swab samples are taken in the HML and analyzed before personnel are readmitted.

CONCLUSION

This chapter has presented the major elements of the design and operating procedures of Radian Corporation's HML. It is hoped that the information presented here and in other papers currently being written and published will help fill some of the information gaps that currently exist in the area of hazardous materials handling. The designs and procedures presented in this chapter are not necessarily the final answers to the problems associated with chemical operations with hazardous compounds, but they are at the forefront of current technology. Hopefully they will serve as catalysts in the evolutionary development of better laboratory designs and procedures. The designs of existing facilities and procedures should be regularly examined with respect to advancing knowledge about the handling of hazardous materials, and they should be modified or replaced if they are not found to provide maximum safety for operating personnel and the surrounding environment.

REFERENCES

1. Nony, C. R., E. J. Treglown and M. C. Bowman. "Removal of Trace Levels of 2-Acetylaminofluorene (2-ARF) from Wastewater," *Sci. Total Environ.* 4:155-163 (1975).
2. Johnson, T. C., and W. D. Marciez. "Permeation of Halogenated Solvents through Dylox Gloves," U. S. Atomic Energy Commission, RFP-1608 (1971).
3. Sansone, E. B. and Y. B. Tewari. "The Permeability of Laboratory Gloves to Selected Solvents," *Am. Ind. Hyg. Assoc. J.,* 39 169-173 (1978).

4. Sansone E. B., and Y. B. Tewari. "The Permeability of Laboratory Gloves to Selected Nitrosamines," in *Environmental Aspects of N-Nitroso Compounds*, E. A. Walker, M. Costeynors, L. Gricinte and R. E. Lyle, Eds. (Lyon: International Agency for Cancer Research, 1978).
5. Nelson, G. O., C. G. Cardenas and J. D. Johnson. "Glove Permeation by Organic Solvents," presented at the Am. Ind. Hyg. Conf., Chicago (May, 1979).
6. Ward, J. T., C. H. Williams, Jr., C. D. Wolbach, L. H. Keith and D. B. Waters, "Transportation of Materials from Radian's Hazardous Materials Laboratory," Chapter 5, this volume.

CHAPTER 5

TRANSPORTATION OF MATERIALS
FROM RADIAN CORPORATION'S
HAZARDOUS MATERIALS LABORATORY

J. T. Ward[*], C. H. Williams, Jr.,
C. D. Wolbach[†] and L. H. Keith
 Radian Corporation
 Austin, Texas

D. B. Walters
 National Institute of Environmental Health Sciences
 Research Triangle Park, North Carolina

INTRODUCTION

Radian has been contracted by EPA and NIEHS to provide repository services for priority pollutants, toxic pollutants, suspected and known carcinogens, mutagens and teratogens, and chromatographic materials. Part of the services requires the preparation, packaging and shipping of repository materials as standards. The nature of these materials which places them in the repository inventory also places them in shipping categories that are intensively regulated. This chapter details:

- regulations pertaining to the shipment of hazardous materials;
- Radian's Hazardous Materials Laboratory (HML) procedures for packaging and labeling materials for shipment;
- the proposed distribution system; and
- the anticipated procedures to protect those who may come in contact with the subject materials.

Part of this chapter deals with regulations that pertain to shipping hazardous materials. This includes a general review of Department of Transporta-

[*]Present address: Sabine Offshore Inc., Sabine Pass, TX.
[†]Present address: Acurex Inc., Mountain View, CA.

tion (DOT) regulations and U.S. Postal Service rules for shipping poisonous, flammable and carcinogenic materials. Also discussed are the repository packaging procedures for various sizes of primary containers and the packing material used for all shipping containers from the Radian HML. General container labeling and means of identification of the chemicals that are being shipped and special handling information for hazardous materials are also covered, including special conditions for preserving materials shipped out of the HML, such as refrigeration, inert gas atmospheres, and the precautions necessary for handling photosensitive compounds. Finally, the safety of personnel who handle materials shipped out of the HML and the safety of those who might come into contact with this material en route to and at the material's final destination is discussed.

The DOT regulations for hazardous materials are structured around two main items—an extensive table of compounds (and classes of compounds), and a series of definitions or classifications for materials. A given substance may be listed in the hazardous materials table or, if not specifically named, it may fall into a certain hazard category because of its chemical and physical properties. If a material is not named but falls within a hazard category, it is termed a "Not Otherwise Specified" (NOS) material. Each named or NOS material must then meet certain packaging, labeling and documenting criteria based on its hazard category. The specific regulations are indexed from the hazardous materials table.

The regulations were designed for the safe transportation of large quantities of materials. The labeling requirements key the transportation personnel to the precautions they must take and the regulations they must follow. Thus, the small quantities that the repository will be shipping may be restricted to expensive and time-consuming modes of transportation not necessary for safe shipment. There are some explicit exemptions from labeling available within the regulations. Again, because the regulations are not designed to cover the type of shipping the repository will be doing, it is not clear whether repository shipments will qualify for these exemptions. Verbal confirmation has been received from the regional DOT office at Fort Worth that exemptions should be obtainable. Written confirmation is presently being sought.

REGULATIONS

The regulations covering shipments from the HML must be abstracted from the general DOT regulations. These are found under Title 49, Transportation, Parts 100 to 199, Code of Federal Regulations. The regulations of interest are in Chapter I (Materials Transportation Bureau), Subchapter D (Hazardous Materials Regulations), Parts 171 to 173. The complexity of these regulations is apparent upon reviewing the indices of these parts.

The regulations affecting the HML can be grouped into three categories: those covering packaging, labeling and documentation. The appropriate rules must be found within a large body of information organized around specific substances and classes of materials. The key sections are from Part 172:

- Subpart B: Table of Hazardous Materials [172.100-172.101];
- Subpart C: Shipping Papers [172.200-172.204];
- Subpart E: Labeling [172.400-172.450];

and from Part 173, Subpart B—Preparation of Hazardous Materials for Transportation [173.21-173.29].

The regulations were written for the shipment of large quantities of hazardous materials (pounds and gallons), not for the very small quantities shipped by the repository. Small quantities and dilute quantities have the potential to fall under several explicit and implicit ememptions. These exemption potentials will be discussed later.

The Hazardous Materials Table

The hazardous materials table (HMT) is the key for a user of the DOT regulations on hazardous materials. It is Section 172.101 of the regulations. An excerpt is presented as Table I for reference in the following discussion. The actual table is over 90 pages long. Materials listed in this table are designated as hazardous for purposes of commercial transportation. The table classifies and specifies DOT regulations and references, requirements for labeling and packaging, quantitative limitations, and methods of transportation of these materials in commerce. If a substance is not named specifically in these tables, a selection must be made from a general description in a section of the table referred to as the NOS group corresponding to the specific hazard class of the material being shipped. For example, a live bacterial organism would fall under the heading, "Etiological Agent—NOS" (see Table I). (Note: A particular problem in using this table is immediately apparent. Compounds are not always named using common scientific terminology, i.e., methyl ethyl ketone is found under ethyl methyl ketone.)

The table is divided into seven major columns, each giving a certain type of information necessary to find the applicable regulations:

- Column 1 contains a code for certain special considerations concerning that compound or material. An asterisk means that a material may have more than one hazard class. An "A" indicates restrictions to shipping this material by aircraft. A "W" indicates restrictions on this material when being shipped by water.
- Column 2 lists the proper shipping name of the material.
- Column 3 lists the hazard class of the material or the term, "forbidden." A material listed as forbidden may not be shipped under any conditions.

Table I. Excerpt from the DOT Hazardous Materials Table

(1) */W/A	(2) Hazardous Materials Descriptions and Proper Shipping Names	(3) Hazard Class	(4) Label(s) Required (If Not Excepted)	(5) Packaging (a) Exceptions	(b) Specific Requirements	(6) Maximum Net Quantity In One Package (a) Passenger Carrying Aircraft or Railcar	(b) Cargo Only Aircraft	(7) Water Shipments (a) Cargo Vessel	(b) Passenger Vessel	(c) Other Requirements
	Ethylene	Flammable gas	Flammable gas	173.306	173.304	Forbidden	300 pounds	1,2	4	
	Ethylene chlorohydrin	Poison B	Poison	173.345	173.346	1 quart	55 gallons	1,2	1	Segregation same as for flammable liquids
AW	Ethylene dibromide (1,2-dibromethane)	ORM-A	None	173.505	173.620	1 quart	55 gallons	1,2	1,2	Stow away from living quarters
	Ethylene dichloride	Flammable liquid	Flammable liquid	173.118	173.119	1 quart	10 gallons	1,2	1	
	Ethylene glycol diethyl ether (diethyl "Cellosolve")	Combustible liquid	None	173.118a	None	No limit	No limit	1,2	1,2	
	Ethylene glycol monoethyl ether ("Cellosolve")	Combustible liquid	None	173.118a	None	No limit	No limit	1,2	1,2	
	Ethylene glycol monoethyl ether acetate ("Cellosolve acetate")	Combustible liquid	None	173.118a	None	No limit	No limit	1,2	1,2	
	Ethylene glycol monomethyl ether (methyl "Cellosolve")	Combustible liquid	None	173.118a	None	No limit	No limit	1,2	1,2	
	Ethylene glycol monomethyl ether acetate (methyl "Cellosolve acetate")	Combustible liquid	None	173.118a	None	No limit	No limit	1,2	1,2	
	Ethylene imine, inhibited	Flammable liquid	Flammable liquid and Poison	None	173.139	Forbidden	5 pints	1,2	1	
	Ethylene oxide	Flammable liquid	Flammable liquid	None	173.124	Forbidden	173.124	1,2	1	Segregation same as for flammable gases
	Ethyl ether. See Ether									
	Ethyl formate	Flammable liquid	Flammable liquid	173.118	173.119	1 quart	10 gallons	1,3	4	
	Ethylhexaldehyde	Combustible liquid	None	173.118a	None	No limit	No limit	1,2	1,2	
	Ethyl lactate	Combustible liquid	None	173.118a	None	No limit	No limit	1,2	1	
	Ethyl mercaptan	Flammable liquid	Flammable liquid	None	173.141	Forbidden	10 gallons	1,2	1	
	Ethyl methyl ether	Flammable liquid	Flammable liquid	None	173.119	Forbidden	10 gallons	1,3	1	Segregation same as for flammable gases

									Remarks
Ethyl methyl ketone	Flammable liquid	Flammable liquid	173.118	173.119	1 quart	10 gallons	1,2	1	
Ethyl nitrate (*nitric ether*)	Flammable liquid	Flammable liquid	173.118	173.119	Forbidden	Forbidden	1,2	1	
Ethyl nitrite (*nitrous ether*)	Flammable liquid	Flammable liquid	None	173.119	Forbidden	Forbidden	1,3	5	
Ethyl phenyl dichlorosilane	Corrosive material	Corrosive	None	173.280	Forbidden	10 gallons	1	5	
Ethyl phosphonothioic dichloride, anhydrous	Corrosive material	Corrosive	173.244	173.245 173.245a	1 quart	1 quart	1	4	
Ethyl phosphonous dichloride, anhydrous	Corrosive material	Corrosive	173.244	173.245 173.245a	1 quart	1 quart	1	4	
Ethyl phosphorodichloridate	Corrosive material	Corrosive	173.244	173.245 173.245a	1 quart	1 quart	1	4	
Ethyl propionate	Flammable liquid	Flammable liquid	173.118	173.119	1 quart	10 gallons	1,2	1	
Ethyl silicate (*tetra ethyl ortho silicate*)	Combustible liquid	None	173.118a	None	No limit	No limit	1,2	1,2	
Ethyl trichlorosilane	Flammable liquid	Flammable liquid	None	173.135	Forbidden	5 pints	1,2	1	
Etiologic agent, n.o.s.	Etiologic agent	Etiologic agent	173.386	173.387	173.386	4 liters			Not permitted except under specific conditions approved by the Department
W Excelsior (shredded wood) *when dry, clear, and free from oil*	ORM-C	None	173.505	173.980			1,3	1,3	Stow away from organic, corrosive, or oxidizing materials
W Exothermic ferrochrome	ORM-C	None	173.505	173.985			1	1	
W Exothermic ferromanganese. *See* Exothermic ferrochrome									
W Exothermic silicon chrome. *See* Exothermic ferrochrome									
Explosive auto alarm	Class C explosive	Explosive C	None	173.111	50 pounds	150 pounds	1,2	1,2	
Explosive bomb	Class A explosive	Explosive A	None	173.56	Forbidden	Forbidden	1,2	5	Magazine stowage authorized. No other cargo may be stowed in the same hold with these items
Explosive cable cutter	Class C explosive	Explosive C	None	173.102	50 pounds	150 pounds	1,3	1,3	
Explosive mine	Class A explosive	Explosive A	None	173.56	Forbidden	Forbidden	1,2	5	Magazine stowage authorized. No other cargo may be stowed in the same hold with this material
Explosive, new approval, and evaluation. See 173.86									
Explosive power device, Class B	Class B explosive	Explosive B	None	173.94	Forbidden	150 pounds	1,2	5	
Explosive power device, Class C	Class C explosive	Explosive C	None	173.102	50 pounds	150 pounds	1,3	1,3	

- Column 4 specifies the required labeling of the material.
- Column 5 references sections of regulations on packaging requirements and labeling exceptions.
- Column 6 indicates the maximum amount of material that may be placed in one package for air or rail shipment. It may also state that a given material is forbidden from shipment by these modes (e.g., ethyl nitrate in Table I).
- Column 7 lists specific locations for storage aboard a cargo vessel or specific instructions as to how the material should be stored. For example: "Do not stow with nitric acid or other oxidizers."

DOT Classification and Definitions of Hazardous Materials

Hazardous materials are classified by DOT into the following hazard categories:

- Explosive A (173.53)
- Explosive B (173.88)
- Explosive C (173.100)
- Combustible Liquids (173.115)
- Corrosive Materials (173.240)
- Etiological Agent (173.386)
- Flammable Gas (173.300)
- Flammable Liquids (173.115)
- Flammable Solids (173.150)
- Irritating Material (173.381)
- Organic Peroxides (173.151)
- Oxidizers (173.151)
- Poison A (173.326)
- Poison B (173.343)
- Pyrophoric Liquids (173.115)
- Pyrophoric Solids (173.150)

Explosive materials are divided into three classes: A, B and C. These are defined in the following manner:

- Class A explosives are explosives that detonate by contact with sparks or flame, or in a drop of 4 in. or less on a standard drop test machine. Some examples of this type of material are dynamite, nitroglycerine, and lead azide or lead staphanate.
- Class B explosives are defined as those explosives which, in general, function by rapid combustion rather than detonation. Examples of this class are smokeless powders, flash powders, some pyrotechnique devices, and jato bottles.
- Class C explosives are defined as certain types of manufactured articles that contain Class A or Class B explosives as a component of the article, but in a restricted amount. Examples include fireworks and sporting ammunition.

A flammable liquid is defined as any liquid having a flash point below 100°F. Ether is an example of a flammable liquid. A combustible liquid is defined as any liquid that has a flash point at or above 100°F, and below 200°F. Kerosene is an example. A pyrophoric liquid is defined as any liquid that ignites spontaneously in dry or moist air at or below 134°F—ethyl aluminum chloride, for example. The flash point is defined by ASTM Methods D56-70, D3278-73 and D93-71.

A corrosive material is defined as any liquid or solid that causes visible destruction or irreversible alterations in human skin tissue at the site of contact, or a liquid that has a severe corrosive rate on steel. Nitric acid is an example of a corrosive material.

An etiological agent is defined as a viable microorganism or its toxins which cause or may cause human disease. This category is limited to material listed by CFR 72.25 (c), Department of Health, Education and Welfare (HEW). The category is not used for carcinogenic or suspected carcinogenic chemicals. This category will not be represented by material in the HML.

A flammable gas is defined as any gas that forms a flammable mixture with air at or below a volume concentration of 13%. In addition, any gas that forms a flammable mixture with air at concentrations above 12% will fall into this category, regardless of the lower limit.

A flammable or pyrophoric solid is defined as any solid material (other than those classified as explosives) which under normal conditions incident to transportation is liable to cause fires through friction or retained heat from processing, or ignite by spontaneous combustion or contact with water (e.g., sodium metal or phosphorus). An oxidizer is defined as a substance such as a chlorate, permanganate, inorganic peroxide, nitrocarbonitrate, or a nitrate that yields oxygen readily to stimulate the combustion of organic material. An organic peroxide is defined as an organic compound containing the bivalent -0-0- structure. The material may be considered a derivative of hydrogen peroxide where one or both of the hydrogen atoms have been replaced by organic radicals (e.g., methyl ethyl ketone peroxide).

An irritating material is defined as any material, solid or liquid, which upon contact with fire, or when exposed to air, gives off dangerous or intensely irritating fumes. Bromobenzyl cyanide and orthochlorobenzal malonitrile are examples. This class of materials is equivalent to the USPS Poison C Category.

Poisonous materials are classified by DOT into two categories: Poison A and Poison B. Class A poisons are defined as gases or liquids that are so toxic that "a very small amount (173.326) of the gas or vapor in air is dangerous to life. Examples of class A poisons are phosgene, cyanogen and bromoacetone.

materials are substances (liquid or solid) that are toxic or suspected to be toxic and can present a health hazard during transportation.

Packaging Requirements

DOT packaging regulations can be divided into two categories: general requirements for each of the classifications of materials, and specific requirements for specifically named materials and given quantities of those materials. The regulations are found in Part 173–Shippers–General Requirements for Shipments and Packagings. The individual subparts (C through N) each cover a given hazard category, first in general, then by specific materials. For example, Subpart H deals with poisonous materials, etiological agents and radioactive materials. Sections 173.343-173.346 discuss the Poison B liquid category in terms of general packaging, limiting quantities, and compounds in this category not otherwise specifically provided for. Sections 173.347-173.362(a) are sections dealing with specific compounds or classes of compounds such as aniline, dinitrophenol solutions, and the phosphate-based pesticides.

In brief, the regulations require that a material be packaged for shipment so that there is no release of a significant amount of hazardous materials into the environment. The package must be constructed to withstand normal transportation conditions. The package must include packing material so that there will be no significant chemical, galvanic or friction reaction among the materials in the package, and container seals must be adequate to prevent inadvertent leakage of the contents under normal conditions incident to transportation [173.24]. Specifically, for flammable liquids (such as methanol, hexane and acetone) and Poison B class materials, limited quantities may be shipped in metal containers of less than 1 quart or in glass containers of less than 1 pint or 16 ounces if the outside container is "strong" [173.118] "Strong" means that if the package is dropped from 4 feet onto concrete, there is no breakage [173.365(a) (7) and 178.205].

Labeling Requirements

All packages that contain hazardous materials and that are to be shipped in interstate commerce must be labeled [172.400]. Certain exceptions are discussed later.

However, if no exception is available, a package containing such materials must carry the particular label or labels specified for that substance in the hazardous materials table (Table I). Figure 1 illustrates the types of labels that are required. The label descriptions are given in 172.407-172. 558. In some instances, a material having two equal hazards may require

Figure 1. Examples of labels required on hazardous materials shipments.

two hazard labels [172.402]. Nitric acid, for example, requires two labels: "oxidizer" and "corrosive." Methyl hydrazine also needs two labels: "flammable liquid" and "Poison A." When a material has several hazardous properties, usually the most hazardous condition is the one that is specified by the label [172.404]. For example, benzene is poisonous, flammable and potentially carcinogenic. In transportation, though, the most immediate problem would be caused by its flammability. Therefore, it would carry the "Flammable liquid" label.

The accepted method of labeling material for shipment is to label the primary container with the contents and warnings as to toxicity, reactivity and flammability. First-aid and fire fighting procedures may also be added. Secondary containers, if they are not the shipping container, also bear the material name and the warnings that appear on the primary label. In addition, the secondary container bears a label informing the recipient that the primary container is on the inside of the secondary container. The external shipping container has the name and address of the recipient and the required DOT hazard labels. A safe handling document may be included inside the shipping container. The shipping container may also give information to persons handling the shipment as to where to receive emergency information if the shipment is damaged or leaking [172.406].

Documentation

Any person who wishes to ship a hazardous material must furnish the carrier firm certain documentation. This documentation is described in Section 172.200 of the DOT regulations. Furthermore, this documentation is specifically forbidden from exemption. A sample document is shown in Figure 2. The specific requirements of the document are outlined below.

- When a hazardous material and a nonhazardous material are described on the same shipping papers, the hazardous materials must be entered first or in a color that contrasts with the description of the nonhazardous materials.
- The shipping papers must be clearly legible and written in English.
- With one exception, no abbreviations or codes are permitted on the shipping document. The only exception is that where there is no specific official shipping name for the material, the abbreviation NOS (Not Otherwise Specified) will be used for a shipping name.
- The shipping document will contain the name and address of the shipper and any additional information consistent with the regulations. The shipping document must be given to the representative of the shipping company who picks up the shipment. The document must accompany the shipment to its final destination.

SHIPPER'S CERTIFICATION FOR RESTRICTED ARTICLES
(excluding radioactive materials)
Two completed and signed copies of this certification shall be handed to the carrier. (Use block letters)

WARNING: Failure to comply in all respects with the applicable regulations of the Department of Transportation, 49-CFR, CAB 82 and, for international shipments, the IATA Restricted Articles Regulations may be a breach of the applicable law, subject to legal penalties. This certification shall in no circumstance be signed by an IATA Cargo Agent or a consolidator for international shipments.

This shipment is within the limitations prescribed for: (mark one)
☒ passenger aircraft   ☐ cargo-only aircraft

Number of Packages	Article Number (Int'l only See Section IV IATA RAR)	Proper Shipping Name of Articles as shown in Title 49 CFR, CAB 82 Tariff 6-D, and (for int'l shipments) the IATA Restricted Articles Regulations. Specify each article separately. Technical name must follow in parenthesis, the proper shipping name for N.O.S. items.	Class	IATA Packing Note No. Applied (int'l only)	Net Quantity per Package	Flash Point (closed cup) For Flammable Liquids °C.	°F.
1	-	Phenol, Limited Quantity	Poison B.	-	5 ml	-	-
2	-	Poisonous Solids, N.O.S. Limited Quantities: (Benzo(a)Pyrene) (Dimethyl Benzidine)	Poison B	- - -	5 g 5 g	- -	- -
1	-	Tetrahydrofuran Limited Quantity	Flammable Liquid		5 ml	-	-

Special Handling Information: Emergency Procedures Documents are Provided in the Sealed Cans, Coded by Aliquot Number.

I hereby certify that the contents of this consignment are fully and accurately described above by Proper Shipping Name and are classified, packed, marked, labelled and in proper condition for carriage by air according to applicable national governmental regulations, and for International Shipments, the current IATA Restricted Articles Regulations.

Name and full address of Shipper	Name and title of person signing Certification
Radian Corporation	C. Herndon Williams
8500 Shoal Creek Blvd.	Senior Scientist
Austin, Texas 78766	*C. Herndon Williams J.*
Date 02 May 1979	Signature of the Shipper (see WARNING above)

Air Waybill No.*	Airport of Departure* Austin, Texas	Airport of Destination* Chicago, Illinois

Figure 2. Sample shipping document for hazardous materials.

Exemptions

Of the three regulated areas, packaging, labeling and documentation, only certain labeling requirements are explicitly exempted. In addition, these exemptions are almost exclusively based on the quantity of material being shipped. For example, materials classified as flammable liquids are exempted from labeling if the quantities fall below those specified in the hazardous materials table (i.e., methanol is classified as a flammable liquid [172.101] but if shipped in less than 1-quart quantities (per container) and packaged in a certain manner, it is exempt from labeling [173.118], except when offered for transportation by air. This is perhaps the most important aspect of the exemptions because it is the labeling requirements that cause the greatest problems and limit the shipping modes that can be used.

All of the solid and liquid compounds in the repository fall under the Poison B classification when shipped as dilute solutions. Because a majority of the compounds are not listed in the hazardous materials table, they fall into the NOS category. These have labeling exemptions for quantities under ~ 6 ounces or ~ 1 quart [172.101 for listed materials, 173.345-346 for NOS materials].

Specific exemptions from labeling which may be applicable to HML shipments are for:

- flammable liquids in quantities below those listed in the hazardous materials table [172.101] for the particular compound (does not apply to shipments by air) [173.118];
- combustible liquids as listed in the hazardous materials table in quantities less than 110 gallons [173.118(a)];
- corrosive liquids as listed in the hazardous materials table in quantities less than 6 fluid ounces (does not apply to shipments by air) [173.244 and 173. 286(b)];
- organophosphates, both named and not otherwise specified, containing less than 2 ounces by weight of the particular component or components [173.359]; and
- "chemical kits" (such as photographic developer kits and soil analysis kits containing corrosive liquids) containing less than 6 ounces of material per internal container [173.286].

Each of these exemptions has specific packaging requirements, and none give exemptions from the transport documentation.

One other exemption in the current regulations may be classified as an "administrative" exemption. This requires application to the Office of Hazardous Materials Operations and extensive documentation concerning every material to be shipped, as well as descriptions of the containers, safety precautions and transportation modes. Under older regulations (pre-1977) an exemption existed for "experimental chemicals." This exemption is no longer available.

U.S. Postal Service Regulations

The U.S. Postal Service (USPS) regulations either ban outright or place specific packaging restrictions on hazardous materials. Specifically forbidden are the DOT Class A Poisons, the USPS Class C Poisons (DOT Irritating

Materials Classification), and materials with flash points below 20°F (e.g., ether, acetone and hexane). DOT Class B Poisons may be mailed; most carcinogens and materials that the USPS has classified as "Other Nonclassified Toxic Materials" may also be mailed. These are mailable only if the packages meet USPS regulations for etiological agents [Postal Service Regulation 53 of Publication 52-T1-L, 2-4-77]. Examples include benzene, β-naphthalamine and β-propiolactone. Also mailable are materials classified as flammable liquids if the flammability limit is above 20°F. This material may be mailed provided the primary container total volume is less than 1 pint. It must be packed in an absorbent material and in a metal secondary shipping container.

All of these materials must be sent by registered mail. They also require certain documents and labels. These conform closely to the equivalent DOT requirements described in the previous sections. The packaging and labeling procedures developed by the Radian HML were designed to meet or exceed all USPS and DOT criteria.

Problem Areas with Shippers

Several problem areas in shipping hazardous materials have been identified. The most serious arise from the labeling requirements and the response of the various carriers to those labels. The individual carriers (other than USPS) and the particular problems are outlined below.

- UPS. United Parcel Service will not accept packages labeled poisonous, corrosive, explosive or radioactive. Their refusal is based on DOT regulation 177.841(e) prohibiting the shipment of hazardous materials labeled poison in carriers that may be transporting substances for human or animal consumption.

- Federal Express. Federal Express will ship most materials. However, those labeled poisonous, flammable or corrosive must be sent under their P-1 designation. The cost for shipping under this designation is $20.00 or more per package. Federal Express will accept poison shipments only on Monday, Wednesday and Friday. Shipments that require dry ice for packaging can be shipped only on Monday and Wednesday.

- Common Carrier. The common carrier shipping companies are the least expensive and the least restrictive. Four problems have been identified, however. Labor disputes can tie up shipments for days or weeks. Packages labeled flammable may be held in a warehouse until a totally flammable load can be made. Packages labeled poisonous may be "bumped" if consumables are being handled (cf. UPS). Common carrier delivery times are usually several days longer than USPS, UPS or Federal Express.

PACKAGING OF MATERIALS

Packaging of materials for shipping is a key area in the safety and handling of repository compounds. The way in which compounds are packaged determines how they may be shipped and what carrier may be used. The following sections discuss packaging procedures and those tests conducted by Radian to verify packaging integrity and establish best shipping methods. Packaging procedures are divided into four categories based on quantity of material and type of shipment.

Packaging of Liquids and Powders in Quantities Not Exceeding 25 Milliliters or Grams

All materials in this category will be packaged for shipment in a packaging kit. Packaging kits consist of:

* a labeled primary container (1 to 25 ml crimp seal vial) wrapped in absorbent material;
* a heat-sealed, labeled plastic bag;
* a second heat-sealed plastic bag (not labeled);
* a bubble plastic packing for cushioning; and
* a sealed can with label.

Packaging of Liquids and Powders Exceeding 25 Milliliters or Grams But Not Exceeding 110 Milliliters or Grams

All materials that fall within this volume/weight category will be shipped in a packaging kit similar to the above kit, with the exception that the primary container will be a 125-ml hypovial and the exterior shipping can will be appropriately larger.

Packaging of Liquids and Powders Exceeding 110 Milliliters or Grams But Less Than 1 Liter or Kilogram

These items will be shipped in a packaging kit consisting of:

* a labeled screw-top primary container wrapped in absorbent material;
* a heat-sealed, labeled plastic bag;
* a second heat-sealed plastic bag (not labeled);
* a cushioning bubble plastic packing; and
* a friction capped metal can (labeled).

Figures 3 and 4 illustrate the packing methods.

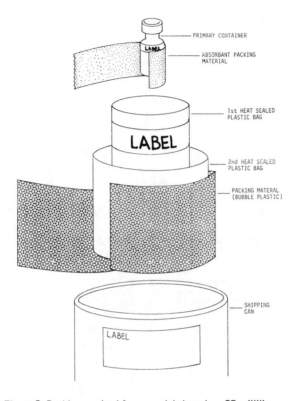

PRIMARY CONTAINER

ABSORBANT PACKING
MATERIAL

1st HEAT SEALED
PLASTIC BAG

LABEL

2nd HEAT SEALED
PLASTIC BAG

PACKING MATERAL
(BUBBLE PLASTIC)

SHIPPING
CAN

LABEL

Figure 3. Packing method for materials less than 25 milliliters or grams.

Packaging of Ampules Containing 5 Milliliters of Liquid or Grams of Powder—Heat-Sealed

Many materials are shipped in 2.5 or 5 ml flame-sealed ampules. These ampules are fitted into a styrofoam block which is labeled and placed in a heat-sealed plastic bag. This package is wrapped in bubble plastic, placed in a metal can, and sealed. The can will then be labeled and boxed for shipping. Figure 5 illustrates the packing method.

Shipping Tests

Radian has conducted a series of tests to verify the "durability" of the shipping containers and establish the best method of shipment. One test

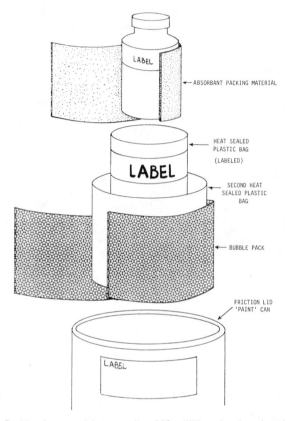

Figure 4. Packing for quantities exceeding 110 milliliters but less than 1 liter in volume.

program involved the destruction of several shipping containers to determine the "survivability" of the primary container. A second program
sent several packages to the same location via different carrier method to
determine delivery times and costs.

To determine the survivability of the primary shipping container a
destructive testing program was carried out. Six 6-ml sample containers
were prepared as described above. Three were packaged containing a dye
powder, and three containing a liquid dye. Two containers from each set
of three were chosen for destruction. Destruction was carried out by
running over each container with a 3/4-ton pickup truck. One container
of each type was placed end-on and one edge-on to the left front wheel
(see Figure 6.) Attempts to perform a "top-bottom" compression were

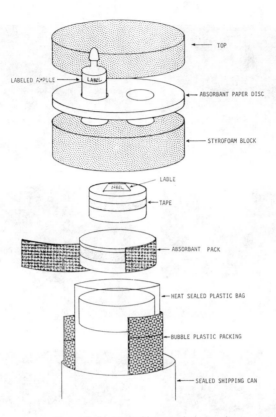

Figure 5. Packing of heat sealed ampules.

unsuccessful. The cans invariably popped out from under the wheel. The calculated pressure on the body of each can was in excess of 2000 lb.

All cans were badly crushed and deformed. The can deformation was such that they had to be cut open with a band saw (see Figure 7). In all four instances the primary container survived intact, as did the two heat-sealed plastic bags that contained the primary containers.

Shipping Studies

Radian has performed an evaluation of transportation methods for small quantities of toxic and hazardous materials packaged to conform to all appropriate DOT regulations. The study was conducted to determine shipping costs, times en route, and condition of packages on arrival at their respective destinations. Each laboratory received three packages,

Figure 6. Edge-on and end-on crush test of hazardous materials shipping container.

each package transported by a different mode. All packages carried the full complement of DOT warning labels.

One to four 5-g aliquots of chemicals that had been packaged as described earlier were sealed in cardboard boxes for shipment to laboratories in Maryland, Ohio and California. Each box weighed between 1 and 2 lb. Each laboratory received three boxes, one each shipped by UPS, Federal Express Air Freight, and USPS. The packages to be shipped by UPS were refused because of the affixed "POISON" labels. UPS

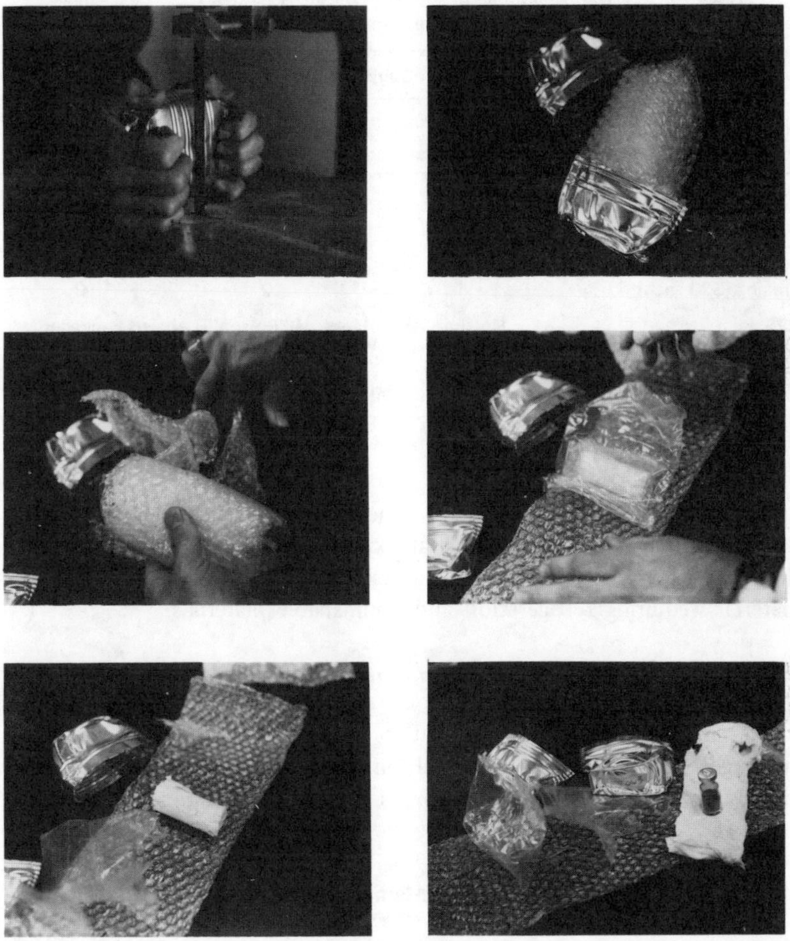

Figure 7. Contents of crushed hazardous materials shipping container after opening.

refuses to handle such items because they cannot be co-shipped with food-containing packages. Samples sent by Federal Express were required to go via the P-1 category at a cost of about $20 each. Packages sent via the USPS were required to be sent as registered mail at a cost of about $6 each. Each package contained a postage-paid return receipt card to be mailed by the receiving laboratory. The results are summarized in Table II.

Until an evaluation of the common carriers (motor freight) mode can be obtained and until the exemption question can be resolved, the USPS

Table II. Results of Shipping Package with a Full Set of DOT Warning Labels
by Various Transportation Modes

Transport Mode (Cost)	Days En Route from Austin to		
	Rockville, Maryland	Cleveland, Ohio	Menlo Park, California
USPS Registered Mail ($6 each)	3,3,3,3	3,3,3,3	3,3,3,3
Federal Express Air Freight ($20 each)	1	2	2
UPS	Refused Acceptance of "Poison"-Labeled Packages		
Common Carrier Motor Freight	Truck Strike—Not Shipped		

registered mail method appears to be the most economical. The apparent saving in shipping time using Federal Express (1-2 days) does not warrant the extra expense. However, Federal Express (P-1) must be used for materials requiring refrigeration and nonmailable materials.

CONTAINER LABELING AND IDENTIFICATION

Container labeling and identification is the most complex aspect of meeting DOT regulations. The multiplicity of compounds and consequently the large number of categories into which a shipment can fall makes each shipment unique.

Internal (Primary and Secondary Container) Labels

There is a sequence of three labels internal to the shipping package: the primary container (ampule or hypovial) label, the heat-sealed plastic bag label, and the secondary container (sealed can) label. The primary container label bears a code number indicating appropriate identifying information on the material. If appropriate, the compound is named. For standard solutions the label also contains a storage code and an expiration date. The storage code tells how the sample should be stored, and the expiration date tells when the concentration of the materials should no longer be considered accurate (Figure 8). The storage code also lists the conditions for safe storage of the material. The storage conditions are abbreviated as temperature ($^{\circ}$C), light (L), air (O) and humidity (H). For example, a compound having the designation (5°), (L), (O), (H),

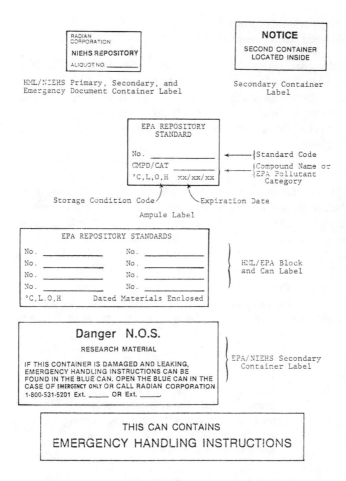

Figure 8. Examples of Radian HML repository labels.

should be stored at 5°C under N_2 or other inert gas, and protected from humidity and light.

The NIEHS samples are labeled with an NIEHS repository aliquot number due to the need of blind-testing for these compounds. Emergency handling information is shipped with a NIEHS sample in a blue sealed can. This can is labeled with an aliquot number corresponding to the sample aliquot number. It contains all the information available about the compound that would be useful in handling an emergency involving the material in question. The labels on the primary container, the secondary container and the emergency document cans are the same. Examples of the HML labels are given in Figure 8.

DOT Regulations-Shipping Labels
and Shipping Documentation

All materials shipped from the Radian HML comply with DOT labeling regulations. Depending on the category of material, each package may have one or more of the labels, "Poison," "Oxidizer," "Organic Peroxide," "Flammable Liquid," "Flammable Solid," "Irritant," "Corrosive," "Explosive," etc. This labeling is in accordance with DOT regulations, Part 172.400-450.

In addition to the labeling required by various federal and state regulations, a document giving general information about the toxicity of the material, special cautions, handling procedures, and first-aid measures is attached to the shipping package when necessary. This document is attached to the package in the same manner as a packing list. It is in an envelope taped to the outside of the package and clearly labeled as containing emergency handling information. Most materials shipped from the EPA repository are below OSHA level concerns. Thus, a simple label on the outside of the package explaining safety procedures for apparent leakage is adequate. This label also lists Radian's toll-free telephone number for the benefit of any responsible party who requires additional information (see Figure 9).

W A R N I N G

In case of leakage avoid skin contact.
Place in plastic bag and return to
shipper C.O.D. Flush contacted skin
areas with water and wash thoroughly
with soap and water. Wash exposed
surfaces with detergent.

For further information call Radian
Corporation Toll Free 1-800-531-5201.

Figure 9.   Radian's package label.

PRESERVATION CONDITIONS–
SPECIAL CONSIDERATIONS

Certain compounds maintained in the repository inventory are unstable under one or more conditions. For example, benzidine should be stored at subambient temperatures ($\leqslant 5°C$), 1,2-dihydrazobenzene is susceptible to oxidation, and several of the polynuclear aromatic compounds decompose when exposed to light. Thus, special precautions must be taken when transporting unstable compounds.

Samples that need refrigeration are shipped in insulated shipping boxes with a quantity of dry ice or ice packs sufficient to maintain the required temperature until the material is delivered to its destination. Shipments of this type will typically go by Federal Express.

Certain compounds in the repository are susceptible to air oxidation and require storage under inert atmosphere. The ampule sealing process (used on all standards) involves an inert gas pre-flush of the ampule followed by another flush after it is filled and before it is sealed. Therefore, all materials shipped from the HML in heat-sealed ampules are under an inert atmosphere. In addition, materials containing compounds identified as being susceptible to air oxidation are so labeled, and instructions for the correct handling procedure are included with the shipment.

Materials shipped in crimp-sealed vials as the primary container are transferred from the bulk supply to the vial inside an inert atmosphere glove box.

Photosensitive chemicals such as the fluorenes must be protected from exposure to light. The primary container (ampule) for these compounds is made of amber glass. The secondary container (sealed cans) prevents light exposure during transportation. Both the primary and secondary containers are labeled to notify receiving personnel that the contents are light-sensitive.

SPECIAL HANDLING INFORMATION

Certain documentation has been developed to give personnel immediate access to information about potentially dangerous compounds. This documentation includes an emergency procedures document and a safety handling document. The current format for these documents has been designed to meet specific NIEHS needs. Examples of the NIEHS forms are given in Figures 10 and 11.

The emergency procedures document gives all pertinent information necessary in case of an accident involving a particular sample. This information includes special handling equipment, fire and first-aid information, symptoms of exposure, and decontamination and disposal procedures.

The safety and handling document lists the types of hazards associated with the particular material, what precautions should be taken against those hazards, safety equipment needed, TLV, storage precautions, and decontamination and disposal procedures.

PERSONNEL SAFETY

Personnel from three areas may come in contact with materials shipped from the HML: the Radian repository personnel, certain members of the general public working in the transportation industry, and laboratory personnel at the receiving location. All personnel must have safety information commensurate with their degree of risk and assumed skills. The degree of risk is highest for repository personnel because they will be handling "pure" materials. The design of the shipping containers makes the degree of risk to the transportation personnel the lowest. This order of risk is also the order of assumed skills (in handling hazardous materials) with transportation personnel expected to have no knowledge of necessary safety precautions.

Repository personnel are trained in the handling of highly toxic and carcinogenic materials. In addition, the HML operating procedures are designed to meet OSHA regulations governing toxic and carcinogenic materials and NIH P3-P4 laboratory requirements for viable pathogens and toxic substances.

Transportation personnel are expected to have no knowledge or training in the handling of hazardous materials. On the other hand, they are expected to have the least risk of exposure. The safety of these people is maintained by three actions: a packaging method secure against all but the most catastrophic accident, a label giving the immediate emergency handling information and source of additional information, and shipment of quantities below OSHA exposure limits. In cases where pure or bulk materials are shipped, additional documentation will be attached to the package detailing exact contents and all available medical, safety and handling information.

Personnel receiving the shipment also receive a safe handling document with all information available on safe handling, emergency procedures, fire fighting, first-aid, and medical treatment and decontamination procedures for leaks and spills. Included are procedures for destroying waste material.

CONCLUSIONS

In summary, it can be seen that packaging and shipping requirements for toxic and otherwise hazardous materials are extremely complex and detailed. Furthermore, the regulations are still in the formative process, and considerations of multiagency rules (e.g., DOT, NIOSH, EPA, OSHA) often must be reviewed before final action is taken. An interesting analogy involved the thousands of EPA water samples shipped by air during

EMERGENCY PROCEDURES DOCUMENT

Number _____

NIEHS Repository for Mutagenic Testing

Primary Name: 4-NITRO-o-PHENYLENEDIAMINE

Primary I.D. #: N-000040   **CAS #:** 000099569

Synonyms: 2-Amino-4-Nitroaniline
1,2-Diamino-4-Nitrobenzene
4-Nitro-1,2-Phenylenediamine
4-Nitro-1,2-Benzenedinamine
4-Nitro-1,2-Diaminobenzene
C.I. 76020

Hygenic Precautions:

Use normal care as in handling potential mutagens. Handle only in approved fume hood. Rubber gloves, laboratory coat with apron, goggles, and half-face respirator with particulate cartridges.

Fire Precautions:

Fire Fighting: Extinguish with water spray, foam, CO_2 or dry chemical. Combustion fumes are extremely toxic. Use full body protection with self-contained breathing apparatus.

First Aid:

Skin: Remove contaminated clothing, wash thoroughly with soap and water for 10 minutes. Transport for medical evaluation.

Eye Contact: Flush eyes for 15 minutes with water. Do not put oil or ointment in eyes. If eyes are photo sensitive, cover with loose dressing and transport for medical evaluation.

Inhalation: Remove personnel to open air and administer oxygen. Transport for medical evaluation.

Ingestion: POISON. Induce vomiting. When vomiting ceases administer two tablespoons of activated charcoal and transport for medical evaluation.

Symptoms:

Unknown. Could be similar to those of p-NITROANALINE, i.e., headache, dizziness, nausea, vomiting, increase in pulse and/or respiration rate, convulsions, difficulty in breathing.

Spills and Leakage:

Wash exposed areas of skin with strong soap and water solution immediately. Contaminated clothing should be washed with strong detergent or destroyed. Use dampened absorbent paper to pick up spill material. Wash contaminated areas with strong soap and water solution. Rinse thoroughly and dry.

Disposal and Waste Treatment:

Destroy waste and/or contaminated material by high temperature ($> 2000°C$) incineration.

Other Instructions:

Report contamination to supervisor.

Figure 10. Emergency procedures document for HML.

SAFETY AND HANDLING DOCUMENT

ALIQUOT NUMBER _____

NIEHS Repository for Mutagenic Testing

Types of Hazards:

POISON; TOXIC COMBUSTION FUMES

Hazards Precautions:

Flammable at elevated temperatures. Do not ingest. Handle as if potential mutagen. Protect from body contact.

Toxicity Level: Toxic. Can cause serious temporary illness or residual injury.

Fire Fighting: Extinguish with water spray, foam, CO_2 or dry chemical; combustion fumes are *extremely* toxic; use full body protection and self-contained breathing apparatus.

Ventilation: Handle only in approved fume hood.

Safety Devices and Protectors:

Fume hood, rubber gloves, half-face respirator with particulate cartridges, laboratory coat with apron, goggles.

TLV: Not specified.

Storage Precautions:

Protect against physical damage. Protect from high temperatures. Store away from areas of normal activity at $< 5°C$.

Spills and Leakage:

Wash exposed areas of skin with strong soap and water solution immediately. Contaminated clothing should be destroyed by incineration. Use dampened absorbent paper to pick up spill material. Wash contaminated areas with strong detergent. Rinse thoroughly and dry.

Disposal and Waste Treatment:

Destroy waste and/or contaminated material by high temperature $(> 2000°C)$ incineration.

Other Instructions:

Report contamination to supervisor.

Figure 11. Safety and handling document for HML.

1976-1978 after first being preserved with a few milliliters of nitric acid. From a theoretical point of view, these water samples were turned into very dilute nitric acid solutions. Since nitric acid cannot be shipped by air in *any* concentration, the practice was halted by DOT.

However, it should be remembered that, frustrating as they often are, these regulations were developed to protect unsuspecting personnel who have to handle hazardous materials and who are not equipped to cope with the accidental release of unknown hazardous materials.

ACKNOWLEDGMENTS

We hope that the many hours of study of these regulations and the resulting packaging and shipping practices we developed in order to meet or exceed required qualifications will be of use to others who encounter the need to ship small amounts of hazardous materials around the country.

Radian is indebted to officials from DOT, NIEHS and EPA for providing the guidance necessary to develop an excellent protocol for carrying out the shipment of a variety of hazardous chemicals ranging from dilute solutions to gram quantities of the pure compounds. In addition, Radian gratefully acknowledges support for this work under NIEHS contract number NO 1-ES-8-2144 and EPA contract number EPA-68-03-2765.

CHAPTER 6

MANAGEMENT OF CARCINOGENIC AND HIGHLY TOXIC CHEMICALS IN A MULTIDISCIPLINARY RESEARCH FACILITY

Harry J. Ettinger, Evan E. Campbell
and George M. Talley
    Industrial Hygiene Group
    Health Division
    Los Alamos Scientific Laboratory
    Los Alamos, New Mexico

INTRODUCTION

Management and control of carcinogenic and other highly toxic chemicals has assumed increased importance due to federal regulations and a greater awareness of the long-term hazards associated with these materials. Research facilities and universities present special problems since they frequently involve multiple small users of a wide variety of ever changing materials and applications. Primary operational aspects of the program require management support and actions by the industrial hygienist to:

1. monitor the issue and/or purchase of chemicals;
2. define for the chemist-user several different levels of constraint relative to chemical issue and/or purchase, depending on the relative hazard or legal requirements associated with the material;
3. work with the individual investigator to define the type of engineering controls, work practices, standard operating procedures (SOP), facilities and training required;
4. follow up to assure compliance; and
5. provide up-to-date toxicological information and guidance regarding newly proposed and adopted regulations.

Management and supervisors must be alert to their prime responsibility to protect the health of their employees and the new technical and legal problems associated with using these chemicals. This management concern must assure adequate facilities before commitments are made for new programs.

Unlike industrial processes or repetitive unit operations, a research and development laboratory is constantly changing the types of materials used and the methods for handling them. Even research scientists dedicated to the same overall objectives may have significantly different potentials for exposure when using the same materials. Under these circumstances, control of toxic materials must incorporate a program directed toward the employee's ability to recognize (by becoming informed), evaluate (by being concerned and securing assistance), and control (by instituting specific work practices, and administrative and engineering controls) the use of toxic materials in the work environment.

Many research facilities and universities are faced with the problem of safely handling relatively small quantities of highly toxic materials. This involves both legal and technical-professional considerations. Frequently, legal considerations receive the most attention based on the formal requirements set down by the Occupational Safety and Health Administration (OSHA), Environmental Protection Agency (EPA), Federal Drug Administration (FDA), or other government agencies. However, legal concerns are probably the simpler of the two considerations since to date OSHA has adopted standards governing fewer than 25 compounds, and a similar situation exists relative to the number of standards for specific chemicals that have been adopted by the other regulatory agencies. The more common situation involves materials where the level of toxicity is poorly defined or where no information exists. In these instances the health professional must evaluate what is known about the specific material of concern, develop analogies on the basis of what is known about similar materials, extrapolate on the basis of what is known about similar materials, extrapolate on the basis of chemical structure and metabolic processes, and assign an uncertainty to this estimating process. When dealing with chemicals of little industrial interest and little prior usage, the health professional frequently faces uncertainties of considerable magnitude. It is not possible to handle each of these materials as if it presents an overwhelming risk to the worker. The health protection program must include continued monitoring of the work environment and the worker's health and obtaining new information to better estimate toxicity. In a research facility much of the work involves handling small quantities of materials that are known to be, or may be, highly toxic and are used in constantly changing work situations. Health protection under these conditions requires considerably more flexibility, professional judgment, and participation by the health professional and technical personnel than would be the case for a routine industrial-production operation.

CONTROL PROGRAM

Industrial hygiene control of the multitude of chemicals and the variety of uses at research and development facilities requires a number of integrated approaches. These include: administrative controls, material substitution, and engineering controls.

Preceding each of these is the need to recognize and evaluate the existence of toxic chemicals that enter a laboratory's research facility. Evaluation should include air sampling to quantitate the presence of a contaminant. This is an important aspect of evaluating the adequacy of control requirements; however, this aspect of the total program will not be discussed in this chapter.

The control program developed at the Los Alamos Scientific Laboratory (LASL) involves the following five phases:

1. categorize chemicals used in the laboratory into four broad groups.
2. monitor all chemicals purchased by the laboratory and used by its employees.
3. develop operating requirements for high toxicity categories noted in (1) above.
4. advise technical and supervisory personnel of those chemicals falling into the more restrictive categories noted in (1) and detail the operating requirements noted in (3) above.
5. reevaluate the adequacy of the controls specified based on changes in regulatory standards and new information concerning levels of toxicological risk and control methods.

Details of such a program must be tailored to the individual organization. The following indicates how such a program is being implemented at LASL.

CATEGORIZATION

The LASL Industrial Hygiene Group reviews the potential toxicity of all new chemicals introduced at the laboratory. This review is aimed at placing each chemical within one of the following four categories:

1. documented cancer-suspect agent (CSA) in humans,
2. controlled highly toxic material,
3. material requiring normal industrial hygiene management, and
4. unknown toxicity.

This categorization of chemicals is probably the most difficult phase in developing a program for the safe handling of toxic materials. In many instances, a clear decision is not possible because of the uncertainties in available toxicological data, limited epidemiological studies, and pending regulatory actions by OSHA, EPA, FDA, or the Consumer Products Safety Commission(CPSC).

Well-documented CSAs are defined to include those chemicals covered by OSHA standards that have been adopted, which at present are limited to vinyl chloride, the 14 OSHA CSAs, benzene, 1,2-dibromo-3-chloropropane (DBCP), arsenic, and acrylonitrile. Also included are materials where microbiological and toxicological documentation of carcinogenicity is unequivocal. Table I shows examples of materials in this category used at LASL. The number in this category will undoubtedly increase significantly in the next several years due to new toxicological information, the impact of the proposed Interagency Carcinogen Standards, and its definition of what constitutes a CSA. Chemicals in the CSA category are not issued until the industrial hygiene controls, isolation facilities, environmental controls, and work practices have been evaluated.

Table I. Cancer-Suspect Agents in Humans

2-Amino-azotoluene	Phenyl Hydrazine
2-Aminofluorene	Benzidine 3,3-Dimethyl
Auramine	Thioacetamide
Benz(a)anthracene	9,10-Dimethyl-1,2-Benzanthracene
Benzidine	3,Methylcholanthrene
Bis-Chloromethyl Ether	Asbestos
Hydrazine Monohydrate	Arsenic Compounds
Hydrazine Sulfate	Benzene
Hydraazobenzene	Acrylonitrile
m-Phenylenediamine	

Controlled chemicals besides CSAs include:

1. those extremely toxic materials that constitute a special risk to the worker,
2. some materials for which proposed OSHA standards claim carcinogenicity (e.g., beryllium),
3. compounds with TLVs that are listed in the ACGIH Appendix A-2 as Industrial Substances Suspect of Carcinogenic Potential to Man,
4. some compounds for which alerts have been issued by the National Institute for Occupational Safety and Health (NIOSH), CPSC or OSHA, and
5. compounds for which toxicological data strongly suggest a high health effects risk to the worker.

Some of these materials will eventually graduate to the CSA category. Table II lists some of the more important controlled chemicals used at LASL.

Table II. Examples of Controlled Highly Toxic Materials

Cadmium	Ethylenediamine
Aniline	Formaldehyde
Beryllium	Biphenol
Creosol	p-Dioxane
Nitrobenzene	Chromate Compounds
Trichloroethylene	

Decisions regarding borderline cases are critical to the success or failure of the control program. There will be a degree of uncertainty in many decisions, but the decision must be made based on the information currently available for each individual material.

TOXICOLOGY TESTING

In some instances toxicological data may be inadequate. A decision must then be made to determine if the planned use warrants development of toxicity data, or a conservative work practices-health protection program adequately serves the purpose of protecting the worker. An approach under consideration at LASL is detailed in Figure 1.

A user would identify new chemicals or materials in proposed or existing projects. The industrial hygienist, with the user or project manager, would estimate the current and projected uses of the materials. Available toxicological data are reviewed to determine appropriate engineering controls. In the absence of adequate toxicological data, interim controls would be recommended to the user, and the available data evaluated by a toxicology review committee to determine if screening short-term toxicity testing is recommended. This decision is based on the following criteria:

a. molecular structure indicating high toxicity potential,
b. significant potential for worker exposure,
c. inadequate toxicity data,
d. continuous use over a projected time, and
e. chemical content greater than 0.1% in a liquid or solid solution.

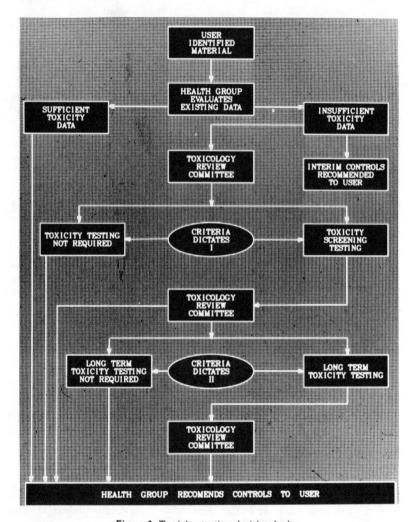

Figure 1. Toxicity testing decision logic.

The review committee may alternately judge that adequate data (possibly by analogy) exist. If so, controls are recommended. When inadequate data exist, screening toxicology is performed to provide data to further identify the hazards associated with the material.

The toxicological review committee continually assesses the test data being accumulated during screening. As early as possible after the initiation of screening testing, a decision will be made regarding the need for long-term toxicology tests, based on the following criteria:

a. probability of continued use and/or commercial involvement,
b. increased amounts to be used or high air concentrations expected,
c. probability of material being a mutagen/carcinogen or highly toxic,
d. no additional toxicity data published or known, and
e. possible introduction into the environment.

Only when it is determined that the material is to be introduced into a routine process is long-term toxicity testing performed. As data are accumulated during toxicity testing, recommendations for controls are adjusted. The desire to do extensive testing must be balanced against the cost of testing a large number of materials that will be used only in small quantities for a limited time span. Under these circumstances, application of conservative work practices may provide adequate protection in a shorter time.

MONITORING USAGE

Chemical issue at central stock is monitored (for accounting and reorder purposes) by a standard punch card system. The user completes the card that identifies the chemical by inserting quantity and using group, date and the worker's name. This information is transferred to a computer tape each week, and a listing is provided to the industrial hygiene group. Issue of any (not just CSA or controlled) chemical in the laboratory can be determined from this data base. The computer output identifies the date, worker, department and quantity issued. Monthly printouts report all chemical users, together with the quantity issued from stock.

For carcinogens, prior approval by the industrial hygiene group and preparation of an SOP are required. For controlled chemicals, the user completes the standard issue card at stock. This will be used to notify the industrial hygiene group of the user's name, group and telephone number. The chemical-use notification card is picked up daily by the industrial hygiene group for immediate review of the work situation and air or biological sampling, if necessary. These procedures are designed to result in minimal inconvenience to the operating technical groups, which is critical if the system is to succeed.

Approximately 100 controlled chemicals are carried in the laboratory's general chemical warehouse. The industrial hygienist immediately reviews with the user the toxicity of the chemical and the conditions under which the chemical will be used. If the controls are satisfactory, the operation is monitored as needed. Whenever possible, substitution of less toxic chemicals is recommended. Controlled chemicals are used in glove boxes, or in hoods with an average velocity of no less than 100 to 150 ft/min, depending on the material and type of operation involved.

Some chemicals are bought individually (as compared to general stock issue) using purchase request forms prepared by the prospective user. These are routinely routed through a chemical buyer who sends a copy to the industrial hygiene group at the time of processing the purchase order. Examination of each chemical purchase request at the time the order is placed enables the industrial hygienist to identify the potential problems before the material is used; permits strong emphasis on considering the use of less toxic materials; or assists in development of necessary control measures before the material must be placed into use. For carcinogens, this may require delay of ordering until control practices have been developed, or more usually a hold at shipping and receiving prior to issue.

OPERATING REQUIREMENTS

Cancer-Suspect Agents in Humans

Operating requirements for materials falling within the legal carcinogen category primarily involves following OSHA requirements. One project involving some of the 14 OSHA carcinogens required construction of a special laboratory facility that satisfied OSHA ventilation and air-cleaning requirements, preparation of an SOP, increased medical examination frequency, designation of a project safety officer (from the operating group) and a carcinogen safety officer (from the industrial hygiene group), and development of special waste disposal practices. In some instances, we have gone beyond OSHA requirements based on our professional evaluation of the problem at hand. This has included installation of charcoal sorbents (in addition to HEPA filters) in the exhaust ventilation air cleaning system, and use of glove box enclosures where the OSHA requirement could have been satisfied by chemical fume hoods.

Operating requirements for materials where the documentation concerning carcinogenicity is extensive are developed on a case-by-case basis. Much of the format, procedures and requirements may be modifications of the "DHEW Safety Standards for Laboratory Operations Involving Chemical Carcinogens." These LASL procedures do not supersede the requirements of any OSHA standard adopted for specific chemicals, but serve as a guide for controlling these materials when detailed OSHA requirements do not exist. Specific requirements depend on the following factors: probable carcinogenic hazard, volatility of material, type of operation to be performed, probability of producing aerosols, risk due to skin contacts, feasibility of monitoring release and potential exposure, practicality of controlling unexpected or accident situations, and other appropriate considerations relevant to protecting the health of the worker, individuals in adjacent areas, and the environment. Extremely small quantities or limited volumes of dilute solutions handled under given specific procedures may be exempt from many of the following detailed requirements, after review by the industrial hygiene group.

Primary responsibility rests with the user. An industrial hygienist is assigned as the carcinogen safety officer to work with the user group's project safety officer to ensure that they meet control requirements, and to provide continuous surveillance of the project. The project safety officer, with the assistance of the industrial hygienist, is responsible for the training of his employees in safe practices, for preventing work practices and conditions that may result in exposure, for informing support organizations of the necessary health and safety precautions, for developing a positive attitude toward safety operations on the part of his employees, and for preparing a comprehensive SOP health and safety plan.

An appropriate preassignment physical examination is performed by the occupational medicine group for each person planning to work with these materials. The purpose of this preassignment examination is to establish a baseline against which changes can be measured and to determine whether there are any existing medical or other conditions that may lead to increased risk in the work situation.

Controlled Chemicals

Since this category includes a variety of materials having different toxic effects, the operating requirements are specific to each substance. These materials cannot be withdrawn from stock without the industrial hygiene group being advised the next day. In this way, the user can be notified of the hazardous nature of the material, control measures and equipment checked, air samples collected and records kept of the rate of usage.

Blanket authorization to withdraw specific items in this category may be given to certain workers who use these material in routine, repetitive operations that are checked regularly. Requirements for handling these materials may include many of the requirements for human cancer-suspect agents.

Materials Requiring Normal Industrial Hygiene Controls

This covers a wide variety of materials, ranging from sodium chloride to lead. We must not lose sight of the fact that carcinogenesis is not the only end-point of concern. Dermatitis, respiratory disease and effects on the central nervous system must be controlled from a wide variety of materials. Again, controls are developed on a case-by-case basis.

INFORMING THE USER

The requirements for handling highly toxic or CSA materials must be distributed to all technical operating personnel. This information is incorporated into the LASL Health & Safety Manual and included in the health and safety section of the new employee orientation handbook. They are also described at the new employee orientation talk on health and safety. It is critical that each organization develop its own mechanism to accomplish transfer of information.

SUMMARY

This chapter summarizes some of the industrial hygiene services required for a research laboratory:

1. emphasizing the worker's awareness of hazards and encouraging him to contact the industrial hygienist for assistance,
2. reviewing and preevaluating all chemical usage, and
3. providing appropriate controls.

This should be supplemented by monitoring the activities as needed.

Control of toxic materials is accomplished by prohibiting the use of extremely toxic materials until satisfactory engineering controls have been implemented, limiting the issue of toxic materials until local exhaust ventilation or other engineering controls are available, or using respirators. In all cases, the use of less toxic substitutes is always considered.

With all of these controls, the variety of toxic materials requires close communication between the industrial hygienist and the user. It is necessary that each user be concerned about his and his fellow workers' health and well-being.

ACKNOWLEDGMENT

This work was performed at the Los Alamos Scientific Laboratory operated under the auspices of the US Department of Energy, Contract No. W-7405-ENG-36.

CHAPTER 7

SAFE HANDLING OF CHEMICAL CARCINOGENS IN THE RESEARCH LABORATORY

J. S. Johnson
University of California
Hazard Control Department
Lawrence Livermore Laboratory
Livermore, California

INTRODUCTION

Toxic and corrosive chemicals have been a part of America's development since the beginning. Only in the last 30 years, however, has any national regulatory attention been given to the safe handling of such chemicals in the workplace. The use of toxic and corrosive materials in the workplace was formally regulated by the Occupational Safety and Health Act of 1970; in 1973, the Occupational Safety and Health Administration (OSHA) issued temporary emergency standards for 14 chemical carcinogens. Now OSHA is attempting to promulgate a generic carcinogen standard. Lawrence Livermore Laboratory has established a chemical carcinogen control program on the basis of applicable standards promulgated by OSHA and has supplemented the program with internal controls for the safe handling of chemical carcinogens in the research laboratory. That control program is outlined here.

Before one can describe a program to safely handle chemical carcinogens in the research laboratory, one must examine the meaning of key words such as safety, safe and risk. *Webster's Dictionary* [1] defines safety as "the condition of being safe from undergoing or causing hurt, harm or risk." It defines safe as being "free from harm or risk" and risk as "the possibility of harm or loss." Thus, to make something safe by definition, one must totally remove the risk. In actual practice, however, one can only reduce, not totally remove, the risk.

To understand the concept of safety, one must realize that the extent of risk reduction is determined by the acceptability of the consequences. This acceptability—judging whether something is safe or unsafe—varies, however, because of the personal, social, economic and national views of the people who are evaluating a particular situation. Because of this variation in risk acceptability, the leaders of this country and the world have been faced with such challenges as nuclear power, supersonic transports, pesticides, DNA research, biohazards, and chemical carcinogens.

The words cancer and carcinogen (environmental, chemical and occupational) are used widely in today's literature without being carefully defined. This careless use of similar words, coupled with related and unrelated observations, results in fear and overreaction—a "cancer mania." It is because cancer is used to identify so many forms of human disease that there is some confusion about its meaning.

Webster's Dictionary [1] defines cancer as a malignant tumor of potentially unlimited growth that expands locally by invasion and systematically by metastasis. And it identifies any substance or agent that produces cancer as a carcinogen. Although no one has been able to determine what causes a substance or agent to be a carcinogen, many hypotheses and bits of information have been and are being used to speculate on the cause, thus adding to the confusion. There is no doubt, however, that cancer incidence and mortality trends in the U.S. are changing.

A recent article [2] from the National Cancer Institute reports that cancer once occurred more frequently among females, but that males now have higher incidence and mortality rates than do females of the same race. Once a predominantly "white" disease, cancer now occurs more frequently and with a higher mortality rate in nonwhite males and results in a higher mortality rate for nonwhite females. Increases have occurred in cancers of the lung, prostate gland, breast (nonwhite females), kidney, bladder (males), and esophagus (nonwhites). Melanomas have increased among members of the white race, and lymphomas have increased in each race-sex group. It is interesting to note, however, that the incidence of cancer among white males would have decreased, rather than increased, in recent years were it not for lung cancer; also, the dramatic increases in cancers among nonwhite males and females would be significantly reduced if lung and prostate cancers could be eliminated. These increases can be partially explained by improved diagnoses, personal habits such as smoking, and occupational exposure; a decrease in stomach cancer must somehow be related to changing eating habits. The observed changes in cancer incidence can also be related to changes in society in the past 40 years, e.g., the increased use of pesticides, greater air pollution, and the wearing of pantyhose. Thus, careful analysis of the cause-effect relationship for these changes can, at best, only provide partial answers to the causes of cancer.

Until the exact causes of chemically induced cancer are determined, one must take steps to reduce human exposure to suspect chemical agents. Regulatory agencies must also take care not to follow the approach of famous English sanitarians, Chadwick and Florence Nightengale. When commenting on medical research in pathogenesis, Florence Nightengale said, "There is no need to know. Only to do" [3].

The control of nonradioactive toxic and/or corrosive materials in the workplace is a relatively new undertaking for the federal government. In 1970 these toxic and/or corrosive materials were formally regulated by the Occupational Safety and Health Act [4], which adopted the American Conference of Industrial Hygienists threshold limit values for chemical substances and physical agents in the workroom environment. OSHA first acted on the carcinogen problem in 1973 by issuing temporary emergency standards for 14 chemicals [5]. Between 1973 and 1978, OSHA issued several additional standards for individual materials; these included vinyl chloride (1974), coke-oven emissions (1977), benzene (1978), 1,2-dibromo-3-chloropropane (1978), and inorganic arsenic (1978).

During 1973-1978, OSHA realized that issuing a separate standard for each nonradioactive toxic and/or corrosive material would be both cumbersome and time-consuming. Therefore, to streamline its regulatory process, OSHA has proposed a generic carcinogen standard approach [6] that defines four categories of carcinogens by their effects on man and animals.

1. Category 1 includes substances whose carcinogenicity has been established in humans, in two mammalian species of test animals, or in one species of test animal if the results are replicated.

2. Category II includes substances whose evidence of carcinogenicity is only suggestive or is positive in only one species of test animal and is not yet replicated.

3. Category III includes substances that require investigation but have not been classified as either Category I or II.

4. Category IV includes substances that OSHA believes are not currently found in the American workplace.

When a substance is found to be a Category I or II carcinogen, OSHA initiates a regulatory action following a standard format. If a substance is classified as a Category I carcinogen because of its effect on man or animals, however, OSHA issues an emergency temporary standard (ETS). In such a case, workplace exposures to the Category I carcinogen would have to be reduced dramatically. If a substitute material were available, a zero exposure level would be required. Each ETS would, according to a preestablished regulatory route, be replaced by a permanent standard. By a similar preestablished route, OSHA would also issue permanent standards for Category II carcinogens.

Public hearings on OSHA's use of the generic carcinogen standard approach were the longest hearings on record, requiring 3 months to complete and producing an 8792-page transcript. Although OSHA proposed the generic carcinogen standard to simplify its standard-setting process for regulating occupational carcinogens, it failed, as in previous attempts to regulate workplace carcinogens, to recognize the need for separating research facilities from the general industry standard. Judging from the number of positive and negative comments this proposed standard received at the public hearings, no fast and easy answer is at hand. The final decision on whether this approach will be used to regulate carcinogens in the American workplace will no doubt be decided in the courts.

Strict application of industrial standards to research facilities can only produce confusion, inefficiency, frustration and monetary waste. A separate standard that recognizes the need for specialized knowledge, special handling facilities, small quantities of chemicals, and rapid small-scale changes must be developed for research facilities. Hopefully, OSHA's reliance on Florence Nightengale's philosophy will change with respect to research facilities in the near future. To encourage this change in philosophy, the professional communities involved must provide technical input to support a separate standard. Until research facilities are regulated by a separate standard, however, all promulgated OSHA standards must be followed when applicable.

Promulgated OSHA standards are recognized in the chemical carcinogen control program outlined in this article. This program, now in use at Lawrence Livermore Laboratory, also includes internal controls that enable one to handle nonradioactive toxic and/or corrosive materials safely and realistically.

LAWRENCE LIVERMORE LABORATORY'S CHEMICAL CARCINOGEN CONTROL PROGRAM

Purpose

The purpose of this program is to outline safety guidelines for handling the chemical carcinogens, presumptive chemical carcinogens, and toxic chemicals used in laboratories at Lawrence Livermore Laboratory (LLL).

Classification Systems

Chemicals controlled by this program are classified as chemical carcinogens, presumptive chemical carcinogens, and toxic chemicals.

Chemical carcinogens are materials designated by OSHA as cancer-suspect agents. The Department of Energy (DOE) requires that all federal regulations for handling chemical carcinogens be followed at LLL. Table I is a

Table I. OSHA Chemical Carcinogens

Chemicals	PCC Solution Control Concentration (wt % or vol %)
4-Nitrobiphenyl	0.1
α-Naphthylamine	1.0
4,4'-Methylene bis(2-chloroaniline)	1.0
Methyl chloromethyl ether	0.1
3,3'-Dichlorobenzidine (and its salts)	1.0
bis-Chloromethyl ether	0.1
β-Naphthylamine	0.1
Benzidine	0.1
4-Aminodiphenyl	0.1
Ethyleneimine	1.0
β-Propiolactone	1.0
2-Acetylaminofluorene	1.0
4-Dimethylaminoazobenzene	1.0
N-Nitrosodimethylamine	1.0

list of chemicals recognized by OSHA as chemical carcinogens and the concentrations at which they can be treated as presumptive chemical carcinogens.

LLL also classifies as chemical carcinogens any chemicals known to produce or that tend to produce tumors in mammals when inhaled, ingested, or absorbed through the skin at a reasonable dose. Guidelines on ceiling doses* have been established by the American Conference of Governmental Industrial Hygienists; they should be followed when idenfifying chemical and presumptive chemical carcinogens.

Some industrial chemicals, e.g., asbestos, benzene and vinyl chloride, are carcinogenic and are controlled by specific federal regulations. Because these regulations are specific, however, they differ from the guidelines outlined in this program and must be applied on an individual basis. Guidance on the use of specific chemicals will be provided by the industrial hygiene and toxicology group of hazards control.

Presumptive chemical carcinogens are materials suspected of being tumorigenic by inhalation, ingestion or skin absorption at a reasonable dose because of chemical structure or questionable research.

---

*A substance should be considered a carcinogen if it produces a tumor by the respiratory route at doses at or below 1000 mg/m^3 for the mouse and 2000 mg/m^3 for the rat; by dermal route at doses at or below 1500 mg/kg for the mouse and 3000 mg/kg for the rat; or by gastrointestinal route at doses at or below 500 mg/kg/d for a lifetime, equivalent to about 100 g dose for the rat and 10 g total for the mouse [7].

Toxic chemicals are materials expected to have a noncarcinogenic adverse effect on persons exposed to low doses.

Procedural Controls

The use of chemical or presumptive chemical carcinogens must be approved by an operational safety procedure (OSP). An OSP may also be required for nonroutine uses of toxic chemicals depending on the hazard potential. The area hazards control safety team will provide assistance when necessary.

Purchasing/Receiving

It is the responsibility of the requester to identify the material being purchased as a toxic chemical, chemical carcinogen or presumptive chemical carcinogen. Reference materials [8] to aid in identification can be found in the main library and its extensions. The industrial hygiene and toxicology group of hazards control will also assist in identification when necessary.

When initiating a purchase requisition (Figure 1), the requester must check "toxic material" on the requisition form. If the requested chemical is a chemical or presumptive chemical carcinogen, the requester must check "toxic material" and add the words "carcinogen, CC" or "carcinogen, PCC" in the "keyword" portion of the purchase requisition. Each week, the procurement department sends a computer printout to the general safety division of hazards control that identifies all toxic and carcinogenic materials requested by LLL personnel.

When ordering carcinogens, the buyer must note on the purchase order that materials management will handle initial distribution. All carcinogens received by LLL receiving are sent unopened to the materials management vault. Materials management personnel open the shipping containers in a ventilated enclosure. After ensuring that the containers are not broken or leaking, they place the material in secondary containers that are properly identified with hazard control material ID tags (Figure 2) and ship them to the health and safety technician in the requester's area.

The health and safety technician is responsible for the initial internal distribution of chemical and presumptive chemical carcinogens. Any transfer of carcinogenic material within the laboratory should be coordinated through the health and safety technician.

General Laboratory Controls

The following practices must be followed whenever toxic chemicals, chemical carcinogens or presumptive chemical carcinogens are handled in the laboratory:

Entrance shall be restricted to personnel directly involved in experimentation or required services.

Local ventilation in the form of fume hoods and close-capture systems shall be available for any experiment that produces significant amounts of airborne gas, vapor or particulate. These systems shall be of the "once-through" type; no recirculation of exhaust air will be permitted.

Eating, drinking, tobacco or gum chewing, food storage, smoking, and application of cosmetics shall be prohibited in the laboratory work area.

Mechanical pipetting aids shall be used for all pipetting procedures.

Minimum protective clothing when handling these materials shall consist of a laboratory coat and safety glasses. Gloves should be worn when skin protection is required.

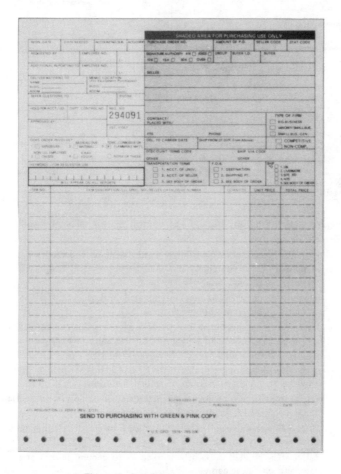

Figure 1. Purchase requisition form.

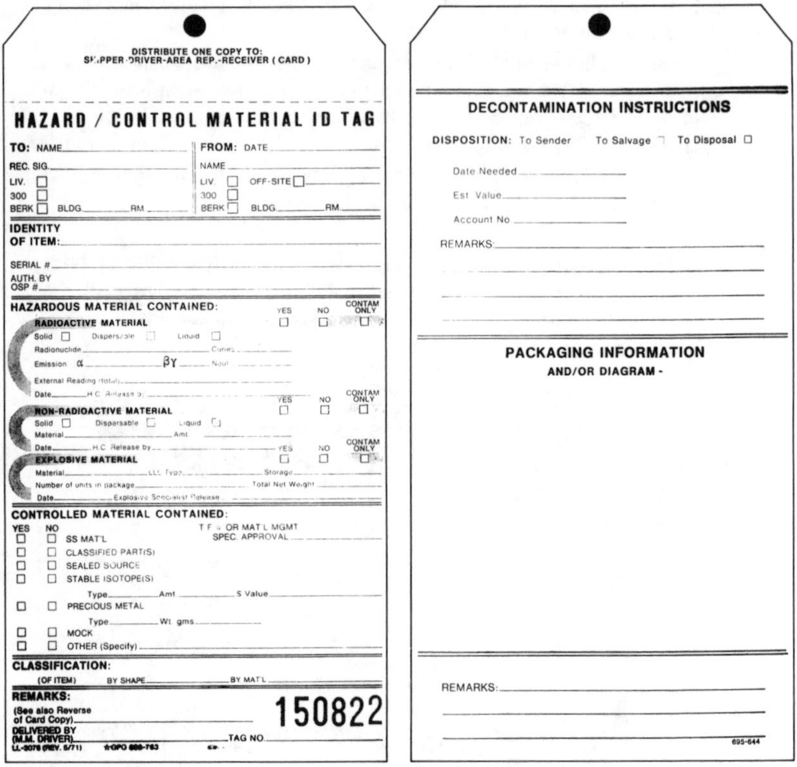
DISTRIBUTE ONE COPY TO:
SHIPPER-DRIVER-AREA REP.-RECEIVER (CARD)

HAZARD / CONTROL MATERIAL ID TAG

TO: NAME ______ | FROM: DATE ______
REC. SIG. ______ | NAME ______
LIV. ☐ | LIV. ☐ OFF-SITE ☐ ______
300 ☐ | 300 ☐
BERK ☐ BLDG. ______ RM. ______ | BERK ☐ BLDG. ______ RM. ______

IDENTITY OF ITEM: ______
SERIAL # ______
AUTH. BY OSP # ______

HAZARDOUS MATERIAL CONTAINED: YES NO CONTAM ONLY
RADIOACTIVE MATERIAL ☐ ☐ ☐
Solid ☐ Dispersible ☐ Liquid ☐
Radionuclide ______ Curies ______
Emission α ______ βγ ______ Neut ______
External Reading (total) ______
Date ______ H.C. Release by ______ YES NO CONTAM ONLY
NON-RADIOACTIVE MATERIAL ☐ ☐ ☐
Solid ☐ Dispersable ☐ Liquid ☐
Material ______ Amt ______
Date ______ H.C. Release by ______ YES NO CONTAM ONLY
EXPLOSIVE MATERIAL ☐ ☐ ☐
Material ______ LLL Type ______ Storage ______
Number of units in package ______ Total Net Weight ______
Date ______ Explosive Specialist Release ______

CONTROLLED MATERIAL CONTAINED:
YES NO T.F. OR MAT'L MGMT SPEC. APPROVAL ______
☐ ☐ SS MAT'L
☐ ☐ CLASSIFIED PART(S)
☐ ☐ SEALED SOURCE
☐ ☐ STABLE ISOTOPE(S)
Type ______ Amt ______ $ Value ______
☐ ☐ PRECIOUS METAL
Type ______ Wt. gms ______
☐ ☐ MOCK
☐ ☐ OTHER (Specify) ______

CLASSIFICATION:
(OF ITEM) BY SHAPE ______ BY MAT'L ______

REMARKS:
(See also Reverse of Card Copy) ______
DELIVERED BY (M.M. DRIVER) ______ TAG NO. 150822
LL-3078 (REV. 5/71)

DECONTAMINATION INSTRUCTIONS

DISPOSITION: To Sender ☐ To Salvage ☐ To Disposal ☐
Date Needed ______
Est. Value ______
Account No. ______
REMARKS: ______

PACKAGING INFORMATION AND/OR DIAGRAM -

REMARKS: ______
695-644

Figure 2. Front (a) and back (b) of control tag for secondary containers.

Properly labeled solid and liquid wastes shall be collected separately in nonpermeable containers and shall be disposed of through the building health and safety technician.

Separate receptacles for noncontaminated broken glass shall be provided in all laboratory work areas.

Hypodermic syringes shall be cut with a Destruclip cutting device and shall be disposed of in appropriate carcinogen waste containers.

Laboratory floor and bench top surfaces shall be made of or covered with a nonpermeable material like stainless steel or polyethylene to facilitate cleanup of spilled materials.

The storage or use of flammable liquids shall comply with Section 25.04 of the LLL Health and Safety Manual.

Safety-shower and eye-wash facilities shall be located within or in close proximity to the laboratory.

All containers shall be clearly marked as to general hazard and complete chemical contents.

Emergency action plans shall be included in the controlling OSP. The workplace shall be exposed only to the amount of material needed to complete the project, and no excess quantity of material should be purchased. Excess chemicals and unusable equipment should be disposed of once the project is completed.

Special Requirements for Working with Presumptive Chemical Carginogens

All persons handling presumptive chemical carcinogens must wear laboratory coats, gloves and safety glasses. When possible, disposable laboratory coats should be worn. These coats should be changed weekly unless contaminated or damaged and should not be worn outside the work area. Receptacles provided by hazards control shall be used for disposal of laboratory coats.

Special Requirements for Working with Chemical Carcinogens

Central carcinogen storage and work areas should be planned for all major laboratory programs using carcinogens. All storage and handling of pure carcinogenic materials should be done in a few primary work areas that are centrally located. This arrangement minimizes duplication of expensive handling facilities and enables better monitoring of the control program's effectiveness.

Primary work areas are locations used for work or permanent storage of undiluted chemical carcinogens. Because of the potentially hazardous nature of pure chemical carcinogens, additional guidelines must be followed:

The responsible department shall, for an indefinite time, maintain a written record of all persons entering and using the work area.

Signs identifying chemical carcinogen work areas shall be posted.

Gloved boxes or equivalent protection shall be used as defined by the industrial hygiene and toxicology group.

Air-cleaning systems shall be used to clean exhaust air contaminated by chemical carcinogens. The air-cleaning device used will depend on the hazard involved [e.g., high-efficiency particulate air (HEPA) filters for particulates and charcoal adsorbers for gases and vapors]. All ventilated systems should be of the "once-through" type; no recirculation of exhaust air shall be permitted. House vacuum systems must also have proper filters if they are used with carcinogens.

Liquid waste-retention systems shall be maintained.

Change rooms and shower facilities shall be available for all laboratory users.

Proper janitorial and maintenance practices and procedures shall be observed.

Chemical carcinogens shall be treated as presumptive chemical carcinogens once they have been diluted to concentrations specified by DOE or LLL standards (see Table I).

Certain carcinogen experiments can be performed in normal chemical laboratories if these laboratories meet all the requirements outlined above. When one of these laboratories is used for a carcinogen experiment, it must be treated as a primary work area. After the experiment is completed, the laboratory can be returned to normal use once the research laboratory has been decontaminated and the carcinogen is properly stored elsewhere.

Carcinogen Packaging

All carcinogens stored on shelves or in refrigerators in the primary work or storage area must be placed in properly labeled, unbreakable outer containers.

Carcinogen Inventory Requirements

The hazards control health and safety technician assigned to each area must keep a carcinogen log that contains the following information:

> purchaser
> Chemical name of carcinogen according to the International Union of Pure and Applied Chemistry (IUPAC)
> quantity of carcinogen received
> storage location
> length of time needed
> date and approximate quantity of carcinogen received for disposal

When the health and safety technician receives carcinogenic material from materials management, he must make appropriate log entries and notify the experimenter that the carcinogen has arrived. Once the carcinogen has been delivered to the experimenter, the experimenter is responsible for completing and maintaining the carcinogen work/storage log. The experimenter's log should be kept on sheets duplicated from Figure 3, and all log sheets should be kept indefinitely by the responsible department.

Signs and Labels

The following sign shall be posted at all entrances to primary carcinogen work and storage areas:

CAUTION

CHEMICAL CARCINOGEN
WORK AREA
AUTHORIZED PERSONNEL ONLY

(Black letters on yellow background.)

CHEMICAL CARCINOGEN LOG

Facility _____

Date of arrival _____

IUPAC chemical name _____

Quantity purchased _____

Purchaser responsible person _____

Storage location _____

Authorized users _____

Disposal date and approximate contents _____

Date	User's name	Approximate quantity used

Date	User's name	Approximate quantity used

Figure 3. Carcinogen work/storage log.

Signs posted in areas where presumptive chemical carcinogens are stored and handled should contain additional information on the specific hazard associated with each presumptive chemical carcinogen (e.g., chemical mutagen or teratogen). These signs should also be used in toxic chemical work areas requiring specific identification (see below).

CAUTION

CHEMICAL HAZARD
WORK AREA
AUTHORIZED PERSONNEL ONLY

(Black letters on yellow background.)

Labels such as those illustrated below should be used on all primary and secondary carcinogen containers:

```
┌─────────────────────────────────────────────────┐
│                                                   │
│                    DANGER                         │
│                  _____                      │
│                                                   │
│              CHEMICAL CARCINOGEN                  │
│                                                   │
│                                                   │
│     Date _____        │
│                                                   │
│     Compound _____         │
│                                                   │
│     Solvent/concentration _____        │
│                                                   │
│                                                   │
│          (Black letters on red background.)        │
│                                                   │
└─────────────────────────────────────────────────┘
```

```
┌─────────────────────────────────────────────────┐
│                                                   │
│                    DANGER                         │
│                  _____                      │
│                                                   │
│                  PRESUMPTIVE                      │
│              CHEMICAL CARCINOGEN                  │
│                                                   │
│                                                   │
│     Date _____        │
│                                                   │
│     Compound _____         │
│                                                   │
│     Solvent/concentration _____        │
│                                                   │
│                                                   │
│          (Black letters on red background.)        │
│                                                   │
└─────────────────────────────────────────────────┘
```

The following label should be used when toxic chemicals are removed from their original bottles and repackaged:

```
┌─────────────────────────────────────────────────┐
│                    CAUTION                       │
│              ─────────────────                   │
│                 TOXIC CHEMICAL                   │
│                                                  │
│   Date _____          │
│                                                  │
│   Compound _____          │
│                                                  │
│   Solvent/concentration _____          │
│                                                  │
│                                                  │
│          (Black letters on red background.)      │
└─────────────────────────────────────────────────┘
```

Decontamination and Disposal

Processes used to decontaminate surfaces that come in contact with chemical or presumptive chemical carcinogens must be evaluated by the area industrial hygienist. Questions about nonroutine decontamination processes for toxic chemicals will be answered by the area industrial hygienist.

Care must be exercised in choosing a decontamination process to ensure that all toxic or carcinogenic materials are destroyed or removed from the work surface. When meaningful, surface swipes should be taken for evaluation by the area industrial hygienist.

All solid and liquid wastes contaminated with carcinogens or toxic chemicals must be disposed of through the health and safety technician or through the hazards control waste disposal group.

Animal Exposure

The care and handling of animals in the laboratory shall follow the recommendations set forth in the U.S. Department of Health, Education and Welfare Publication 74-23. Additional information on the care and handling of animals can be obtained from the director of animal facilities, LLL biomedical division.

Medical Surveillance for Carcinogen Workers

The department head or division leader is responsible for informing the medical department in advance when any LLL employee will be routinely working with chemical carcinogens. This advance notice will enable the medical department to review the employee's file and provide necessary counseling.

The medical department's minimum medical surveillance program for carcinogen workers includes a review of employee medical records and an annual examination of each employee's physical health and laboratory work. Questions about who will be part of this medical surveillance program will be answered by the medical department.

The medical department shall disqualify from carcinogen work all pregnant women and all employees with a past or present history of cancer, excluding skin cancer that has been cured. (This exclusion may be waived after consultation with the plant physician.) In addition, each nonpregnant woman of childbearing age should consult with the plant physician to determine her suitability for carcinogen work.

ACKNOWLEDGMENT

This work was performed under the auspices of the U.S. Department of Energy by Lawrence Livermore Laboratory under Contract No. W-7405-Eng-48.

REFERENCES

1. *Webster's New Collegiate Dictionary* (Springfield, MA: G. and C. Merriam Company, 1976).
2. Olvesa, S. S., and D. T. Silverman. "Cancer Incidence and Mortality Trends in the United States: 1935-74," *J. Nat. Cancer Inst.* 60:545-571 (1978).
3. Higginson, J. "A Hazardous Society? Individual Versus Community Responsibility in Cancer Prevention," *Am. J. Phys. Hyg.* 66:359-366 (1976).
4. Occupational Safety and Health Administration. "General Industrial Safety and Health Administration Regulations, Part 1910.93," *Federal Register* 39(25):23540 (1974).
5. Occupational Safety and Health Administration. "Emergency Temporary Standard on Certain Carcinogens," *Federal Register* 38(85):1092ʯ (1973).
6. Occupational Safety and Health Administration. "Identification, Classification, and Regulation of Toxic Substances Posing a Potential Occupational Carcinogenic Risk," *Federal Register* 42(192):54148 (1977).
7. "TLV's Threshold Limit Values for Chemical Substances in the Workroom Environment," American Conference of Governmental Industrial Hygienists, Washington, D.C. (1977), p. 40.
8. *The Registry of Toxic Effects of Chemical Substances,* National Institute of Occupational Safety and Health, Washington, D.C.

CHAPTER 8

DESIGN, IMPLEMENTATION AND MONITORING OF LABORATORIES FOR HANDLING CHEMICAL CARCINOGENS AND MUTAGENS

Vincent F. Simmon* and M. Virginia Peirce

SRI International
Menlo Park, California

DESIGN AND IMPLEMENTATION

Several laboratories at SRI perform biological assays with chemicals suspected of being mutagens or carcinogens. During the last six years, we have developed procedures consistent with current and expected government guidelines for handling known carcinogens. Many samples are coded, and their potential biological hazards are not known. Therefore, all samples are handled as if they are subject to Occupational Safety and Health Administration (OSHA) guidelines, even when the amount of chemical involved is less than a milligram.

When a sample is received, it is brought to a central chemical storage room that serves all of the laboratories performing short-term assays for identifying carcinogens. Only two people work in the chemical storage room. When working in the room, they wear disposable lab gowns, caps, shoe covers and gloves. The laboratories and the storage area are restricted, with access limited to authorized personnel. Eating, drinking, smoking, chewing gum, and application of cosmetics are not permitted in these regulated areas. All janitorial functions are performed by experienced laboratory staff. The entryway to the chemical storage facility is shown in Figure 1.

---

*Present address: Genex Corporation, Rockville, MD.

153

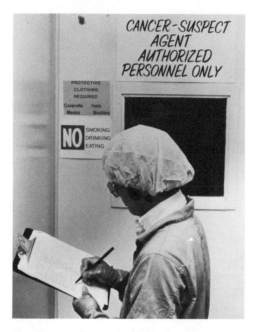

Figure 1. Entryway into chemical storage-weighing area. A logbook of entry and exit time and date is kept in the change room leading into the room, and in all laboratories where suspect chemicals are tested.

Each sample is logged in a manner similar to that used for radioactive materials. The sample is identified by project number, client, approximate volume or weight, date received, storage site (refrigerator, freezer, room-temperature cabinet), and current disposition. A form from the log book is shown in Figure 2.

Chemical Log Sheet No. ___468___

Date	Date Chemical Received	Name or Code of Chemical	Client	SRI Project Number	Investigator	Storage Site	Amount Chemical Received	Amount Chemical Removed
4-10-78	4-7-78	06182	NCI	5848	Simmon	RF	5g	
4-18-78					Cahill			0.5g
4-24-78					Cahill			1.3g
5-17-78					Cahill			1.15g
2-8-79					Remainder (~ 2g) given to Health & Safety as per Simmon			

Figure 2. Sample log book entry.

Chemicals received are placed in secondary containers (Figure 3) to ensure safety in transport and storage. Unless otherwise specified, chemicals are stored under ambient conditions in a storage cabinet (Figure 4). The

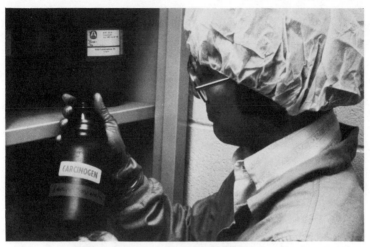

Figure 3. Primary containers of chemicals are placed in screw-top secondary containers before being stored.

Figure 4. Ambient-temperature storage cabinets. The cabinets are connected to an exhaust air system which maintains them under slightly negative pressure with respect to the room. This prevents the accumulation of hazardous vapors or dust from the chemicals.

cabinets are connected to the air discharge system so that they are under
a constant, slightly negative pressure. When required, samples are stored
frozen or refrigerated. The refrigerators/freezers have vents along their openings (Figure 5). A simple catch prevents the door from being opened fully;
it must be manually overridden to fully open the door.

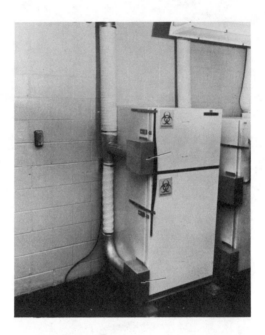

Figure 5. Chemical storage refrigerator-freezer. Exhaust vents are placed along the
lower edge of each door. The door opening is limited by a catch (arrows)
that must be manually overridden. This allows the air inside the refrigerator-
freezer to be exhausted before the person opening the door is exposed.

When an investigator wishes to test a sample, he or she submits a requisition identifying the project and stating: when the chemical is needed, code
number or name, and the amount of chemical desired. A requisition slip
is shown in Figure 6. The sample requested is transferred from its storage
area in its secondary container to a glove box (Figure 7). The air from
the glove box is passed through a 0.45-μ filter and an activated carbon
filter before it is exhausted. After being placed in the glove box, the secondary container is opened and an aliquot of the sample is placed in a pre-
weighed sterile screw-top test tube. After it is closed, its exterior is wiped
clean and the closed test tube is reweighed to determine the weight of
the sample. The closed test tube is then placed in a passthrough for pickup by the investigator (Figure 8).

```
Requestor:_____   Date:_____   Charge #:_____
Chemical name, lot #,   _____
    and amount:         _____
                        _____
                        _____
                        _____
Experiment #:_____   Date chemical required:_____
                                                         Form 377.001-1
```

Figure 6. A sample chemical requisition slip.

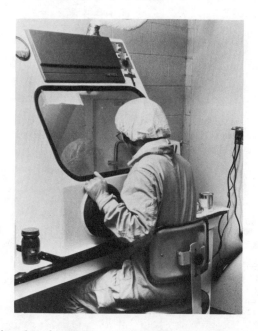

Figure 7. The glove box for opening chemical containers. An activated carbon filter is fitted inside the glove box (behind the panel at the top), along with a 0.45-μ membrane filter.

For microbial mutagenicity tests, the closed sample tube is transferred to a vertical laminar flow hood (Figure 9), where an appropriate amount of solvent is added to the sample. This hood is set up for performing the Ames *Salmonella*/mutagenicity assay. The working surface of the hood is lined with an absorbent diaper and contains separate plastic-lined waste containers for burnable materials, such as plastics, and for nonburnable materials, such as glass. This type of hood exhausts approximately 80% of the air on each cycle. The exhausted air is passed through a 0.45-μ filter

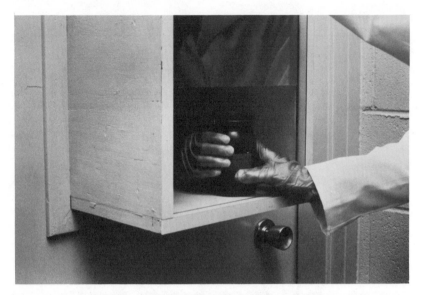

Figure 8. The passthrough from the chemical storage area into the laboratory where chemicals are tested. Closure is provided by a sliding plexiglass door. The passthrough is built into an emergency exit door.

Figure 9. A vertical laminar flow hood with equipment set up for performing the Ames *Salmonella*/microsome assay. Plastic-lined waste containers[1] are provided for disposal of burnable and nonburnable waste. A heat block[2] is used to maintain the top agar at 43°C. The liver homogenate (S-9 mix) is kept at 0°C in a thermos container.[3] Manual pipetting equipment[4] is used for all pipetting operations.

and two activated carbon filters before being discharged to the outside air. Monitoring equipment is in place to detect chemical breakthrough of the first activated carbon filter. Burnable waste from the operation is placed in a plastic-lined box. An exhaust system above the container limits the amount of dust reentering the work area when material is placed in the waste container (Figure 10). When they are filled, the boxes are sealed, labeled to indicate that they contain hazardous material, and incinerated (Figure 11). All liquid wastes and diluents are pooled and poured into polyethylene 1-gal jugs. Disposable glassware is placed in a plastic-lined drum. These operations are carried out under a standard fume hood (Figure 12). Liquid and nonburnable materials are buried in a restricted, class 2 dump site.

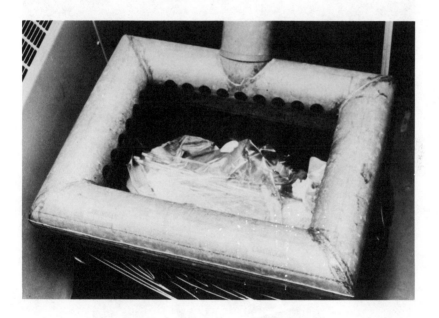

Figure 10.   Disposal of burnable waste in a vented, plastic-lined waste container.

MONITORING

As with radioactive samples, it is necessary to monitor storage and work areas for chemical contamination, or to assess the efficiency of the cleanup when there has been a chemical spill. Because of the large number of chemicals used, and because many of the chemicals are coded, it would be impractical to develop specific analytical procedures for each chemical.

Figure 11. A sealed box of burnable waste. Burnable waste includes all plastic, paper and petri plates.

Figure 12. View of the fume hood in which solid and liquid wastes are disposed. All liquid wastes, including diluents, are pooled into plastic 1-gal jugs. Glassware and other nonburnable materials are collected in a plastic-lined cardboard drum.

In collaboration with Lawrence Livermore Laboratory, we evaluated the feasibility of using the Ames *Salmonella*/microsome assay for routine monitoring of laboratory surfaces. The Ames assay does not identify what chemicals are present, but it can detect many classes of chemicals that are mutagenic to bacteria.

An outline of the protocol used to evaluate this procedure is presented in Figure 13.

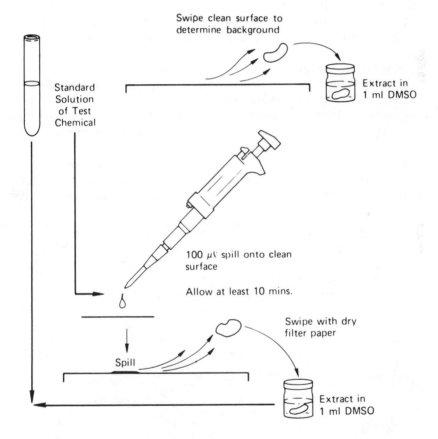

Figure 13. Protocol for the evaluation of the use of the Ames *Salmonella*/microsome assay for detecting chemicals on laboratory surfaces. A series of concentrations of each chemical was prepared. Each concentration was tested for mutagenic activity, and 100 µl of each concentration also was spilled onto a clean laboratory surface. After 10 min, the area of the spill was wiped with a clean, dry filter paper, which was then placed in a vial with 1 ml of DMSO. The mutagenic activity of the DMSO extract was compared with the mutagenic activity of the stock solution, after correction for the DMSO dilution.

For negative controls, an ostensibly clean lab surface (exposed several days to airborne laboratory dust) was swiped once with a dry Whatman #40, 41 or 50 1-in.-diameter filter paper tab. The filter tab was folded or rolled to fit into a 1-dram screw-capped vial, and 1 ml of dimethylsulfoxide (DMSO) was added to the vial to extract the material absorbed by the filter paper.

Five standard solutions of each test chemical were prepared, usually in the range from 0.01 to 3%; 100 μl of each standard solution was applied to a clean lab surface. After at least 10 min, a dry filter paper tab was swiped over the spill area, fit into a 1-dram vial, and 1 ml of DMSO was added to the vial. Two aliquots (50 and 150 μl.) of the DMSO extracts were tested for mutagenic activity. For positive controls, some of the standard solutions were tested directly for mutagenicity at the same time as the DMSO extraction mixtures. Mutagenicity was assayed in one Ames strain (the most sensitive strain for the chemical being tested), and S-9 mix metabolic activation was included when required. All mutagenicity experiments were performed in triplicate.

Results for four chemicals tested are shown in Figures 14 through 17.

Figure 14 is a graph of results of three spills of 9-aminoacridine (9AA). The Ames strain selected was TA1537, and no S-9 mix metabolic activation

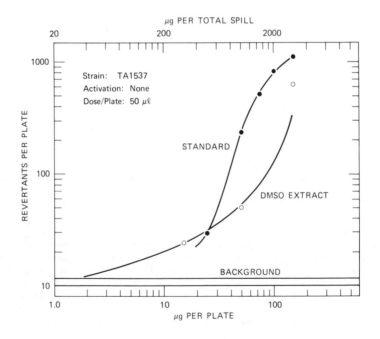

Figure 14. Results of controlled spills with 9-aminoacridine.

was included. The top axis indicates total micrograms of 9AA spilled; the bottom axis indicates the equivalent amount of 9AA potentially available in the 50-μl test dose of the DMSO extract of the spill. The vertical axis indicates average number of his^+ revertants per plate. The lines labeled "background" indicate the range in number of revertants per plate for the negative control (50-μl plate of the DMSO extract swipe of "clean surface"). The range (10 to 12 revertants per plate) is consistent with the spontaneous reversion frequency of TA1537; therefore, there was no apparent interference from background mutagens, toxic chemicals or microbes. The dark circles represent revertants per plate for the standard solutions tested directly for mutagenicity. This positive control dose-response indicated how mutagenic 9AA was at known doses under test conditions. The three open circles represent three different spills of 9AA. The total amount of the first spill was 300 μg (top axis). This would have made a maximum of 15 μg (bottom axis) potentially available in the 50-μl dose of DMSO extract plated. The second open circle represents total spill of 1000 μg 9AA—which would have made a maximum of 50 μg available in the 50-μl dose of DMSO extract plated. The average number of revertants per plate is plotted as a function of the amount of 9AA potentially available per plate. When the standard curve and the results for the three spills are compared, it can be seen that the two curves are close at flat parts of the dose-response curve and not so close at steep parts of the curve, where small changes in the amount of 9AA present make a big difference in the number of revertants per plate.

Figure 15 presents results of controlled spills of MNNG. Enough MNNG was recovered from spills greater than 200 μg to be toxic to the bacteria. This provides an example of the need for testing several doses of the DMSO extract of a field sampling swipe. A response of around 250 revertants per plate could indicate the presence of 0.5 μg or a toxic dose of 50 μg MNNG per plate (total spills of 10 μg or 1000 μg, respectively). Testing several doses, both less than and greater than 50 μl, of the DMSO extract of a field sampling swipe would give a better indication of the quantity of mutagen present.

Figure 16 presents results of controlled spills of 2-naphthylamine. There is a dose-response curve with increasing concentration of the spill paralleling the standard curve.

Figure 17 presents results of tests with spills of 2-aminoanthracene on two different types of lab surfaces. The bottom line represents four spills onto a vinyl tile surface collected with a dry filter paper tab; recovery was barely above background. The middle line represents spills on the same vinyl tile surface, but recovered with a swipe dampened with ethanol; recovery was improved. The top line represents spills on a polyethylene

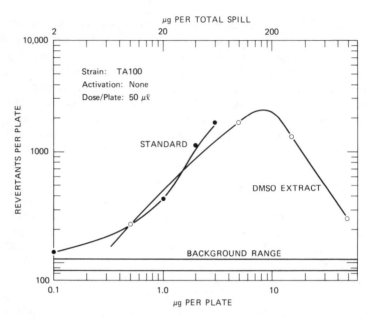

Figure 15. Results of controlled spills with N-methyl-N-nitro-N-nitrosoguanidine (MNNG).

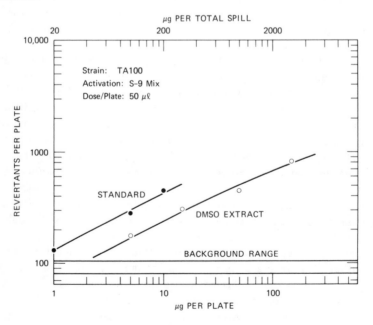

Figure 16. Results of controlled spills with 2-napthylamine.

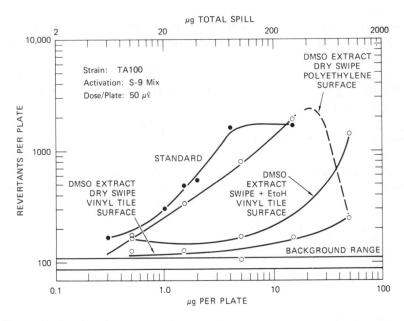

Figure 17. Results of controlled spills with 2-aminoanthracene. The spills were onto either vinyl tile or a polyethylene surface. In one experiment, the vinyl surface was wiped with a filter paper moistened with ethanol.

Table I. Summary of Detection of Mutagens on Laboratory Surfaces Using the Ames *Salmonella*/Microsome Assay. (The minimum amount of chemical that could be detected, the *Salmonella* strain, and use of an activation system (if required) are indicated.)

Compound	Approximate Spill Limit Detection (μg)	Strain	S-9 Mix Metabolic Activation
4-Nitroquinoline-1-oxide	1	TA100	−
MNNG	10	TA100	−
2-Aminoanthracene	10	TA100	+
4-Methoxynaphthylamine-HCl	10	TA100	+
N-Acetylaminofluorene	20	TA98	+
Benzo[a]pyrene	20	TA100	+
2-Naphthylamine	30	TA100	+
Ethylnitrosourea	50	TA100	−
9-Aminoacridine	100	TA1537	−
Nitrogen Mustard-HCl	1000	TA100	−
Benzidine	3000	TA100	+
8-Hydroxyquinoline	3000	TA100	−
Triethylthiophosphoramide	10000	TA100	−
Hydrazine Sulfate	Not detected	TA100	−
Thiourea	Not detected	TA100	+

surface; recovery was very close to the standard curve. These results provide further evidence that using less porous surfaces in carcinogen/mutagen labs is important.

Table I summarizes the minimum detectable amounts of all the chemicals tested. Spills of 3 mg or less were detected for most chemicals. Spills of less than 10 μg were detected for 2-aminoanthracene, MNNG, and 4-nitroquinoline-1-oxide. Hydrazine sulfate and thiourea were not detected as mutagens, in either the standards or the spills.

In conclusion, we found that the Ames assay was free of interference from background chemicals or microbes, the chemicals tested retained mutagenicity to Ames strains after spill and recovery, and recovery was efficient enough to determine the presence of mutagenic chemicals.

SECTION II

CHEMICAL MONITORING
AND
MEDICAL SURVEILLANCE

CHAPTER 9

MONITORING TRACE AMOUNTS OF ORGANIC CHEMICALS IN THE LABORATORY ATMOSPHERE

Richard Glenn Melcher

Dow Chemical U.S.A.
Michigan Division
Analytical Laboratory
Midland, Michigan

INTRODUCTION

To ensure a safe working environment in the laboratory and production plants, it is often necessary to determine trace quantities of organic chemicals in the work atmosphere. For a successful program good communication must exist between the toxicologist who assesses the toxicity of the compound, the industrial hygienist who investigates the hazard of exposure to personnel, and the analytical chemist who determines the concentration of the compound in the environment and in biological samples for metabolism and pharmacokinetic studies. The factors that affect the collection and determination of trace quantities can be quite complex, and each specialist involved in method development, sampling or analytical measurements must have a basic understanding of the total effort.

It is beyond the scope of this chapter to discuss the complexities of toxicological industrial hygiene or analytical techniques. However, discussion will be directed toward some general factors which interface the collection of trace organics in air and their recovery for quantitative determination. The main emphasis will be on collection with solid sorbents followed by thermal desorption or desorption with a suitable solvent. This includes a majority of the samples presently being collected and new methods being developed. Solid sorbents are convenient to use, can concentrate trace contaminants, and can be used for area samples as well as for employee breathing-zone samples.

169

DEFINITION OF PROJECT

Once a problem or potential for a problem has been recognized, careful definition of the project is necessary to determine its purpose and scope. The laboratory or plant area must be studied to determine the personnel involved, ventilation, engineering controls and the type and quantity of chemicals in the area.

The type and extent of analytical coverage must be defined since different collection and quantitation techniques may be employed to determine short-term exposures and/or long-term, time-weighted-average exposures. Area, as well as personal samples, are sometimes necessary, and onsite monitors with alarms may be warranted.

A detailed checklist is useful in the planning and execution of a successful survey [1]. After the survey is completed, the data must be reviewed and recommendations made for the solution of the problem.

METHOD DEVELOPMENT AND VALIDATION

Although detailed, validated methods are available for many compounds in books [2-10], literature and reviews [11-13], and in government publications [1,14-17], one must be aware of the factors that affect collection and recovery and the procedures checking the method's reliability for the specific application intended. Methods are not available for many compounds and must be developed and validated. Suggested steps for the development and validation of air sampling methods are summarized in Tables I and II.

Table I. Progressive Development Steps

Suggest Procedure (little or no experimental work)
1. Chemical, physical, and toxicological properties listed.
2. Concentration range and required sensitivity estimated.
3. Sorbent-desorption system(s) extrapolated from similar compounds.
4. Analytical procedure suggested.
5. Possible interferences indicated.

Tentative Procedure (limited experimental work)
1. Analytical procedure tested.
2. Desorption efficiency determined.
3. Optimized desorption parameters.
4. Preliminary breakthrough and bias study.
5. Preliminary onsite samples.
6. Effect of interferences, coadsorption and temperature (if indicated).

Table II. Validation Steps

Validated Method (systematic study)

1. Determination of breakthrough volume at concentrations of 2 times TLV and relative humidity of 85% or greater.
2. Five samples at each concentration, 0.1, 0.5, 1 and 2 times TLV, for relative humidities less than 50% and greater than 85% (40 samples).
3. Six samples at the TLV concentration (three collected at each humidity) and stored for at least 14 days.
4. Statistical evaluation of data.
5. Onsite validation by comparison to accepted method or by "field spiking."
6. Collaborative studies with other laboratories.

Criteria for Successful Validation

1. Accuracy and precision of combined analytical and collection procedures for concentration range of 1/10 TLV to 2 TLV, ± 16% relative at the 95% confidence level.
2. Total recovery efficiency of at least 75%.
3. Bias between total recovery and desorption efficiency less than ± 10% relative.
4. Capable of taking 10-to-15-min samples at ceiling and excursion levels.
5. Minimum sampling time 1 hr, preferred 4 to 8 hr for TWA.
6. Storage samples should be compared within ± 10% relative to initial samples after being stored for 14 days.
7. The flowrate of the sampling pump should be known with the accuracy of ± 5%.

The exact protocol and amount of testing necessary depends on the extent of the sampling project. Methods for limited surveys, where the sampling conditions and concentrations are defined and relatively constant, can be validated for that specific situation. Long-term or on-going surveys which involve a variety of compounds, geographical locations, temperatures, humidities and storage times require a greater collection and recovery data base as well as a continuing quality control program [7,18]. If additional sampling variables are subsequently introduced, additional data should be obtained.

The first experimental step in method development is obtaining a suitable analytical procedure. Although the procedure may be changed or replaced for the final validation and survey, an adequate technique must initially be available to evaluate recoveries and determine concentration ranges. Table III lists some recommended characteristics that should be considered before and during the sampling procedure development. Gas chromatography is the most widely used analytical technique for stable, volatile organic compounds because of its selectivity and sensitivity. Gas chromatographic procedures are available or can be developed for a wide range of organic compounds by proper selection of columns and detectors.

Table III. Interfacing Analytical and Sampling Procedures

1. Sensitivity	Sensitivity range compatible with amount of compound to be collected.
2. Specificity	Interferences in the area and on a broader scale investigated.
3. Reproducibility of Analysis	Over concentration range to be studied.
4. Reproducibility of Apparatus	Operating conditions well defined, and columns and reagents widely available.
5. Adaptability	Compatible with desorption solvents and other reagents used in method.
6. Simplicity	Rapid, uncomplicated procedure.
7. Automated	Automatic injection and data handling systems for extended projects.

The range can be broadened by using chemical derivatives and gas chromatographic/mass spectrometric techniques.

Many other analytical techniques, such as liquid chromatography, infrared and absorption spectroscopy, are useful for the determination of trace compounds, particularly those which are nonvolatile, heat-sensitive or highly reactive.

Area Monitors

Many laboratories have facilities in the immediate area to monitor trace quantities of experimental chemicals. A program can be set up for periodic sampling and analysis using the laboratory research equipment. A dedicated automatic sampling system with alarm potential may also be used in areas where careful scrutiny is necessary.

Although area monitors may be preferred for detection of excursions and short-term data points, it is often difficult to correlate the results to actual personal exposures, especially when the employees spend only sporadic periods in the area. In order to obtain the high sensitivity and actual time-weighted-average personal exposure, it is often necessary to incorporate solid sorption collection in the monitoring program.

Collection on Solid Sorbents

Solid sorbent collection methods for many compounds have been reported in the literature, and the extrapolation of this information serves as a guide to the selection of suitable collection sorbent and desorption conditions. Many of the parameters which affect collection have been studied in detail, but the number of variables encountered in actual samples is often too great to rely solely on these extrapolations for untested compounds. High concentration of collected compounds on the backup section of a collection tube can be used to detect deteriorative effects on the collection efficiency. However, if these factors are recognized before or during sampling, modification may be made in the collection procedure which will reduce the number of invalid samples. A false indication of breakthrough may be caused by migration of the compounds collected on the front section to the backup section over an extended storage period.

Factors Affecting Collection Efficiency

Factors which affect collection efficiency are listed below. The degree to which each factor contributes depends on the specific sorbent and sorbate.

Contaminant's Chemical and Physical Properties

It is usually more efficient to obtain experimental breakthrough data on specific collection systems for the compounds of interest, although some equations have been developed to relate the properties of the compound to collection efficiencies [19-21].

Sorbent

In selecting a sorbent for high collection efficiency, the subsequent recovery of the compound must also be considered. A compromise may be necessary to obtain a useful system.

Size of Collection Tube

In general, if the amount of sorbent is doubled, the beakrthrough volume is doubled. Tubes containing at least 600 mg should be used for sampling periods of 1 hr or more.

Flowrate

As long as equilibrium conditions have not been exceeded, the breakthrough volume is not greatly affected by flowrate. The linear velocity at optimum conditions should be an important consideration when extrapolating data to different size tubes [22].

Concentration

Breakthrough occurs sooner for higher concentrations. For charcoal, the Freundlich isotherm appears to apply [20,23].

Humidity

In general, an increase in humidity will result in some increase in breakthrough [24,25].

Coadsorption

More strongly held compounds displace others along the sorbent bed and may cause premature breakthrough [19].

Temperature

An increase in temperature will result in an increase in breakthrough [24].

Recovery From Solid Sorbents

Two basic techniques are used to recover organic compounds from solid sorbents.

Thermal Desorption

In the thermal desorption technique, the collection tube is heated and a carrier flow purges the collected organics into a gas chromatograph or other measuring device [25-40]. The main advantage of this technique is the high sensitivity obtained since the total sample collected in 1-3 liters of air can be injected at one time. Sensitivity is in the low parts-per-billion range for most compounds. One disadvantage is the "one-shot" nature of the analysis. Multiple samples must be taken in order to run duplicate analyses and/or to examine by more than one technique. An unpredicted interference or instrumental miscue results in a lost sample. Some typical sorbents and conditions are shown in Table IV [25,41-45]. It is important to thoroughly condition each sampling slug before it is used by heating and purging with nitrogen. When determining trace quantities the background pattern becomes quite important. Decomposition and oxidation products of the sorbent can interfere with the analysis and extra care is needed in conditioning and in choosing desorption temperature and rate.

The apparatus used for desorption can be relatively simple [25] or more complex [33]. The basic components of a simple system are shown in Figure 1. The collection tube, usually 4-6 in. long and 0.25 in. in diameter, is connected directly to the gas chromatographic column or through a heated valve. The tube is heated with a heating tape, and the desorbed compounds are purged into a cold gas chromatographic column. After desorption, the column is temperature-programmed to obtain the chromatogram. Other thermal desorption systems can be integrated with an onsite chromatograph

Table IV. GC Conditions for Thermal Desorption Analysis

	Increase in Boiling Point of Collected Compound			
Sampling Tube	4-in. Carbosieve B adsorbent, 100/120	4-in. Porapak N porous polymer 80/100	4-in. Tenax-GC porous polymer, 60/80	2-in. 20% DC-200 silicone oil on C.W., H.P. support 100/120
Sampling Tube Desorption	5 min at 270°C	5 min at 200°C	5 min at 260°C	5 min at 230°C
Column	2 ft x 0.125 in. s.s., Carbosieve B adsorbent, 100/120	4 ft x 0.125 in. s.s., Porapak N porous polymer, 80/100	8 ft x 0.25 in. s.s., 10% OV-17 silicone oil on Gas Chrom Q support, 60/80	6 ft x 0.25 in. glass, 10% OV-17 silicone oil on Gas Chrom Q support, 100/120
Column Temperature	5 min at 80°C program 20°C/min to 290°C and hold	5 min at 60°C program 15°C/min to 200°C and hold	5 min at 60°C program 15°C/min to 280°C and hold	5 min at 90°C program 15°C/min to 260°C and hold
Injection Port Temperature	80°C	120°C	220°C	200°C
Carrier Gas Flow (ml N_2/min)	20	20	30	20

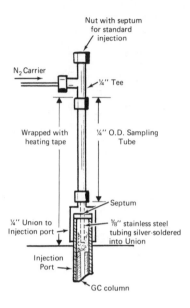

Figure 1. Basic components for a simple thermal desorption system.

where the sample is collected, thermally desorbed and analyzed in a 5- to 10-min periodic cycle [46,47].

Solvent Desorption

Solvent desorption of collected compounds from solid sorbents is the most commonly used technique. The procedure is relatively simple; once the compound is desorbed, the extract can be analyzed by gas chromatography or other standard analytical techniques. The solvent desorption system permits duplicate analyses by different techniques allows special procedures to separate and identify interferences and special procedures such as derivatization [48]. It also permits automatic injection by available liquid handling systems.

Parts-per-million concentrations in air are usually determined, although parts-per-billion sensitivity can be obtained for some compounds by using large sample volumes and high-sensitivity detectors.

Table V lists some of the most widely used sorbents and general types compounds collected. Overlap of useful sorbents allows some flexibility when sampling mixtures. The desorption solvent is selected on the basis of recovery and analytical procedure. Mixed solvents [14] and two-phase systems [49] have been used to improve recovery.

Table V. General Sorption-Desorption Systems for Organic Compounds

Sorbent	Desorption Solvent	Types of Compounds
Activated Carbon	Carbon disulfide, methylene chloride, ether (1% methanol or 5% isopropanol sometimes added)	Miscellaneous Volatile Organics: methyl chloride, vinyl chloride and other chlorinated aliphatics, aliphatic and aromatic solvents, acetates, ketones, alcohols
Silica Gel	Methanol, ethanol diethyl ether, water	Polar Compounds: alcohols, phenols, chlorophenols, chlorobenzenes, aliphatic and aromatic amines
Activated Alumina	Water, diethyl ether, methanol	Polar Compounds: alcohols, glycols, ketones, aldehydes
Porous Polymers	Ether, hexane, carbon disulfide, alcohols, thermal	Wide Range of Compounds: phenols, acidic and basic organics, multi-functional organics
Chemically Bonded	Ether, hexane, methanol, thermal	Specialized: high boiling compounds, pesticides, herbicides, polynuclear aromatics

Charcoal [50] and silica gel [51,52] are widely used sorbents while porous polymers and chemically bonded packings [55] are used for specialized applications. Most methods require a sampling pump to pull the air through the sorbent tube, and small battery-operated personal pumps are available. Pumpless dosimeters have recently been developed; they rely on the diffusion [56] or permeation [57] of compounds through a membrane into a chamber containing a sorbent.

Factors Affecting Recovery Efficiency

A number of factors influence the recovery efficiency (that fraction recovered of the total compound collected when no breakthrough has occurred). They can cause errors unless they are understood and related to the chemical and physical properties of the compound collected.

Desorption Efficiency

The desorption efficiency is the most significant of the factors defining the sorption-solvent desorption system. For many systems the desorption efficiency can be written in terms of an equilibrium constant; it is dependent on the ratio of solvent to sorbent for the distribution of the compound between the two phases [58].

Temperature

The temperature effect on recovery can be significant. It is a common practice to cool the solvent before desorbing samples to reduce the heating effects. However, the equilibrium constant will change with temperature, and the final desorption temperature may be critical.

Humidity

High humidity during collection may produce low recoveries for compounds which are easily hydrolyzed. If a large amount of water is collected, good contact with a nonpolar desorption solvent may be prevented or the equilibrium may change.

Coadsorption

Collection of other compounds can also affect recovery. The chemistry of all compounds collected must be considered and the relative effects tested in the laboratory.

Desorption Time

Desorption time of 30 min to 1 hr with good agitation is usually sufficient for most systems. Once optimum desorption has taken place, the system is generally stable; however, some exceptions have been observed [59]. Some compounds react or are readsorbed after an optimum desorption time as shown in Figure 2. The active surface of the sorbent may act as a catalyst. Methanol has been shown to react with carbon disulfide in the presence of charcoal to form polysulfides, mercaptans and polyether-thioether compounds [59].

Concentration

The equilibrium model predicts that desorption efficiency should not vary with concentration. However, some factors that affect recovery will have a greater percentage effect on lower concentrations. As a result the recovery of some compounds decreases at lower concentrations as shown in Figure 2. The effects of concentration and desorption time should be identified early in the method development.

Validation Procedures

Various techniques have been used to introduce a known amount of test compound into a collection tube in order to determine collection and

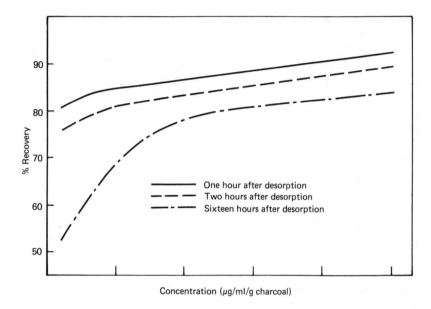

Figure 2. Effect of concentration and desorption time on recovery. Once optimum desorption has taken place, the system is generally stable; however, some exceptions have been observed.

recovery efficiencies accurately [60]. These include direct injection, air bags, permeation tubes, diluters and chambers. A device described in the literature [61] has been successful for liquids over a wide boiling point range. Air, which is pulled through a saturated salt solution to create a known humidity, is swept through a U-tube and carries the compound vapors into the collection tube. This system is portable and useful for field validation. A modification of this idea can be used for very low concentrations of high boiling point materials [55]. An extra glass wool plug is placed in the front end of a collection tube. A few microliters of a dilute solution are injected into the plug at the start of a collection test. Analysis of the plug, separate from the sorbent, will give a mass balance.

Preliminary Breakthrough Studies

In setting up a validation study for an untested compound, some preliminary studies will determine the feasibility of the solid sorbent/solvent desorption system. A number of solid sorbents and desorption solvents can be checked using the phase equilibrium technique [58] where the sorbent is added to a solution containing a known amount of the test compound.

The partition ratio at equilibrium predicts the optimum desorption efficiency attainable. After a system is selected, direct injections of the test compound are made into collection tubes with and without air being pulled through. If the desorption efficiencies as determined by direct injection are considerably lower than phase equilibrium values, interaction or reaction on the sorbent surface is indicated. If the total recovery from the simulated air collection is lower than the direct injection efficiency, even though no breakthrough has occurred, hydrolysis, oxidation, or another reaction may be indicated. Some indication of collection efficiency is indicated by the collection volume and the amount of breakthrough in the backup section.

Once a tentative procedure has been selected, an in-depth validation study can be designed as outlined by Table I. The specific guidelines for a successful validation [59] suggested in Table II have been developed from the literature and from study of a wide range of organic compounds in industrial areas. They are intended to indicate the degree of reliability that should be obtained from an acceptable method using diligent but practical application of developmental and sampling techniques. If a method fails to meet some of the criteria, it can still be used if its limitations are known and dealt with effectively.

Onsite Testing

Although many of the collection and recovery parameters can be tested in the laboratory, it is not often possible or feasible to simulate actual onsite sampling conditions. Judicious onsite testing during method development and after a successful validation will either uncover unpredictable circumstances or increase confidence.

One technique used in onsite testing is comparison to an established (but possibly inconvenient) alternate method. The alternate procedure may be a time-averaging technique such as an impinger, a continuous monitoring technique such as a portable infrared, or use of periodic short-term or instantaneous grab samples.

"Field spiking" is also a useful technique where a duplicate sampling system is set up in an onsite area. One of the collection tubes is then spiked with an appropriate amount of the test compound. Identical treatment and analysis of the duplicate tubes will indicate the unknown concentration in the area as well as the recovery factor from the spiked tube by difference.

REFERENCES

1. Soule, R. D. "An Industrial Hygiene Survey Checklist," in *Industrial Environment—Its Evaluation and Control*, NIOSH, U.S. Government Printing Office (1973), p. 711.
2. Ruch W. E. *Quantitative Analysis of Gaseous Pollutants* (Ann Arbor, MI: Ann Arbor-Humphrey Science Publishers, Inc., 1970).
3. Stevens, R. K., and W. F. Herget. *Analytical Methods Applied to Air Pollution Measurements* (Ann Arbor, MI: Ann Arbor Science Publishers, Inc., 1974).
4. Linch, A. L. *Evaluation of Ambient Air Quality by Personnel Monitoring* (Cleveland OH: CRC Press, 1975).
5. Gunther, F. A., Ed. "Pesticides in Air: Sampling Methods," in *Residue Reviews, Vol. 55* (New York: Springer-Verlag, 1975).
6. Stevens, R. K., and W. F. Herget. *Analytical Methods Applied to Air Pollution Measurements* (Ann Arbor, MI: Ann Arbor Science Publishers, Inc., 1974).
7. Katz, M., Ed. *Methods of Air Sampling and Analysis*. 2nd ed. (Washington, DC: American Public Health Association, 1977).
8. Fishbein, L. *Chromatography of Environmental Hazards: Carcinogens, Mutagens and Teratogens, Vol. 1* (Amsterdam: Elsevier Publishing Company, 1972).
9. Fishbein, L. *Chromatography of Environmental Hazards: Metals, Gaseous and Industrial Pollutants, Vol. 2* (Amsterdam: Elsevier Publishing Company, 1973).
10. Fishbein, L. *Chromatography of Environmental Hazards: Metals, Gaseous and Industrial Pollutants, Vol. 3* (Amsterdam: Elsevier Publishing Company, 1975).
11. Saltzman, B. E., and W. R. Burg. "Air Pollution," *Anal. Chem.* 49:1R-16R (1977).
12. Saltzman, B. E. and J. E. Cuddeback. "Air Pollution", *Anal. Chem.* 47:1R-15R (1975).
13. Lande S. S. "Measurement of Atmospheric Vinyl Chloride," *Am. Ind. Hyg. Assoc. J.* 40:96 (1979).
14. "NIOSH Analytical Methods" Sets A-J Standard Completion Program, National Technical Information Service, Springfield, VA 22151.
15. Taylor, D. G., R. E. Kupel and J. M. Bryant, Eds. *Documentation of the NIOSH Validation Test*, DHEW Publication 77-185 U.S. Government Printing Office (1977).
16. "Ten NIOSH Analytical Methods," Sets 1-5 National Technical Information Service, Springfield, VA 22151 (1977).
17. Ballou, E. V., Ed. *Second NIOSH Solid Sorbents Roundtable*, U.S. Government Printing Office (1976).
18. Linch B. E. "Quality Control for Sampling and Laboratory Analysis," in *Industrial Environment— Its Evaluation and Control*, NIOSH, U.S. Government Printing Office (1973), p. 277.

19. "Package Sorption Device System Study," MSA Research Corporation, EPA Contract EHSD 71-2, National Technical Information Service, Springfield, VA 22151, PB-221-138 (1973).
20. Nelson, G. O., and C. A. Harder. "Respirator Cartridge Efficiency Studies: VI: Effect of Concentration," *Am. Ind. Hyg. Assoc. J.* 37: 205 (1976).
21. Wood, G. O., and R. G. Anderson. "Personal Sampling for Vapors of Aniline Compounds," *Am. Ind. Hyg. Assoc. J.* 36:538 (1975).
22. Faust, C. L., and F. R. Hermann. "Charcoal Sampling Tubes for Organic Vapor Analysis by Gas Chromatography," *Am. Ind. Hyg. Assoc. J.* 27:68 (1966).
23. Hill, R. H., Jr., C. S. McCammon, A. T. Saalwaechter, A. W. Teass and W. J. Woodfin. "Gas-Chromatographic Determination of Vinyl Chloride in Air Samples Collected on Charcoal," *Anal. Chem.* 48: 1395 (1976).
24. Nelson, G. O., A. N. Correia and C. A. Harder. "Respirator Cartridge Efficiency Studies: Effect of Relative Humidity and Temperature," *Am. Ind. Hyg. Assoc. J.* 37:280 (1976).
25. Russell, J. W. "Analysis of Air Pollutants Using Sampling Tubes and Gas Chromatography," *Environ. Sci. Technol.* 9:1175 (1975).
26. Urone, P., and J. E. Smith. "Analysis of Chlorinated Hydrocarbons With the Gas Chromatograph," *Am. Ind. Hyg. Assoc. J.* 22:36 (1961).
27. West, P. W., B. Sen and N. A. Gibson. "Gas-Liquid Chromatographic Analysis Applied to Air Pollution Sampling," *Anal. Chem.* 30:1390 (1958).
28. Altshuller, A. P., T. A. Bellar and C. A. Clemons. "Concentration of Hydrocarbons on Silica Gel Prior to Gas Chromatographic Analysis," *Am. Ind. Hyg. Assoc. J.* 25:646 (1964).
29. Bellar, T. A., M. F. Brown and J. E. Sigsby, Jr. "Determination of Atmospheric Pollutants in the Part-Per-Billion Range by Gas Chromatography," *Anal. Chem.* 35:1924 (1963).
30. Cropper, F. R. and S. Kaminsky. "Determination of Toxic Organic Compounds in a Mixture in the Atmosphere by Gas Chromatography," *Anal. Chem.* 35:735 (1963).
31. Novak, J., V. Vasak and J. Janak. "Chromatographic Method for the Concentration of Trace Impurities in the Atmosphere and Other Gases," *Anal. Chem.* 37:660 (1965).
32. Pellizzari, E. D. "Development of Method for Carcinogenic Vapor Analysis in Ambient Atmospheres," Environmental Protection Agency, National Technical Information Service, Springfield, VA 22151, PB-239-770 (1974).
33. Pellizzari, E. D. "The Measurement of Carcinogenic Vapors in Ambient Atmospheres," Environmental Protection Agency, National Technical Information Service, Springfield, VA 22151, PB-269-582 (1977).
34. Parkes, D. G., C. R. Ganz, A. Polinsky and J. Schulze. "A Simple Gas Chromatographic Method for the Analysis of Trace Organics in Ambient Air," *Am. Ind. Hyg. Assoc. J.* 37:165 (1976).

CHEMICAL MONITORING & MEDICAL SURVEILLANCE 183

35. Parsons, J. S., and S. Mitzner. "Gas Chromatographic Method for Concentration and Analysis of Traces of Industrial Organic Pollutants in Environmental Air and Stacks," *Environ. Sci. Technol.* 9:1053 (1975).
36. Brenner, N., and L. S. Ethe. "Condensing System for Determination of Trace Impurities in Gas by Gas Chromatography," *Anal. Chem.* 31:1815 (1959).
37. Williams, F. W., and M. E. Unstead. "Determination of Trace Contaminants in Air by Concentration on Porous Polymer Beads," *Anal. Chem.* 40:2233 (1968).
38. Dravnieke, A., B. K. Krotoszynski, J. Whitfield, A. O. Donnell and J. Burgwald. "High Speed Collection of Organic Vapors from the Atmosphere," *Env. Sci. and Technol.* 5:1220 (1971).
39. Shadoff, L. A., G. J. Kallos and J. S. Woods. "Determination of Bis-(chloromethyl) Ether in Air by Gas Chromatography-Mass Spectrometry," *Anal. Chem.* 45:2341 (1973).
40. Aue, W. A., C. R. Hastings-Vogt and D. R. Younker. "A Gas Chromatographic Cartridge Desorption Port," *J. Chromatogr.* 114:184 (1975).
41. Gallant, R. F., J. W. King, P. L. Levins and J. F. Piecewicz. "Characterization of Sorbent Resins for Use in Environmental Sampling," National Technical Information Service, Springfield, VA 22151, PB-284 347.
42. Pellizzari, E. D., J. E. Bunch, B. H. Carpenter and E. Sawicki. "Collection and Analysis of Trace Organic Vapor Pollutants in Ambient Atmospheres," *Env. Sci. Technol.* 9:552 (1975).
43. Pellizzari, E. D., J. E. Bunch, B. H. Carpenter and E. Sawicki. "Collection and Analysis of Trace Organic Vapor Pollutants in Ambient Atmospheres," *Env. Sci. Technol.* 9:556 (1975).
44. Raymond, A., and G. Guiochon. "The Use of Graphitized Carbon Black as a Trapping Material for Organic Compounds in Light Gases Before a Gas Chromatographic Analysis," *J. Chromatogr. Sci.* 13:173 (1975).
45. Vidal-Madjar, C., M. F. Connord, F. Benchah and G. Guiochon. "Performances of Various Adsorbents for the Trapping and Analysis of Organohalogenated Air Pollutants by Gas Chromatography," *J. Chrom. Sci.* 16:190 (1978).
46. Frankel, L. S., and R. F. Black. "Automatic Gas Chromatographic Monitor for The Determination of Parts-Per-Billion of Bis-chloromethyl Ether," *Anal. Chem.* 48:732 (1976).
47. Melcher, R. G., and V. J. Caldecourt. "Parts-Per-Billion Determination of Organic Compounds in Air and Water Using the Delayed Injection Technique," *Anal. Chem.* (submitted).
48. Blau, K., and G. S. King. *Handbook of Derivatives for Chromatography* (London:Heyden and Son Ltd., 1977).

49. Langvardt, P. W., and R. G. Melcher. "Simultaneous Determination of Polar and Non-Polar Solvents in Air Using a Two-Phase Desorption From Charcoal," *Am. Ind. Hyg. Assoc. J.* (in press).
50. White, L. D. et al. "A Convenient Optimized Method for the Analysis of Selected Solvent Vapors in the Industrial Atmosphere," *Am. Ind. Hyg. Assoc. J.* 31:225 (1970).
51. Campbell, E. E., and H. M. Ide. "Air Sampling and Analysis With Microcolumns of Silica Gel," *Am. Ind. Hyg. Assoc. J.* 27:323 (1966).
52. Feldstein, M., S. Bolestrieri and D. A. Levaggi. "The Use of Silica Gel in Source Testing," *Am. Ind. Hyg. Assoc. J.* 28:381 (1967).
53. Kaminski, F., and R. G. Melcher. "Collection and Determination of Trace Amounts of Organo-Thiophosphates in Air Using XAD-2 Resin," *Am. Ind. Hyg. Assoc. J.* 39:678 (1978).
54. Farwell, S. O., F. W. Bowes and D. F. Adams. "Evaluation of XAD-2 as a Collection Sorbent for 2,4-D Herbicides in Air," *J. Environ. Sci. Health.* B12:71 (1977).
55. Melcher, R. G., W. L. Garner, L. W. Severs and J. R. Vaccaro. "Collection of Chlorpyrifos and Other Pesticides in Air on Chemically Bonded Sorbents," *Anal. Chem.* 50:251 (1978).
56. Bamberger, R. L., G. G. Esposito, B. W. Jacobs, G. E. Podolak and J. F. Mazur. "A New Personal Sampler for Organic Vapors," *Am. Ind. Hyg. Assoc. J.* 39:701 (1978).
57. Nelms, L. H., K. D. Reisner and P. W. West. "Personal Vinyl Chloride Monitoring Device with Permeation Technique for Sampling," *Anal. Chem.* 49:994 (1977).
58. Dommer, R. A., and R. G. Melcher. "Phase Equilibrium Method for Determination of Desorption Efficiencies," *Am. Ind. Hyg. Assoc. J.* 39:240 (1978).
59. Melcher, R. G., R. R. Langner, and R. O. Kagel. "Criteria for the Evaluation of Methods for the Collection of Organic Pollutants in Air Using Solid Sorbents," *Am. Ind. Hyg. Assoc. J.* 39:349 (1978).
60. Saltzman, B. E. "Preparation of Known Concentrations of Air Contaminants," in *The Industrial Environment–Its Evaluation and Control*, NIOSH, U.S. Government Printing Office (1973) p. 123.
61. Severs, L. W., R. G. Melcher and M. J. Kocsis. "Dynamic U-Tube System for Solid Adsorbent Air Sampling Method Development," *Am. Ind. Hyg. Assoc. J.* 38:321 (1978).

CHAPTER 10

STATE-OF-THE-ART TECHNIQUES FOR MONITORING ENVIRONMENTAL CARCINOGENS, MUTAGENS AND TERATOGENS

E. D. Pellizzari

Research Triangle Institute
Research Triangle Park, North Carolina

INTRODUCTION

The presence of organic components in ambient air is a fact of life in a modern industrialized society since volatile organic compounds are virtually ubiquitous. Many thousands of organic constituents are suspected to be introduced directly into the environment by industrial pollution. Carcinogenic and mutagenic compounds find frequent use as intermediates in organic synthesis, for example, in the preparation and use of plastics, fabrics, dyes, resins, cosmetics and pharmaceuticals. Organic solvents heavily used in industry are also sources of high ambient levels or organic vapors whether in the workplace or in the environment.

Comprehensive studies on levels of carcinogenic and mutagenic agents in air and correlation of this information with health effects in man are mandatory if we are to better understand the current genetic diseases as well as problems in carcinogenesis and mutagenesis. Intermediate and life threatening effects of some compounds are obvious, but the consequences of chronic low levels of exposure are often not known for many years. Qualitative and quantitative analysis of industrial ambient atmospheres is vital if the etiology of types of cancers and other diseases is to be established. It is also essential to understand the complete organic composition of the atmosphere because of the existence of anti- and co-carcinogenic factors. In statistical studies it has been demonstrated that the incidence of cancer associated with the respiratory system is elevated where high air pollution occurs.

Discussed here are analytical techniques which are available for the collection and analysis of vapor-phase organics in the workplace as well as in the general environment. Problems associated with collecting vapor-phase organics and transferring the samples to instrumental techniques for analysis are also discussed.

The detection limits and dynamic range for several instrumental methods for industrial and environmental air pollution analysis are given in Table I. The detection mode and whether the method is selective for certain chemical classes are indicated. The range of linearity and the detection limit are also depicted. In general, three instrumental methods are considered to be the most sensitive among the analyst's arsenal of tools. The thermal energy analyzer operates principally on chemiluminescent phenomena [1,2]. It is particularly sensitive and specific for N-nitrosamines. Electron capture and mass spectrometry are very well known, of course [3-5]. An important point in comparing detection modes is the minimum amount of material that is necessary to evoke a detector response. Obviously, the direct analysis of organics in ambient air is not possible in most cases since the concentration is below the detection limit or the techniques require preliminary purification before detection.

COLLECTION OF HAZARDOUS VAPORS

Many parameters and factors require consideration in designing a collection technique for organics. First, the analyst should consider the chemical and physical properties of the substances to be collected and analyzed.

The general volatility sequence for chemical classes is depicted in Figure 1. Represented here are only a few chemical group types. But, in general, for quantitative collection of *all* organics in air, it is important to note the dynamic range of vapor pressure (physical state) and chemical reactivity of compounds to be analyzed in a single sample.

Alkane $>$ Aldehyde $>$ Alcohol $\cong$ Nitrate Ester $>$
Carboxylic Acid $\cong$ Dialdehyde $>$ Diol $\cong$ Dinitrate $\cong$
Alcohol $C_{n+b}{}^6 \cong$ Acid Aldehyde $\gg$ Dicarboxylic Acid

Figure 1. Volatility sequence for C_n compounds (based on boiling and melting points).

Table I. Detection Limits/Dynamic Range for Several Instrumental Methods

Detection Mode	Selectivity	Grams
		10^{-13} 10^{-12} 10^{-11} 10^{-10} 10^{-9} 10^{-8} 10^{-7} 10^{-6} 10^{-5} 10^{-4} 10^{-3} 10^{-2} 1
Thermal Energy Analyzer	+	
Photoionization	±	
Electron Capture	+	
Mass Spectrometry		
Electron Impact	−	
Multiple Ion Det.	+	
Neg. Chemical Ion.	+	
Fluorescence	+	
Flame Ionization	−	
Thermal Conductivity	−	
FT/IR	±	
UV	−	

Figure 2 illustrates a more detailed relationship between chemicals and their presence as a gas/vapor or aerosol/particulate as a function of vapor pressure and polarity. Within a chemical class there is a significant differential in vapor pressure between compounds, and a greater degree of variance exists between chemical class types [6]. Thus, in designing an analytical tool for the collection of organic substances from the atmosphere, the analyst is confronted with a large range of chemical and physical properties for which the technique must be adapted.

A three-dimensional visualization of vapor pressure vs chemical class type and atmospheric complexity is depicted in Figure 3. For an analytical method to be used successfully for collecting and analyzing organic compounds in the atmosphere, it should possess the ability to tie together as many of the "cubes" as possible. Such a method has great versatility and assures that the analyst is providing a maximum amount of chemical information about the industrial and environmental atmosphere.

Numerous methods are described in the literature for the collection and analysis of volatile organics from ambient air [7-18]. Most techniques are too restrictive; that is, they focus on one or a few substances at a given time. Recently, our laboratory has developed and perfected techniques that provide for a polypollutant approach and yield a more representative and quick chemical makeup of the ambient air [8-14]. The polypollutant method is based on the use of a solid sorbent, followed by capillary gas chromatography/mass spectrometry/computer (GC/MS/COMP) analysis for qualitative and quantitative determinations.

Because organic constituents in air are usually present at parts-per-trillion (ppt) to parts-per-million (ppm) levels in a vast amount of diluting medium (air and water vapor), it is generally not practical to attempt in situ analysis of all the organic compounds in air. There is no widely applicable method of detection that can distinguish each compound from all others at such low concentrations. Therefore, to achieve the requisite sensitivity, vapors must be concentrated from a large volume of air.

The four basic steps to analyze for organic vapors in industrial and environmental atmospheres are:

1. collection/concentration of vapors,
2. their transfer to an analytical system,
3. their separation and identification, and
4. measurement of each of the compounds of interest.

There are several possibilities for the collection/concentration process. Cryogenic sampling is excellent for extremely volatile compounds such as acetylene, NO_x, SO_x and freons; liquid nitrogen, oxygen or solid CO_x/

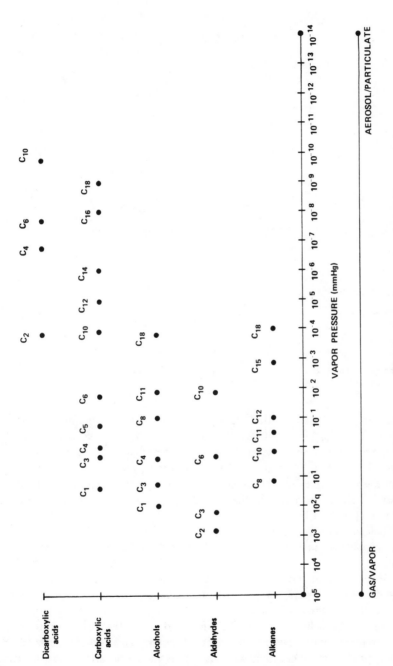

Figure 2. Relationship between vapor pressure and physical state of organics in air.

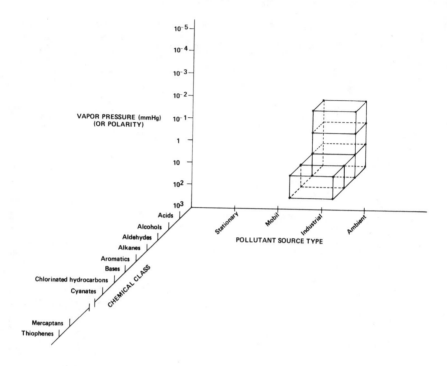

Figure 3. Three dimensional matrix between vapor pressure, chemical class and atmospheric complexity.

acetone can be used as the cooling medium. However, this method condenses considerable quantities of water vapor. The reactive gases NO_x, SO_x and ozone can cause artifacts by reacting with amines, oxygenates and olefins. Also, in inaccessible field locations, setting up and maintaining cryogenic traps can be difficult, and cryogenic samples are difficult to store or ship. Furthermore, the use of oxygen (or nitrogen which condenses out oxygen) can be dangerous.

Solvent impingers are also employed, but handling and shipping volumes of solvent also present problems. Artifacts during collection are also prevalent.

Reasonably effective concentration of organic components can be achieved by the use of a solid sorbent such as Tenax GC. Sorbent cartridges can be made clean, light-weight and compact. Vapors collected from a large volume of air can be delivered to an analytical system by thermal desorption of the trapped vapors. During collection of vapors on a sorbent, each adsorbed compound is in equilibrium with its vapors in the air stream so that it is moving slowly through the bed. The partition ratio between the air stream of the sorbent surface for each compound is unique. It depends on the temperature and structure of the sorbent, and it determines selectivity for the compound because it controls the rate at which it moves through the bed. Compounds are qualitatively collected until sufficient air has passed through the bed to elute them. For quantitative analysis, a breakthrough volume must be known as a function of temperature for any compound that is to be collected.

Once collected, the concentrated vapors must be recovered from the collection system and delivered to an analytical system. If cyrogenic traps are used, a substantial quantity of water is collected. Solvent impingers use liquid as a collection medium. In either case, the collected compounds must be separated from a substantial volume of liquid. This can be done by inert gas purge, by solvent extraction and concentration or, for highly volatile compounds, by low-temperature vacuum distillation. These procedures are tedious, sample throughput is low and substantial losses of the collected compounds may occur. Generally, only a small aliquot of the sample can be analyzed ($\sim$1%), and thus the sensitivity is poor.

The vapors can be recovered from a sorbent bed by solvent extraction or by thermal desorption. The disadvantages of solvent extraction have already been mentioned. Thermal desorption is accomplished by heating the sorbent in an inert gas stream.

But, the basic question remains—which sorbent should be used? What factors should be considered in its selection? There are several criteria that must be fulfilled if a sorbent is to be acceptable for industrial and environmental air pollution studies. These criteria are as follows [8-14,19-22]:

1. The sorbent must withstand repeated use without deterioration, and it must not contaminate the sample.
2. In order to collect a compound, it must adsorb nearly all the vapor passing into it.
3. The adsorbed vapors must be released completely upon thermal desorption.
4. It should possess a sufficient breakthrough volume or retention volume if the method is to be used for quantitative analysis.
5. It must not catalyze in situ reactions on its surface during and after vapors have been adsorbed on its surface. In other words, it should not be involved in hydrolysis, rearrangement, synthesis or decomposition of compounds.

Before Tenax was selected, several sorbents—carbon, Porapak, chromosorbs—were evaluated in our laboratory according to the first four criteria [8-10,19-22].

The four general methods used to determine breakthrough volumes are as follows:

1. Cartridges are purged into a monitoring system, and the response of the flame ionization detector is observed.
2. Disappearance of vapor from cartridges during purging under laboratory and field conditions is determined.
3. Appearance of vapor in backup cartridges during purging is also determined. This approach calls for loading cartridges with a compound and then sampling air that does not contain that compound. Backup cartridges are changed periodically during sampling. The volume of air required to cause appearance of half the vapor in the backup cartridge is then determined. This approach has been used to test the possibility of premature breakthrough or displacement chromatography when sampling in the presence of high ambient levels of hydrocarbons (e.g., auto exhaust).
4. The elution volumes may be determined on a gas chromatographic column packed with a known quantity of sorbent.

The breakthrough volumes determined by all of these methods generally are in substantial agreement.

The breakthrough volumes for a few organics are given in Table II. This characteristic has been determined for approximately 150 compounds and extrapolated to more than 400.

TRANSFER AND ANALYSIS OF HAZARDOUS VAPORS

Once a collection device has been thoroughly tested, it is interfaced with an analytical system [3,8-14].

An inlet manifold has been used to desorb the vapors thermally at 270°C from the cartridges in a helium stream from which vapors are trapped at -196°C. Then the trap is switched into the carrier gas stream of the capillary gas chromatograph and rapidly heated to 250°C. A GC/MS/COMP or GC Fourier transform infrared spectrometer/computer system may be used for the analysis. The mixture is resolved using glass capillary columns. Generally, however, the detector is the mass spectrometer. It is coupled to a computer which stores full scan data on disk or magnetic tape. After data acquisition is complete, the system plots normalized mass spectra indexed to a total ion current chromatogram. Mass fragmentograms may also be derived from the acquired mass spectra.

The advantages of this type of collection and analysis system are as follows:

1. It is easy to transport and operate the samplers in the field even under adverse weather conditions.
2. Little water is collected.
3. The entire sample is delivered for analysis.

Table II. Breakthrough Volumes for Several Priority Pollutants[a]

Priority Pollutants	bp	Temperature °F (°C)										
		50(10)	55(12.7)	60(15.5)	65(18.3)	70(21.1)	75(23.9)	80(26.7)	85(29.4)	90(32.2)	95(34.9)	100(37.8)
1,1-Dichloroethylene	32	2.4	2.2	1.8	1.6	1.4	1.3	1.2	1.1	1.0	0.97	0.87
Dichloromethane	40	14	12	9.7	8.3	6.9	5.9	4.9	4.1	3.5	2.9	2.4
1,2-trans-Dichloroethylene	47.5	1.90	1.81	1.73	1.68	1.65	1.51	1.44	1.38	1.31	1.25	1.20
1,1-Dichloroethane	57	8.9	7.9	7.0	6.3	5.6	5.0	4.5	3.9	3.5	3.1	2.7
Chloroform	61.2	17	14	12	10	9.1	7.7	6.6	5.6	4.8	4.2	3.5
1,1,1-Trichloroethane	74	23	21	18	16	15	14	12	10	9	8	7
Carbon Tetrachloride	76.8	41	34	29	24	20	17	14	12	10	8	7
1,2-Dichloroethane	84	49	42	36	31	27	23	20	17	15	12	11
Trichloroethylene	87	90	78	67	58	50	44	38	33	28	24	21
Bromodichloromethane	90	83	70	61	52	45	39	34	29	25	22	19
1,2-Dichloropropane	96.2	229	199	162	138	115	98	81	69	58	49	41
1,1,2-Trichloroethane	113	309	245	208	177	151	128	109	93	79	67	57
Tetrachloroethylene	121	361	361	267	250	196	170	144	125	106	92	78
Chlorobenzene	132	899	776	653	563	473	408	344	296	249	215	181
1,1,2,2-Tetrachloroethane	146	477	406	353	308	262	228	199	173	147	128	112
Bromoform	149.5	511	445	388	330	287	245	213	186	158	138	117
1,3-Dichlorobenzene	172	2,393	2,075	1,758	1,524	1,291	1,119	948	885	697	603	510
1,4-Dichlorobenzene	174	2,390	2,071	1,752	1,520	1,289	1,113	937	812	688	592	497
bis-(2-Chloroethyl)ether	178	1,692	1,440	1,226	1,043	888	768	653	560	477	406	354
1,2-Dichlorobenzene	179	2,422	2,191	1,960	1,716	1,463	1,301	1,139	989	839	769	699
Acrolein	52	1.9	1.8	1.7	1.5	1.4	1.3	1.2	1.1	1.0	0.91	0.83
Acrylonitrile	77	8.5	7.4	6.6	5.7	5.0	4.4	3.9	3.4	3.0	2.6	2.3
Benzene	80	108	92	77	65	54	46	38	32	27	23	19
Toluene	110.6	494	421	348	296	245	209	173	147	122	104	86
Ethylbenzene	136	1,393	1,188	984	838	693	590	487	415	344	293	243

[a]Breakthrough volume is in l/cartridge (1.5 cm i.d. × 6.0 cm bed of 35/60 mesh Tenax GC).

4. Nearly complete chromatographic resolution of individual compounds is obtained.
5. Resolution of individual compounds by mass fragmentography is virtually complete.
6. Vapors present in the ppb to ppt range can be quantitated.
7. Gas chromatographic retention times in mass spectra can be used for positive identification.

A disadvantage is that the volume of data produced is very large: 1000 mass spectra per sample, 8000 per day, or 40,000 mass spectra per week. Fast data processing systems are needed to assist in the identification of components as represented by the mass spectra. Current computer/mass spectral search systems are costly and inaccurate. However, efforts to improve these problems are in progress in several laboratories.

Another disadvantage is that some compounds are not seen because they are too volatile to be efficiently collected on Tenax GC. Other sorbents, such as XAD, Poropak, chromosorbs and amosorbs, have higher adsorption affinities, but they do not meet the criteria outlined earlier. They collect too much water, exhibit artifact reactions, have poor thermal stability or yield poor recoveries. Generally, these criticisms can be raised regarding other sorbents.

In addition to GC/MS/COMP, the other instrumental tools listed in Table I are available to the analyst in conjunction with the collection and transfer techniques described here. For example, GC Fourier transform infrared computer techniques can be used in combination with Tenax GC and thermal desorption. Also, GC with thermal energy analysis or with electron capture detection can be used with these collection and transfer techniques.

Only vapor-phase organics in the atmosphere are covered in this discussion. Of course, there is a continuum between the vapor phase and the aerosol or particulate, without sharp demarcation as to the physical state in in which the compound may be present. Figure 2 depicts the relationship between vapor pressure versus chemical type. The problem of collection is compounded by this phenomenon, and the analyst needs to apply several collection techniques in order to cover the range of physical states in which the organics may appear. Chemicals which exhibit very low vapor pressure will exist primarily in the aerosol or particulate state, and collection techniques should emphasize the ability to collect aerosol particulate with the subsequent recovery of the chemicals by simple extraction techniques. Because of their very low vapor pressures, these compounds presumably will not be entirely amenable to GC analysis. Other methods of analysis are available to complement the GC techniques. The combination of high-performance liquid chromatography (HPLC) and mass spectrometry computer or with thermal energy analyzer [24] extends the range of analysis to include the aerosol particulate-bound organics.

Finally, one of the most useful tools for atmospheric analysis—although limited for workplace studies—is the use of the long-path Fourier transform infrared (FTIR) computer. This analytical tool allows the in situ analysis of organics and thus introduces less pertubation of the sample. Perturbation can lead to potential artifacts, a problem that must be addressed in selection of the collection techniques. Long-path FTIR generally offers the ability to examine the atmosphere through a 1-km pathlength in order to achieve adequate sensitivity. Even under these circumstances, low level detection (sub-ppt) is beyond the capability of this technique. It is useful in performing high resolution, which is mandatory in differentiating the constituents in a mixture when no preliminary purification is performed.

REFERENCES

1. Krull, I. S., and M. H. Wolf. *Lab.* 11(5):84 (1979).
2. Fine, D. H., R. Rufeh, D. Lieb and D. P. Rounbehler. *Anal. Chem.* 47:1188(1975).
3. Pellizzari, E. D., J. E. Bunch, R. E. Berkley, and J. McRae. *Anal. Chem.* 48:803 (1976).
4. Pellizzari, E. D., J. E. Bunch, R. E. Berkley and J. T. Bursey. *Biomed. Mass Spec.* 3:196(1976).
5. Bursey, J. T., D. Smith, J. E. Bunch, R. N. Williams, R. E. Berkley and E. D. Pellizzari. *Am. Lab.* 9:35 (1977).
6. Grosjean, D. "Aerosols from Ozone and Other Photochemical Oxidants," NAS, Washington, DC, 87 (1977).
7. Kaiser, R. E. *J. Chromatogr. Sci.* 12:36 (1974).
8. Pellizzari, E. D. "Development of Method for Carcinogenic Vapor Analysis in Ambient Atmospheres," EPA-650/2-74-121, July 1974, 148 pp.
9. Pellizzari, E. D. "Development of Analytical Techniques for Measuring Ambient Atmospheric Carcinogenic Vapors," EPA-600/2-75-076, November, 1975, 186 pp.
10. Pellizzari, E. D. "The Measurement of Carcinogenic Vapors in Ambient Atmospheres," EPA-600/7-77-055, June 1977, 288 pp.
11. Pellizzari, E. D. "Analysis of Organic Air Pollutants by Gas Chromatography and Mass Spectroscopy," EPA-600/2-77-100, June 1977, 104 pp.
12. Pellizzari, E. D. "Measurement of Carcinogenic Vapors in Ambient Atmospheres," EPA-600/7-78-062, April 1978, 273 pp.
13. Pellizzari, E. D. "Analysis of Organic Air Pollutants by Gas Chromatography and Mass Spectroscopy," EPA Contract No. 68-02-2262, Final Report, submitted.

14. Pellizzari, E. D. "Improvement of Methodologies for the Collection and Analysis of Carcinogenic Vapors," EPA Contract No. 68-02-2764, Annual Report, submitted.
15. Rasmussen, R. A., and F. W. Went. *Proc. Nat. Acad. Sci.* 53:215 (1965).
16. Tyson, B. J., W. A. Dement and M. A. Mooney. *Nature* 252:119 (1974).
17. Tyson, B. J., and G. C. Carle. *Anal. Chem.* 46:610 (1974).
18. Tyson, B. J. *Anal. Lett.* 8:807 (1975).
19. Pellizzari, E. D., B. Carpenter, J. Bunch, and E. J. Sawicki. *Environ. Sci. Technol.* 9:552 (1975).
20. Pellizzari, E. D., J. E. Bunch, R. E. Berkley and J. McRae. *Anal. Lett.* 9:45 (1976).
21. Berkley, R. E., and E. D. Pellizzari. *Anal. Lett.* 4:327 (1978).
22. Pellizzari, E. D. *J. Chromatogr.* (in press).
23. Pellizzari, E. D., B. Carpenter, J. Bunch and E. Sawicki. *J. Environ. Sci. Technol.* 9:552 (1975).
24. Krull, I. S., T. Y. Fan, M. Wolf, R. Ross and D. H. Fine. In: *LC Symposium I. Biological and Biomedical Applications of Liquid Chromatography*, G. Hwak, Ed. (New York: Marcel Dekker, Inc.) (1978), p. 443.

CHAPTER 11

DEVELOPMENT OF A PERSONAL MONITORING DEVICE FOR THE DETECTION OF DIRECT-ACTING ALKYLATING AGENTS

Alvin Segal

Laboratory of Organic Chemistry
and Carcinogenesis
Institute of Environmental Medicine
New York University Medical Center
New York, New York

Gordon Loewengart

Allied Chemical
Corporate Research Laboratories
Morristown, New Jersey

INTRODUCTION

The use of personal monitoring devices to detect and measure various environmental chemicals has been reviewed extensively [1]. There appear to be no published reports describing personal monitoring devices for the detection of the direct-acting carcinogenic biological alkylating agents, a group of highly reactive, fairly unstable organic compounds. The term direct-acting implies that metabolic activation is not a prerequisite to biological activity. This chapter describes how the need to detect in our laboratory and animal facility atmospheres the monofunctional, direct-acting, alkylating carcinogen [2-5] and mutagen [6], β-propiolactone (BPL) led to the development of a personal monitoring device.

Early studies showed that BPL reacts with various guanine derivatives in vitro [7-9] and with DNA and RNA in mouse skin to form 7-(2-carboxyethyl)guanine [10, 11]. More recent studies in this laboratory have shown

197

that BPL binds to the three major components of chromatin—DNA, histones and nonhistone chromosomal proteins [12]. Binding of BPL to DNA in chromatin was 29% of that to naked DNA, suggesting that in some manner, chromatin proteins protect DNA against alkylation [12]. Among the histone classes in chromatin, BPL was found to bind to the greatest extent to the lysine-rich histone Hl [12]. Reinvestigation of the in vitro interaction between BPL and DNA has shown that 1-(2-carboxyethyl)adenine [13] and 3-(2-carboxyethyl)thymine [14] are formed in addition to 7-(2-carboxyethyl)guanine and also that the in vitro reaction between BPL and histones results in acylation of the ε-amino group of L-lysine to form ε-N-(3-hydroxypropionyl)lysine [15].

Many of the uses of BPL in industry and medicine have been reviewed [16]. The potential of BPL as a carcinogenic hazard to man has been recognized by the Occupational Safety and Health Administration (OSHA). OSHA has included BPL in a list of carcinogens whose handling and use are governed by a series of rules and regulations designed to protect the health of individuals working with carcinogens [17].

MATERIALS AND METHODS

BPL and p-nitrobenzyl pyridine (p-NBP) were obtained from the Aldrich Chemical Company, Milwaukee, WI. Deoxyguanosine (dG) was purchased from the Nutritional Biochemicals Corporation, Cleveland, OH. Reagent-grade ammonium hydroxide (28-30%), was supplied by Matheson, Coleman and Bell, Rutherford, NJ. Polygram cel 300 precoated plastic sheets for thin-layer chromatography (TLC) coated with cellulose MN 300 (0.1 mm thick) were purchased from Brinkmann Instruments, Westbury, NY. TLC (2.375 x 9 in.) developing tanks were obtained from Brinkmann Instruments. Gardray film-badge holders were purchased from R. S. Landauer Jr. and Company, Glenwood, IL. A Mineralight UVS-54 short-wave ultraviolet (uv) lamp was obtained from Ultra-Violet Products, San Gabriel, CA.

A 10-µl aliquot of an acetone solution containing 2 µg (9.3 nmol) of p-NBP per µl was applied to a cellulose TLC strip by micropipette within a diameter of approximately 0.6 cm.

A 10-µl aliquot of an aqueous solution containing 0.2 µg (0.75 nmol) of dG per µl was spotted on the cellulose TLC strip by micropipette within a diameter of approximately 0.6 cm adjacent to p-NBP. The cellulose TLC strip was then inserted into the film-badge holder.

BPL was dissolved in ethyl ether to establish a desired concentration, and in all experiments 100 µl of the ethyl ether solution was transferred to a 4,175-ml Erlenmeyer flask by micropipette. The film-badge holder containing the cellulose TLC strip was suspended approximately halfway into the

Erlenmeyer flask attached to the cork stopper by copper wire. At the end of the desired time exposure to BPL vapors, the film-badge holder was removed and the cellulose strip examined under uv light for fluorescence of dG. The film-blade holder was then suspended half-way into the TLC developing tank over 20 ml of ammonium hydroxide and examined for the development of the characteristic blue color indicating alkylation of p-NBP by BPL.

In a similar manner, cellulose TLC strips containing p-NPB were exposed to the vapors of the direct-acting alkylating carcinogens *bis*(chloromethyl) ether, chloromethyl methyl ether, ethyleneimine, dimethylcarbamyl chloride, diepoxybutane and glycidaldehyde.

Cellulose strips containing p-NPB were stored in vacuo ($\sim$ 1 mm) in a vacuum desiccator. They were also exposed to the atmosphere on the roof of the NYU Medical Center in midtown Manhattan and in a laboratory (containing no direct-acting alkylating agents) at the Institute of Environmental Medicine in Tuxedo, NY, a rural area about 45 miles from New York City.

RESULTS

The results of the work described above are summarized in Table I. In each case the sensitivity of the reaction is related to the length of exposure of the cellulose surface to the BPL vapors. For the reaction of BPL with p-NBP, the limits of detection are in the lower ppb range for exposures longer than 1 hr; for exposures equal to or less than 1 hr, the detection limit is always less than 1 ppm. The detection limits of the reaction between BPL and dG are generally 10 to 100 times greater than the reaction with p-NBP. Maximum sensitivity was reached by 4 hr of exposure with p-NBP, but not until 24 hr with dG.

The intensity of the blue color produced by the reaction between BPL and p-NBP is proportional to the concentration of BPL. This color on the TLC strip, which is visualized by exposing the strip to an atmosphere containing ammonia vapors, can be made to appear and disappear repeatedly. The authors observed this to be the case with a strip that had been exposed to BPL 3 weeks previously.

The absolute limit of detection using dG as the trapping reagent was determined independently using pure alkylated dG and was found to be 0.5 μg of alkylated dG. Under the conditions employed for the gas/solid phase reactions, and at a detection limit of 60 ppb, 1.5 μg would be the maximum amount of alkylated dG that could be formed. This assumes that all the BPL reacts with dG, and none is hydrolyzed to β-hydroxpropionic acid.

Table I. Limits of Detection of β-Propiolactone

Exposure Time (hr)	Detection Limits	
	p-Nitrobenzyl Pyridine[a]	Deoxyguanosine[b]
0.25	0.6 ppm	60 ppm
0.50	0.6 ppm	6 ppm
1	60 ppb	6 ppm
4	6 ppb	6 ppm
8	6 ppb	0.6 ppm
24	6 ppb	60 ppb

[a]10 μl of an acetone solution containing 20 μg of p-NBP was spotted on a cellulose TCL strip within a diameter of approximately 0.6 cm.
[b]10 μl of an aqueous solution containing 2 μg of dG was spotted on a cellulose TLC strip within a diameter of approximately 0.6 cm.

Preliminary results indicate that the direct-acting alkylating carcinogens *bis*(chloromethyl)ether, chloromethyl methyl ether, ethyleneimine, dimethylcarbamyl chloride, diepoxybutane and glycidaldehyde can be detected in the lower ppb range when their vapors are exposed to cellulose TLC strips containing p-NBP.

The cellulose TLC strips were removed from the vacuum desiccator after 7 days and remained colorless after exposure to NH_3 [18]. Cellulose TLC strips exposed to the atmosphere at the Institute of Environmental Medicine for 5.5 hr gave no color reaction when exposed to NH_3. A faint blue color was detected after a 22-hr atmospheric exposure and darkened considerably after a 7-day exposure [18]. Similar results were obtained when cellulose TLC strips were exposed to the atmosphere on the roof of the NYU Medical Center [18].

DISCUSSION

The use of p-NBP and dG on cellulose TLC strips provides a sensitive, simple and inexpensive method of personal monitoring for BPL and other direct-acting carcinogens. The p-NBP was chosen because it has been used to assay alkylating agents in general [19, 20], BPL specifically [21], and it has also been reported to react with a direct-acting acylating carcinogen (dimethylcarbamyl chloride) to give an acylated derivative [22]. The mechanism of color formation of alkyl derivatives of p-NBP has been determined [23]. As small a quantity as 20 μg of alkylating agent has been detected on Kieselgel G thin-layer plates sprayed with an acetone solution of p-NBP [24]. The dG was chosen because alkylation at the N-7 position of guanine produces highly fluorescent compounds [25, 26] and because it is an integral part of the genetic material in cells, DNA. The dG has proved to be less sensitive than the p-NBP, but it can be useful as a backup procedure. Also the fact that dG is less sensitive can become useful in practice; when both the p-NBP and dG spots show exposure to BPL, it is indicative of a higher exposure than if the p-NBP is positive and the dG negative.

The results of the exposure of cellulose TLC strips containing p-NBP to the atmospheres at the Institute of Environmental Medicine and midtown Manhattan are significant in that they suggest that a low-level background of alkylating agents is part of our environment.

The p-NBP is not specific to BPL and will react with a variety of direct-acting alkylating agents; it can serve as a litmus-like test for direct-acting alkylating agents. In this laboratory the p-NBP reagent on cellulose TLC strips has been applied to detecting the direct-acting alkylating carcinogens bis(chloromethyl)ether, chloromethyl methyl ether, ethyleneimine, dimethylcarbamoyl chloride, diepoxybutane and glycidaldehyde.

In many laboratories and industrial settings only one or a very limited number of alkylating agents are used at any one time, and further identification might not be necessary. When several alkylating agents are present in one area, more complicated, expensive equipment requiring highly trained personnel could verify the specific chemical involved after a TLC strip indicates an exposure. In order to equal the sensitivity of this simple method, one would generally have to resort to gas chromatography-mass spectrometry.

The TLC strip monitoring badges are easy to prepare from readily available materials. There should be no personnel resistance to their use since they are not cumbersome. Monitoring at the end of an exposure period is simple and requires no expensive equipment or specialized personnel.

ACKNOWLEDGMENTS

This research was supported by USPHS Grants CA 16992 and CA 13343 from the National Cancer Institute and Grant ES 00260 from the National Institute of Environmental Health Sciences. We wish to thank Mr. Sidney Sudberg for technical assistance with this work. A portion of this paper has appeared in *Archives of Environmental Health* 33(1):33-35 (1978)

REFERENCES

1. Linch, A. L. *Evaluation of Ambient Air Quality by Personnel Monitoring* (Cleveland, OH:CRC Press).
2. Roe, F. S. C., and O. M. Glendenning. "The Carcinogenicity of β-Propiolactone in Mouse Skin," *Brit. J. Cancer* 10:357-362 (1956).

3. Palmes, E. D., L. Orris and N. Nelson. "Skin Irritation and Skin Tumor Production by β-Propiolactone," *Am. Ind. Hyg. Assoc. J.* 23:257-264 (1962).

4. Dickens, F., H. E. H. Jones and H. B. Waynforth. "Oral, Subcutaneous and Intratracheal Administration of Carcinogenic Lactones and Related Substances: The Intratracheal Administration of Cigarette Tar in the Rat," *Brit. J. Cancer* 20:134-144 (1966).

5. Van Duuren, B. L., L. Langseth, L. Orris, G. Teebor, N. Nelson and M. Kuschner. "Carcinogenicity of Epoxides, Lactones and Peroxy Compounds. IV. Tumor Response in Epithelial and Connective Tissue in Mice and Rats," *J. Nat. Cancer Inst.* 37:825-834 (1966).

6. Smith, H. H., and A. M. Srb. "Induction of Mutations with β-Propiolactone," *Science* 114:490-492 (1951).

7. Roberts, J. J., and G. P. Warwick. "The Reaction of β-Propiolactone with Guanosine, Deoxyguanylic Acid and RNA," *Biochem. Pharmacol.* 12:1441-1442 (1963).

8. Colburn, N. H., R. G. Richardson and R. K. Boutwell. "Studies of the Reaction of β-Propiolactone with Deoxyguanosine and Related Compounds," *Biochem. Pharmacol.* 14:113-118 (1965).

9. Roberts, J. J., and G. P. Warwick. "The Reaction of Some Compounds of Biological Interest with Nucleic Acids," *Biochem. J.* 87:14P (1963).

10. Colburn, N. H., and R. K. Boutwell. "The Binding of β-Propiolactone to Mouse Skin DNA in Vivo; Its Correlation with Tumor-initiating Activity," *Cancer Res.* 26:1701-1706 (1966).

11. Boutwell, R. K., N. H. Colburn and C. C. Muckerman. "In Vivo Reactions of β-Propiolactone," *Ann. N. Y. Acad. Sci.* 163:751-764 (1969).

12. Segal, A., M. Schroeder, P. Barnett and B. L. Van Duuren. "Studies of the Effects in Vitro of β-Propiolactone and β-Propiolact[^{14}C]one on Whole Mouse Skin Chromatin," *Biochem. Pharmacol.* 23:937-946 (1974).

13. Mate, U., J. J. Solomon and A. Segal. "In Vitro Binding of β-Propiolactone to Calf Thymus DNA and Mouse Liver DNA to Form 1-(2-Carboxyethyl)adenine," *Chem. -Biol. Interact.* 18:327-336 (1977).

14. Segal, A., J. J. Solomon and U. L. Mate. "Isolation of 3-(2-Carboxyethyl)thymine Following in Vitro Reaction of β-Propiolactone with Calf Thymus DNA," *Chem. Biol. Interact.* (in press).

15. Segal, A., and S. J. Garte. "In Vitro Acylation of the ε-Amino Group of L-Lysine in Calf Thymus Histones by the Carcinogen, β-Propiolactone," *Chem. -Biol. Interact.* 15:319-326 (1976).

16. Fishbein, L. "Degradation and Residues of Alkylating Agents," *Ann. N. Y. Acad. Sci.* 163:869-894 (1969).

17. "Carcinogens. Occupational Health and Safety Standards," *Federal Register* 39(20III):3756-3797 (1974).

18. Daisey, J. Personal communication, Department of Environmental Medicine, N. Y. U. Medical Center.

19. Epstein, J., R. W. Rosenthal and R. J. Ess. "Use of γ-(4-Nitrobenzyl) pyridine as an Analytical Reagent for Ethyleneimines and Alkylating Agents," *Anal. Chem.* 27:1435-1439 (1955).

20. Preussman, V. R., H. Schneider and F. Epple. "Investigations Concerning the Detection of Alkylating Agents. II. The Detection of Various Classes of Alkylating Agents by a Modification of the Color Reaction with 4-(4-Nitrobenzyl)pyridine (NBP)," *Arzn. -Forsch.* 19:1059-1973 (1969).

21. Fayet, M. T., H. G. Peterman, J. Fontoine, J. Terre and M. Roumrantzeff. "The Use of β-Propiolactone as an Inactivating Agent in the Preparation of Anti-foot and Mouth Vaccine," *Ann Inst. Pasteur (Paris)* 112:65 (1967).

22. Goldschmidt, B. M., B. L. Van Duuren and R. C. Goldstein. "The Reaction of 4-(p-Nitrobenzyl)pyridine with Some Electrophiles," *J. Het. Chem.* 13:517-519 (1976).

23. Koenigs, E., K. Kohler and K. Blindow. "Pyridone Methides," *Chem. Ber.* 58B:933-940 (1925).

24. Fischer, G. W. "Acylated Vinyl Compounds. XV. Thin-layer Chromatography of Toxicologically Relevant 2-Halogenvinylketones," *J. Chromatog.* 117:137-142 (1976).

25. Lawley, P. D., and P. Brookes. "Further Studies on the Alkylation of Nucleic Acids and Their Constituent Nucleotides. Some Observations on O-alkylation," 89:127-138 (1963).

26. Farmer, P. B., A. B. Forster, M. Jarman and M. J. Tisdale. "The Alkylation of 2-Deoxyguanosine and of Thymidine with Diazoalkanes. Some Observations on O-alkylation," *Biochem. J.* 135:203-213 (1973).

CHAPTER 12

ANALYSIS OF CARCINOGENIC AND MUTAGENIC AROMATIC AMINES

Lawrence Fishbein

U.S. Department of Health, Education and Welfare
Food and Drug Administration
National Center for Toxicological Research
Jefferson, Arkansas

INTRODUCTION

Aromatic amines represent a category of considerable importance as organic intermediates for the manufacture of a wide variety of organic chemicals and intermediates and dyes, a large number of which have been widely used in textile, leather, plastic and paper products as well as in permanent and semipermanent coloring products. Hence, exposure to these agents primarily through skin contact and inhalation covers a societal spectrum—occupational, the consumer and the general public. The major objective of this presentation is to highlight a number of the recent techniques for the analysis of a spectrum of carcinogenic and/or mutagenic aromatic amines, with a focus of their analysis in environmental and occupational samples. The analytical procedures will primarily focus on chemical subclasses including benzidines, naphthylamines, aminobiphenyls, methylene bis(2-chloroaniline), aminofluorene, phenylene, nitrophenylene and toluene diamines. However, it is important at the outset to discuss the aromatic amines as a class in terms of germane aspects of their activity and metabolism, utility and occurrence.

It is generally acknowledged that the class of compounds in which the molecular basis of carcinogenic activity is the most clearly understood is the aromatic amines [1-9]. Figure 1 illustrates a spectrum of typical hydro-

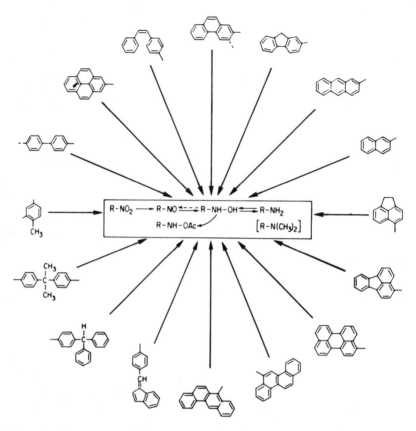

Figure 1. Spectrum of typical hydrocarbon moieties present in carcinogenic aromatic amines.

carbon moieties present in carcinogenic aromatic amines [8]. These are (from the top, clockwise): phenanthrene, fluorene, anthracene, naphthalene, acenaphthene, fluoranthene, perylene, crysene, benz(a)anthracene, benzalindene, triphenylmethane, 2,2-*bis*-phenylpropane, toluene biphenyl, pyrene and stilbene. The unconnected bond or bonds on these moieties indicate the positions where attachment of amino or *amine-generating group or groups* can give rise to carcinogenic compounds or which very substantially increases the carcinogenicity of the hydrocarbon moiety itself [5]. For example, the two possibilities indicated on the biphenyl moiety correspond to 4-aminobiphenyl and benzidine, two well-recognized carcinogens.

METABOLISM AND ACTIVATION

Because of the possible metabolic interconversion of the amino group with hydroxyl amino and nitroso substituents, and the metabolic reduction of the nitro group to these (as illustrated in the center block of Figure 1), the latter three groups have been termed amine-generating groups [2,5]. It should also be noted that in some, but not all instances a dimethylamino group may replace the amino group without significant loss of carcinogenic activity [5]. The aromatic amines require metabolic activation for carcinogenicity, and it is generally acknowleged that the mechanism of the activation, compared to other classes of carcinogens, is now known in considerable detail. Evidence exists that the metabolism of aromatic amines occurs via ring hydroxylation, N-hydroxylation of the monoacetyl derivative, and conjugation with sulfate and glucuronic acid [1,6-9]. The hydroxylamino form of the functional group represents this activated form, or, in some instances, the first phase of a two-stage activation mechanism [5]. The N-hydroxy form (also known as hydroxamic acid) in some (and possibly all) instances, undergoes a second activation step, e.g., conjugation with an acyl group which can be acetyl, sulfonyl or phosphoryl. These acyloxy amines are highly reactive species which can readily undergo covalent combination with cellular nucleophiles, nucleic acids and proteins. Indeed, the arylation of DNA and/or RNA is generally regarded to be the critical initiating step in carcinogenesis [1-9].

Oxidation of either a primary or secondary aromatic amine is the major route to N-hydroxy compounds in animals. The oxidation can take place within a number of organs in the body; however, it occurs primarily in the liver [1,6-8]. Although N-hydroxylation is a prerequisite for tumor induction by carcinogenic aromatic amines, not all N-hydroxy derivatives are carcinogenic, e.g., N-phenylhydroxylamine, N-ethyl-N-phenyl hydroxyl amine and N-hydroxy-N-1-fluorenylacetamide were all noncarcinogenic when tested [1].

In recent studies of hepatic microsomal N-glucuronidation and nucleic acid binding of N-hydroxy arylamines in relation to urinary bladder carcinogens, it was found by Kadlubar et al. [9] that arylamine bladder carcinogens are N-oxidized and N-glucuronidated in the liver and that the N-glucuronides are transported to the urinary bladder. The hydrolysis of the glucuronides to N-hydroxy arylamines and the reactive electrophilic arylnitrenium ions in the normally acidic urine of dogs and humans may be critical reactions for tumor induction in the urinary bladder [9]. Figure 2 illustrates the formation and transport of possible proximate and ultimate carcinogenic metabolites of arylamines for the induction of urinary bladder cancer as suggested by Kadlubar et al. [9].

An additional summary of the metabolic pathways by which aromatic amines may modify nucleic acids and proteins is shown in Figure 3 using 4-aminobiphenyl as an illustrative example [10].

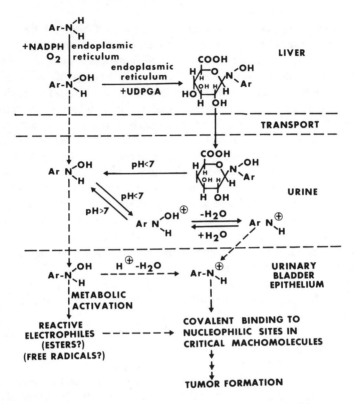

Figure 2. Formation and transport of possible proximate and ultimate carcinogenic metabolites of arylamines for the induction of urinary bladder cancer. (Ar: aryl substituent.)

The aromatic amines have long occupied a position in the forefront of investigations in the etiology of chemically induced carcinogenesis. Most of the organic compounds known to be carcinogenic to man are aromatic amines or derivatives of aromatic amines [11-14].

The Occupational Safety and Health Administration (OSHA) in 1973 called for the regulation of 14 chemical compounds including the aromatic amine derivatives: benzidine; 3,3′-dichlorobenzidine; 4-aminobiphenyl; α-and β-naphthylamines; 2-acetyl aminofluorene (2-AAF) and 4,4′-methylene-bis(2-chloroaniline) or (MOCA). These compounds are known to cause or suspected of causing human cancer from occupational exposure, and hence there is no assigned TLV for these compounds in the U.S. [15].

A statistically significant association between exposure and subsequent tumor development has been found for 4-aminobiphenyl, benzidine, 2-naphthylamine, and a strong association is suspected for 3,3′-dichlorobenzidine, 2-acetylaminofluorene, 4-dimethylaminoazobenzene, diphenylamine,

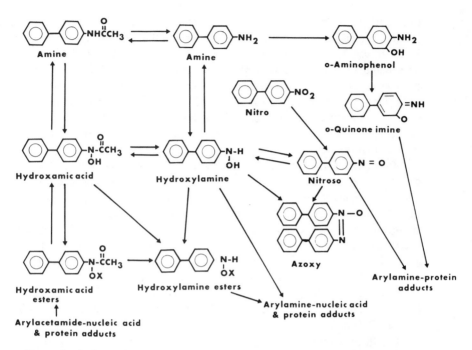

Figure 3. Pathways by which 4-aminobiphenyl may be activated metabolically. (Source: Baetcke, K. "Mechanistic Approaches to Carcinogenics," Aromatic Amines Program, NCTR Report, Nov. 6, 1976.)

o-tolidine (3,3′dimethylbenzidine) and *o*-dianisidine (3,3′dimethoxybenzidine) [16].

Human absorption of the aromatic amines in an occupational setting occurs via inhalation of the dust or vapors, absorption through intact skin and by ingestion. Individual hygiene is considered a most important factor.

UTILITY AND OCCURRENCE

Benzidine, its salts and a number of its derivatives and analogs occupy a paramount position both in their use applications as well as their potential health risks. Benzidine has been used for over 60 years primarily as an intermediate in the production of azo dyes, sulfur dyes, fast color salts, naphthols, and other dyes and dyeing compounds. Over 250 commercial dyes based primarily on the coupling of tetrazotized benzidine with phenols and aromatic amines have been reported [17]. Benzidine is also used as a hardener for polyurethane and in the past was extensively used in analytical and chemical chemistry as a chromogenic spray reagent for the detection of chlorinated organic pesticides in thin-layer chromatography, for determining hydrogen peroxide, nicotine, sugars, occult blood, bacterial cytochromes and for the detection of inorganic ions. The production of benzidine-derived dyes in 1948 was 35 million pounds, which accounted for 25% of all domestic dyes manufactured and almost all of the direct class dyes [18]. U.S. production of direct benzidine-derived dyes dropped to 11.4 million pounds in 1971 [19], and 681 metric tons in 1972 [20]; domestic production in 1978 was estimated to be limited to 12 benzidine dyes [21]. Available data indicate that U.S. production and importation of benzidine and benzidine compounds may exceed 3.5 million kg/yr [20].

Other derivatives of benzidine are employed to a lesser degree. 3,3'-dichlorobenzidine is employed as a coupling agent in the production of dyes and pigments with color plastic resins, rubber, printing inks, metal finishes, textiles and wall paper prints, and in interior-grade, lead-free finishes (paints), toy enamels and floor coverings. It is also used to a lesser extent as a curing agent for liquid-castable polyurethane elastomers. In 1971 about 1.6 million kg of 3,3'-dichlorobenzidine were produced in the U.S., and an additional 635,000 kg were imported [20].

More than 44,000 kg of 3,3'-dimethylbenzidine (o-toluidine) and 122,000 kg of 3,3'-dimethoxybenzidine (o-dianisidine) were imported into the U.S. during 1970 and 1971, respectively. These compounds are components of nearly 100 different dyes [20].

Although benzidine and its congeners are not known to occur in nature, they can be introduced to the aquatic environment via effluent discharge from manufacturing plants for the chemical as well as from pigment wastes containing the respective unreactive aromatic amine. Benzidine can also be formed *in situ* by the introduction of benzidine-based azo dyes into waste streams containing hydrogen sulfide or sulfur dioxide [22]. Adverse health effects might arise from the contamination of drinking water supplies or through potential bioaccumulation in fish which are subsequently used as food [23].

CARCINOGENIC BENZIDINE-DERIVED DYES AND PRECURSORS OF CARCINOGENIC AROMATIC AMINES

The potential carcinogenic hazard of three widely used benzidine-derived dyes, Direct Black 38, Direct Blue 6, and Direct Brown 95 (Figure 4) was noted in a recent National Institute for Occupational Safety and Health (NIOSH) advisory which recommended that these benzidine-based dyes be handled in the workplace as if they were human carcinogens. Based on the data from NCI short-term studies with rats, it was strongly stressed that a cancer-causing potential exists upon exposure to the benzidine-derived dyes, most likely through the mechanism of metabolic conversion of the dyes to

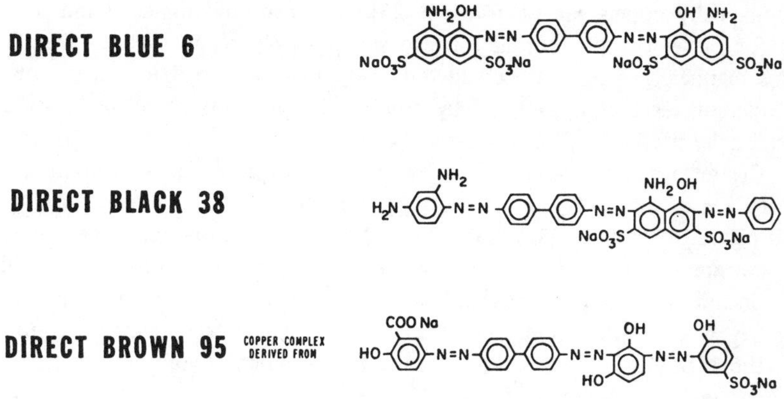

DIRECT BLUE 6

DIRECT BLACK 38

DIRECT BROWN 95 COPPER COMPLEX DERIVED FROM

Figure 4. Benzidine-derived dyes.

benzidine in the animal system [21]. Caution is also indicated by preliminary results from NIOSH field studies showing that humans working with these same dyes also excrete higher than expected levels of benzidine in their urine. Both laboratory and field studies indicate that these benzidine-derived dyes can be metabolized to benzidine, which is present in the urine of animals and humans [21]. The residual free benzidine content of the bulk benzidine-based dyes ranged from 1 to 19 ppm. It was conservatively estimated that about 20 times more benzidine and up to 200 times more monoacetyl benzidine were present in the urine of these dye workers (in two benzidine dye manufacturing operations, two textile finishing companies and a leather tannery), than if they had been exposed only to the dyes' residual benzidine content. In addition, NIOSH reported that concentrations of benzidine found were "significant fractions" of those associated with a high incidence of bladder cancer.

It is also important to note other industrial examples of precursors of carcinogenic aromatic amines. For example, recent reports indicate that phenyl-β-naphthylamine (PBNA), which is not currently regulated by OSHA, is converted by man into the human carcinogen β-naphthylamine [23]. PBNA is widely used in the rubber industry as an antioxidant as well as in the petroleum industry, where it is formulated into greases and oils as an antioxidant. PBNA is also used in the production of seven dyes of which C.I. Acid Blue 98 appears to be of commercial world significance [24]. It has also been reported that samples of commercial PBNA were contaminated with 20-30 mg/kg of β-naphthylamine [23].

It should also be stressed that a number of aromatic amines, particularly α-and β-naphthylamine, can be formed in situations outside factories and chemical laboratories. For example, if nitrogen compounds such as amino acids or proteins are pyrolyzed or burned, small but measureable amounts of naphthylamines can be formed [25]. The naphthylamines found in the air of gas works [26] or in tobacco smoke [27] are believed to arise in this manner. Hence, it is considered likely that carcinogenic amines can be present in air that is polluted by combustion products of nitrogen-containing materials, particularly proteins such as hides, hair or leather.

Cigarette smoke was reported by Hoffman et al. [27] to contain 2.2 x 10^{-8}/g of β-naphthylamine per cigarette smoked. Thus a man smoking 30 cigarettes per day could absorb 200 μg of β-naphthylamine per year. There are possibly other bladder carcinogens in cigarette smoke and polluted air in addition to β-naphthylamine; hence it is extremely difficult at present to say whether the increased bladder cancer incidence of cigarette smokers in the U.S. and Denmark [28] is due to the β-naphthylamine present in some cigarette smoke [27].

ANALYTICAL METHODOLOGY

One major goal in analytical methodology is the development of increased sensitivity and specificity in the determination of the aromatic amines and their metabolites in biological fluids and the environment. This would better enable both the monitoring of this important class of environmental hazard as well as permit a better correlation between an exposure or dose of the aromatic amine carcinogen and cancer incidence in man. The aromatic amines, particularly benzidine, its congeners and their metabolites, can be determined in biological and environmental media by a variety of procedures including: gas-liquid, high-pressure liquid and thin-layer chromatography (GLC, HPLC and TLC), spectrophotometry and spectrophotofluorimetry. It should be emphasized that the sensitivity, precision and accuracy vary not only among different methods, but also among various models of analytical instruments and among different operators [20,29].

Since benzidine is primarily a human bladder carcinogen, urine is by far the most commonly analyzed biological medium. The various procedures utilized are those wherein the urinary benzidine is extracted in a solvent (e.g., either-benzene, 3:2) and thereafter frequently determined colorimetrically by procedures based on diazotization and coupling reactions [30-34]. The sensitivity of these methods generally ranges from 0.5 to 0.1 μg of benzidine per liter of urine. A more generally used colorimetric procedure involves the formation of a yellow meriquinodal complex with chloramine-T (CH_3-C_6H_4-SO_2NNaCl) which offers a convenient means for a rapid quantitation determination (35-39). The general sensitivity achieved with the chloramine-T procedure is in the order of 0.01 mg of benzidine [39]. The color reaction is not specific for benzidine (e.g., all p,p'diaminodiphenyl derivatives from the yellow oxidation product to some degree) and is photosensitive, requiring rapid reading of the samples to prevent inaccurate results. Although organic bases interfere with the analysis as well as do compounds structurally related to benzidine, the chloroamine-T method is convenient and can also be applied to benzidine or its derivatives in samples of air, urine, feces and blood if suitable sample preparation steps are taken [20]. Chloramine-T has been employed by industrial hygienists to determine occupational exposure to benzidine and a number of its analogs [35-37]. The U.S. Environmental Protection Agency (EPA) in 1975 adopted the chloramine-T method as its recommended procedure for the determination of benzidine [40]. The accuracy of the method is generally ± 10% or better in the 2-10 μg amine range [37].

However, these colorimetric procedures generally lack both sensitivity and selectivity for many trace level investigations of a variety of carcinogenic aromatic amines.

In contrast to colorimetric procedures, GLC readily distinguishes individual components of aromatic amine mixtures, including closely related derivatives. Jenkins and Bairs [41] utilized a Perkin-Elmer Model 900 gas chromatograph equipped with FID and dual 6 ft x 1/8 in. i.d. glass column packed with a mixture of OV-17 (4.7%), QF-1 (5%) and DC-200 (0.5%) on 80/100 mesh Gas-Chrom Q to analyze samples of wastewater containing benzidine, 3,3′-dimethoxybenzidine, diphenylamine and 1-naphthylamine in the parts-per-billion (ppb) range. Although programmed thermal operation gave decreased sensitivity for benzidine when compared with isothermal analysis (e.g., 0.5 mg/1 compared to 0.1 mg/1), resolution was improved and complete separation of benzidine, 3,3′-dimethoxybenzidine, diphenylamine and 1-naphthylamine was obtained as illustrated in Figure 5. The procedure for pretreatment of sample prior to analysis by GLC, TLC or colorimetry is shown in Figure 6.

The fate of benzidine (as well as aniline and N,N-dimethylaniline) was recently investigated under controlled conditions to approximate the process chlorination of raw water supplies and wastewater secondary effluents [42]. GLC analysis of chlorination mixtures was accomplished using a 10% DC-200/Gas Chrom Q column with operating parameters as previously described by Jenkins and Baird [41]. Although a polymeric product was found on chlorination of benzidine, GLC analysis of the chlorination supernatant showed no ring-substituted isomers of benzidine.

Bowman and his colleagues [43-49] recently described a number of analytical procedures at the National Center for Toxicological Research (NCTR) used to augment a variety of investigations involving short-term and chronic low dose feeding of aromatic amines [benzidine, 3,3′-dimethylbenzidine (diorthotoluidine), 3,3′-dimethoxybenzidine (dianisidine),

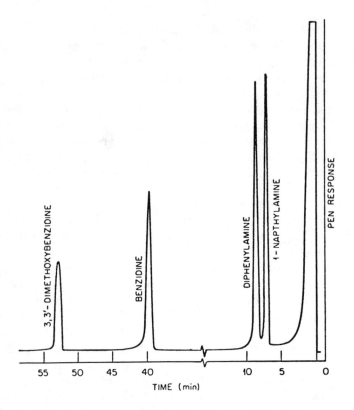

Figure 5. Resolution of four aromatic amines by the column mixture OV-17 (4.7%), QF-1 (5.0%) and DC-200 (0.5%) on 80- to 100-mesh Gas-chrom Q, using PTGC (150-250°C at 3/min, holding 12 min at 150°C) [41].

3,3'-dichlorobenzidine, 4-aminobiphenyl and 2-acetylaminofluorene] to experimental animals. Hence, requisite analytical methodology for these compounds was required to:

1. verify purity, proper dosages and chemical stability of the compounds administered in drinking water and feed;

2. monitor clothing, work areas and urine of personnel to signal any accidental spillage or exposure to these agents;

3. monitor wastewater resulting from decontamination of the test areas; and

4. develop methods for decontamination.

Bowman and Rushing [47] described trace analysis of 3,3'-dichlorobenzidine and its dihydrochloride salt in animal chow, wastewater and human urine by three gas chromatographic procedures. The major features of the method for these carcinogens in chow are: extraction of the residues as

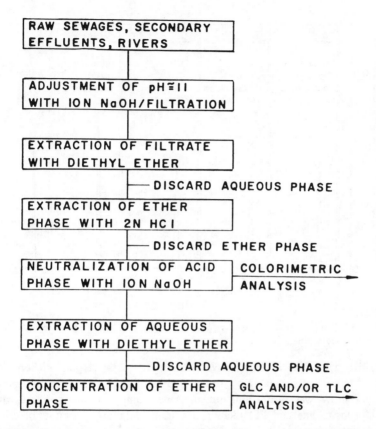

Figure 6. Procedure for pretreatment of sample prior to analysis by GLC, TLC or colorimetry [41].

the free amine and a cleanup via acid-base liquid-liquid partitioning with benzene, followed by passage over a silica gel column. With wastewater and human urine, residues were adsorbed by percolating the sample through a column of XAD-2 resin eluted with acetone, and cleaned up with acid-base partitioning and a silica gel column. Residues then were assayed by GLC, either as the free amine or after conversion to the pentafluoropropionyl derivative by using an electron-capture or a rubidium-sensitized thermionic-type (N/P) detector. Minimum detectable residues in chow, wastewater, and human urine are about 18 ppb, 18 parts-per-trillion (ppt) and 60 ppt, respectively, as determined by electron-capture GLC of the pentafluoropropionyl derivative. Typical electron-capture gas chromatograms of pentafluoropropionyl (PFP), trifluoroacetyl (TFA) and heptafluorobutyryl (HFB) derivatives of dichlorobenzidine are illustrated in Figure 7. The PFP and HFB derivatives gave about equal responses, the TFA-dichlorobenzidine was about half as

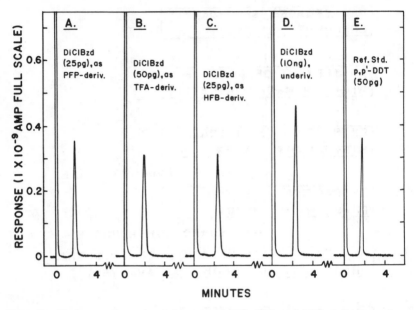

Figure 7. Electron capture chromatograms of PFP, TSA and HFB derivatives of dichlorobenzidine.

sensitive, while the PFP derivative enhanced detector responses about 300-fold. Figure 8 illustrates gas chromatograms of underderivatized extracts of animal chow, wastewater and human urine, compared with standards of dichlorobenzidine and PFP-dichlorobenzidine. Minimum amounts of dichlorobenzidine detectable in human urine, based on twice background, were about 0.060 ppb by electron-capture GLC of the PFB derivative and 1.8 ppt by N/P-GLC [47].

A procedure has recently been reported by Bowman [48] for determining 11 aromatic amines (as well as the estrogens estradiol and diethylstilbestrol) (Figure 9) in admixture at low ppb or sub-ppb levels which is applicable to wastewater, urine and samples from air filters and swabs from the monitoring of work areas. A scheme for the extraction, separation and analysis of the 13 compounds in admixture is shown in Figure 10. Salient features of the procedure are: separation of the residues into basic, phenolic and neutral fractions; hydrolysis of the 2-AAF in the neutral fraction to 2-AF; conversion of all residues to the PFP derivatives; and analysis on a 5% Dexsil column by electron-capture GLC using three isothermal operating conditions. Gas chromatograms of derivatized fractions from untreated wastewater along with 1-ppb amounts of ten of the compounds as PFP derivatives (superimposed) are presented in Figure 11. Good recoveries (72-85%) were obtained at the 10-ppb level in assays of wastewater spiked with 0.10, 1.0 and 10 ppt

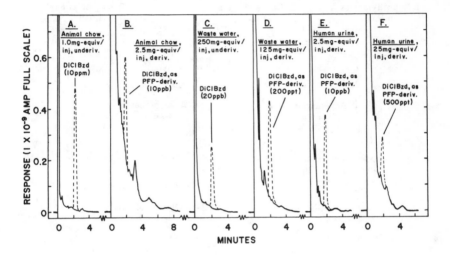

Figure 8. Gas chromatograms of underivatized extracts of animal chow wastewater and human urine compared with standards of dichlorobenzidine and PFP-dichlorobenzidine.

of eight aromatic amines and the two estrogens, but tended to drop significantly at the 1- and 0.1-ppb levels. The procedure also served as an excellent means of monitoring for residues of the compounds at levels of 1 to 2 ppb in the urine of laboratory and animal caretaker personnel [48]. Although extensive studies of cleanup procedures were evaluated employing XAD-2 resin and Sephadex LD-20 prior to derivatization and alumina and silica gel column chromatography before and after derivatization, no system could be devised that allowed good recoveries of all 13 compounds at the levels tested [48].

Spectrophotofluorimetric (SPF) methods were described for the trace analysis of benzidine, 3,3'-dimethylbenzidine, 3,3'-dimethoxybenzidine [43], 4-aminobiphenyl, 2-naphthylamine and their hydrochloride salts [45] in wastewater, potable water, human urine and rodent blood. The salient features of the methods for these known or suspected carcinogens are: extraction of the residues as the free amine with benzene, rapid cleanup

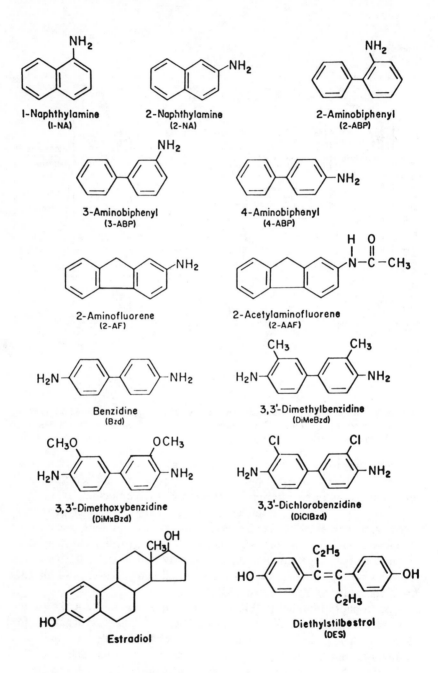

Figure 9. Structures of aromatic amines and estrogens analyzed in admixtures.

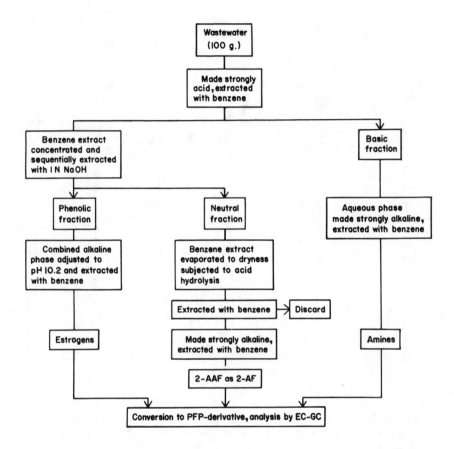

Figure 10. Scheme for the extraction, separation and analysis of the compounds in admixture shown in Figure 9.

on an alumina column, and quantification of the free amine in methanol via SPF. Potable water solutions of the salts are diluted with buffer (pH 4) and quantified directly by SPF. Spectrophotofluorimetry is based on the measurement of fluorescence radiation emitted by a sample previously excited by ultraviolet (UV) or visible light. The intensity of the emission is proportional to both the concentration of the analyte and the intensity of the exciting radiation. Hence, SPF is inherently extremely sensitive; under favorable conditions it can be four orders of magnitude more sensitive than molecular absorption spectrophotometry [50]. In addition, SPF is potentially important as an analytical method for benzidine and its congeners since these compounds emit distinctive fluorescent spectra by which each can be identified and quantified (Table I). The detection limits of the

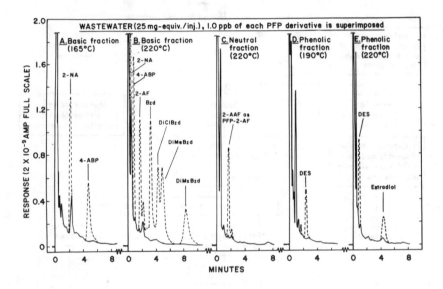

Figure 11. Gas chromatograms of derivatized fractions from untreated wastewater along with 1-ppb amounts of ten of the compounds as PFP derivatives superimposed.

amines and their salts were 2 ng/ml and 10 ng/ml, respectively. Good precision was obtained in a variety of sample types: relative standard deviations of 0.0 to 5.0% were reported for trypticase soy dextrose and brain heart infusion medium containing 0.1 ppm and 1.0 ppm benzidine and wastewater containing 20 ppb benzidine. Somewhat poorer results (1% to 25%) were obtained with human urine (20 ppb) and rat blood (10 ppm). The relative errors in the above analyses varied from 10 to 35%, except for the samples of rat blood, which averaged about 85%. This level of accuracy is generally adequate for all samples mentioned other than rat blood.

4-Aminobiphenyl was also determined by SPF utilizing the same substrates and techniques as previously described [45]. Recovery rates ranged from 81 to 95% in biological growth, media and wastewater, from 45 to 95% in human urine, and from 6 to 70% in mouse whole blood. Best recovery from urine occurred without prior hydrolysis, while best recovery from blood occurred after acid hydrolysis (67 to 72%) [45].

Table I. Wavelengths for Maximum Fluorescence and Corresponding Relative
Intensities for Benzidine and Congeners, Biphenyl, Isomeric
Aminobiphenyls and Naphthylamines [43,45].[a]

Compound	λ_{Ex}(nm)	λ_{Em}(nm)	R1 (μg/ml)
Benzidine	295	396	33.5
Benzidine · 2HC1	302	410	7.45
3,3′-Dimethylbenzidine	300	384	51.8
3,3′-Dimethylbenzidine · 2HC1	310	410	12.2
3,3′-Dimethoxybenzidine	312	380	64.3
3,3′-Dimethoxybenzidine · 2HC1	318	422	8.25
Biphenyl	260	312	3.90
2-Aminobiphenyl	312	392	6.25
3-Aminobiphenyl	255	398	5.50
3-Aminobiphenyl · HC1	260	410	7.0
4-Aminobiphenyl	290	368	55.0
4-Aminobiphenyl · HC1	260	382	7.80
1-Naphthylamine	332	425	14.6
1-Naphthylamine · HC1	285	444	2.1
2-Naphthylamine	242	400	18.5
2-Naphthylamine · HC1	286	406	10.4

[a]All dilutions of the free amines were prepared in methanol and those of the salts
were in water—2% buffer (pH-4). The instrument was frequently calibrated to produce a R1 of 5.0 with a dilution of 0.3 μg quinine sulfate/ml of 0.1 N sulfuric
acid (λ_{Em} = 350, λ_{Em} = 450). Readings were corrected for solvent blanks and R1
was plotted vs concentration of the six compounds on log–log paper to produce a
standard curve.

However, quantitative determination of benzidine and its congeners in
admixture is somewhat difficult because of spectral overlap and large differences in relative intensities. It should be noted, however, that the importance
of this deficiency depends on the composition and type of sample to be
analyzed; in many instances it is not significant [43]. Figure 12 illustrates
SPF excitation and emission spectra and standard curves for benzidine and
benzidine–2HC1 [43]. The excitation and emission spectra and standard
curves of 4-aminobiphenyl, 1-naphthylamine and 2-naphthylamine and
their hydrochloride salts are depicted in Figures 13 through 15, respectively.
The relative intensities of the free amines in methanol were as much as
five to seven times greater than the corresponding hydrochloride salts in
0.01-HC1 solutions. In these solvents, the limits of detection, expressed
as twice background, were about 1-2 and 2-5 μg/ml for the free amines
and salts, respectively.

SPF techniques were found to be quite useful for the monitoring of
work areas such as cages, floors, benches and apparatus suspected of being

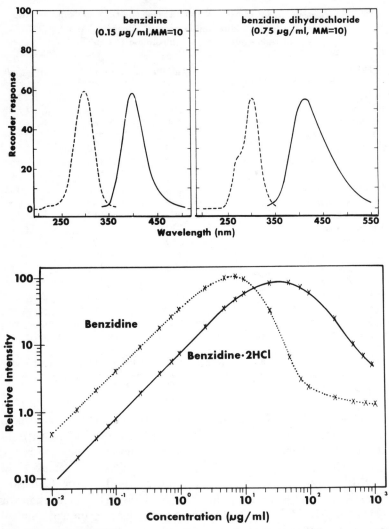

Figure 12. SPF excitation and emissions spectra at standard curves for benzidine and benzidine hydrochloride.

contaminated with the above carcinogenic amines or their salts. Background fluorescence is generally equivalent to 0.10 µg of the aromatic amine (benzidine). Areas contaminated with as little as 0.30 µg of the salt are readily detected and the identity of the agent confirmed by its characteristic excitation and emission maxima [43,45].

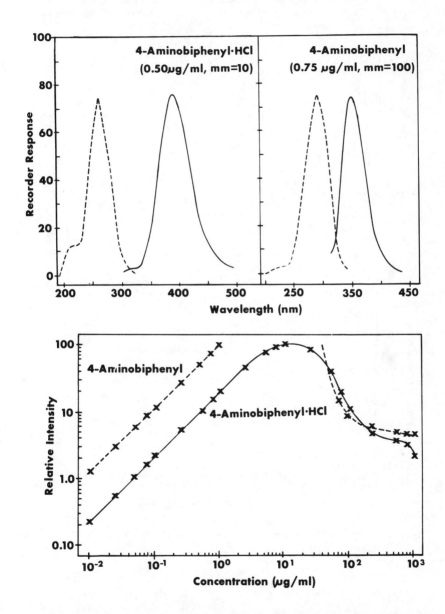

Figure 13. SPF excitation and emissions spectra at standard curves for 4–aminobiphenyl and 4–aminobiphenyl hydrochloride.

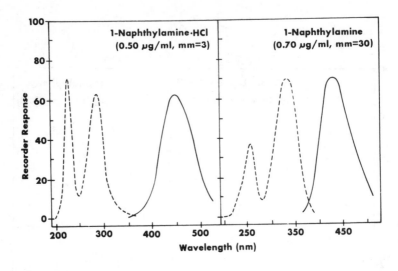

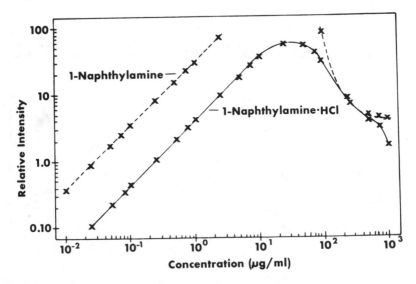

Figure 14. SPF excitation and emissions spectra at standard curves for 1–napthylamine and 1–napthylamine hydrochloride.

A number of procedures utilizing HPLC for the determination of a number of carcinogenic aromatic amines have been reported [51-57]. Riggin and Howard [56] described an HPLC method for the determination of benzidine, 3,3′-dichlorobenzidine and 1,2-diphenylhydrazine in aqueous media.

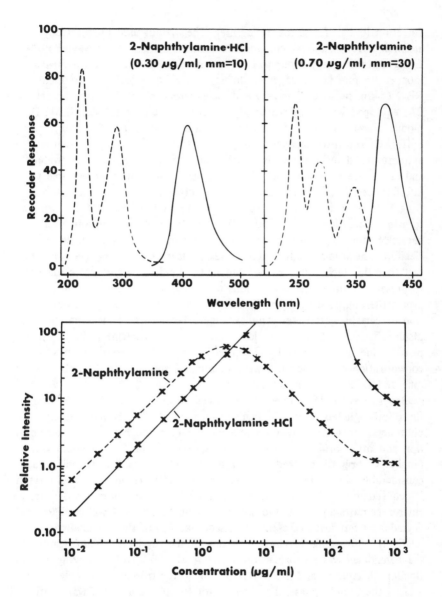

Figure 15. SPF excitation and emissions spectra at standard curves for 2–napthyla-mine and 2–napthylamine hydrochloride.

These compounds can be assayed either by direct injection, or by solvent extraction or resin desorption of the aqueous sample prior to analysis with detection limits of less than 1 μg/liter. The system used in this study was assembled from modular components consisting of an Altex Model 110A liquid chromatographic pump, a Rheodyne 7010 injector with a 50-μl loop, a 4.6 mm i.d. x 25 cm stainless steel column packed with Lichrosorb RP-2 (5-μm particle diameter) and an electrochemical detector (Model LC-2A) equipped with a thin-layer glassy carbon electrode (Model 7L5). The mobile phase consisted of 50/50 acetonitrile/pH 4.7, 0.1 M sodium acetate buffer. Of the three analytical approaches (e.g., direct injection, solvent extraction and resin absorption) that were applied to actual wastewater and/or surface water samples, direct injection, while most susceptible to interferences, is very rapid and has a detection limit of approximately 1 μg/l. Solvent extraction serves to clean up and concentrate the sample to give a detection limit of 50 ng/l or better. Resin adsorption offers a detection limit of approximately 100 ng/l and offers some degree of cleanup. The primary advantages of resin adsorption are its speed and the fact that this technique can be used in the field. This eliminates the need to preserve dilute aqueous solutions of compounds of interest and also avoids the emulsion problems frequently encountered during solvent extraction of certain wastewater samples. Figure 16 illustrates the separation of dichlorobenzidine (DCB), benzidine and diphenylhydrazine (DPH) by reverse-phase liquid chromatography. Figure 17 depicts the chromatograms for resin concentration of municipal sewage of samples spiked with 10 ppb of benzidine and DCB, respectively [56].

Banerjee et al. [57] recently employed HPLC techniques to elaborate the photodegradation of 3,3'-dichlorobenzidine. DCB was very rapidly photodegraded under environmental conditions through reductive dechlorination and other processes to monochlorobenzidine (MCB), benzidine and a number of brightly colored water–insoluble substances. The reaction was considerably slower in organic solvents, and the mechanism of dechlorination is believed not to involve simple carbon–chlorine bond homolysis. From an environmental standpoint, the action of sunlight on DCB will lead to its degradation but not necessarily to its detoxification since benzidine, a relatively photostable carcinogen, is one of the products. Quantification of the benzidines was performed on a Waters M6000A HPLC utilizing a μC₁₈ μC_{18} Bondapack column and a 1:1 mixture of acetonitrile and 5% aqueous acetic acid as the mobile phase. The identity of the photoproducts was confirmed by GLC using an HP5730 FID instrument and a 10% UCN 932 on Chromosorb W column maintained at 225°C and by mass spectrometry [57]. Gutman [51] employed HPLC for fractionating 2–AAF (2-acetylaminofluorene) and some of its hydroxylated metabolites formed by an *in vitro* microsomal system. Fullerton and Jackson [47] utilized HPLC and a 4-ft Carbowax 400 column for the determination of 2–AAF and its major metabolites in mouse urine samples.

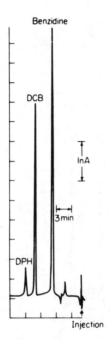

Figure 16. Separation of DCB, DPH and benzidine by reverse–phase liquid chromatography. Volume injected, 25 μl; amount injected 3 ng each; flowrate, 0.8 ml/min; mobile phase, 50/50 acetonitrile/pH 4.7, 0.1 M sodium acetate buffer; stationary phase, 4.6 mm i.d. x 25 cm RP-2 (5 μm); electrode potential, 0.9 V.

A more efficient separation of 2-AAF and the ring-hydroxy metabolites was accomplished by reverse-phase liquid chromatography on a 2-ft column of C_{18}/Corasil using acetonitrile:water as the mobile phase. The response to each of the ring-hydroxylated metabolites and N-OH-AAF on the C_{18}/Corasil column was linear from approximately 10 ng to 2 μg [52].

A combination of the two columns (Carbowax and C_{18}/Corasil) was found to provide an excellent method for resolving and quantitating 2-AAF, N-hydroxy-AAF and the 1-, 3-, 5- and 7-hydroxy AAF metabolites in the presence of urinary components. The response of the system to each of the metabolites was linear over a range of 10 ng to 2 μg with the exception of N-OH-AAF which deviated from linearity below 100 ng.

Stanley et al. [55] recently described an analytical approach to metabolic profiling of aromatic amines for both conjugated and "free" metabolites in biological systems utilizing HPLC. Initially, an ethyl acetate extraction removes the less polar metabolites. A salting-out procedure using Sephadex G-10 is combined with HPLC to analyze the water-soluble conjugates

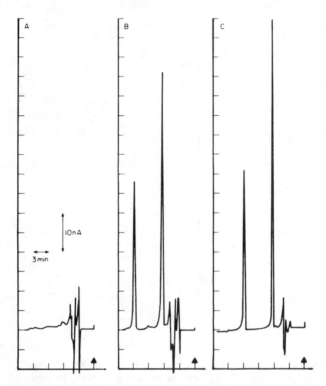

Figure 17. Chromatogram for resin concentration of municipal sewage: (A) unspiked; (B) spiked with 10 ppb benzidine and DCB; (C) standard corresponding to 100% recovery of spike.

directly using sequential UV and fluorescence detection. The "free" metabolites are also derived from individual conjugate peaks by enzymatic or hydrolytic procedures and then rechromatographed by HPLC. Metabolites in the ethyl acetate fraction are similarly analyzed by reverse–phase HPLC. Figure 18 illustrates an HPLC profile of standards of 2-AAF, 2-AF, and ring-hydroxy metabolites using reverse-phase mode and methanol/water phase. N-hydroxy AAF did not elute under the conditions that adequately separated the remaining metabolites. An HPLC chromatogram of the water-soluble metabolites of $9\text{-}^{14}C\text{-}2\text{-AAF}$ isolated from urine of a mouse which had been stomach intubated with 0.5 mg of $9\text{-}^{14}C\text{-}2\text{-AFF}$ and the urine collected for 16 hr is shown in Figure 19. As indicated in this figure, there are five major components, one of which is a doublet (peak 2) observed in BALB/c female mice. The insert in Figure 19 is an HPLC chromatogram of N-hydroxy-2-AAF glucuronide determined under identical conditions showing that peak 4 has the same retention time, hence demonstrating that this

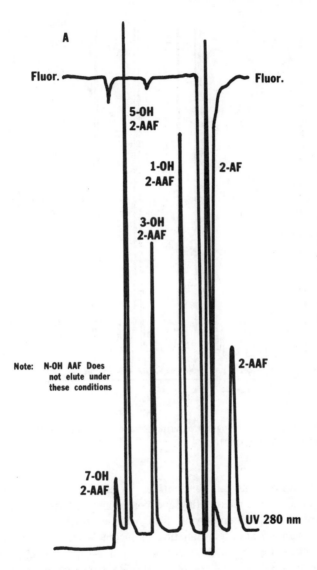

Figure 18. HPLC profile of standards of 2–AAF, 2–AF and ring metabolites using reverse-phase mode and methanol/water phase.

procedure provides a direct approach for the separation and identification of the amounts of N–OH–2–AAF that are excreted in the urine.

Treatment with β-glucuronidase releases a compound with identical chromatographic properties as N–OH–2–AAF. Figure 20 depicts how indi-

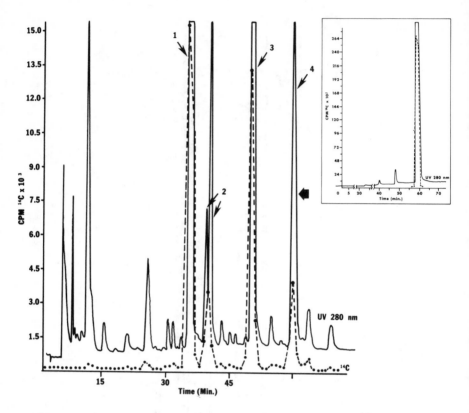

Figure 19.   HPLC chromatogram of water-soluble metabolites of 9-^{14}C-2-AAF isolated from mouse urine.

vidual conjugate peaks can be identified by collecting and treating with β-glucuronidase, then reextracting and confirming with authentic standards.

Mefford et al. [54] employed HPLC with electrochemical detection to effect a separation and determination of picomole quantities of 1- and 2-naphthylamine. Equimolar mixtures of 1- and 2-naphthylamine were readily separated on a 35-cm du Pont SCX cation-exchange column using an acetate-citrate buffer, pH 5.2 (0.027 M citric acid; 0.06 M NaOH, 0.05 M sodium acetate; 1.05 ml glacial acetic acid) at a flowrate of 0.94 ml/min. Calibration curves of each separate component at even lower levels (0-2 pmol) were linear.

A mixture of benzidine and *o*-dianisidine was also easily separated on a 25-cm SCX column using 0.1 M ammonium acetate as eluant at a flowrate of 0.35 ml/min. Calibration curves for each component were linear over the range 0-10 pmol.

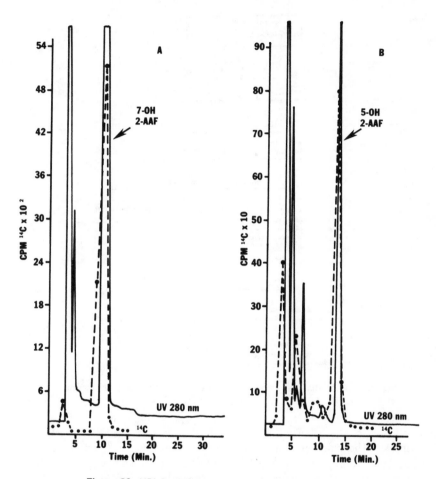

Figure 20. HPLC of individual 2-AAF conjugate peaks.

The quantitative determination of 1- and 2-naphthylamine in cigarette smoke has been reported by Hoffman and co-workers [27,58]. The basic nonvolatiles of the smoke of 300 cigarettes were reacted with pentafluoropropionic anhydride and the resulting neutral components chromatographed on Florisil. The concentrates of N-pentafluoropropionamides of 1- and 2-naphthylamines were analyzed by electron-capture GLC, which had a sensitivity limit of less than 1 ng. The mainstream smoke of an 85-mm U.S. nonfilter cigarette contained 27 ng of 1-naphthylamine and 22 ng of 2-naphthylamine. Figure 21 illustrates the analytical procedure employed for the separation and determination of the naphthylamine from cigarette

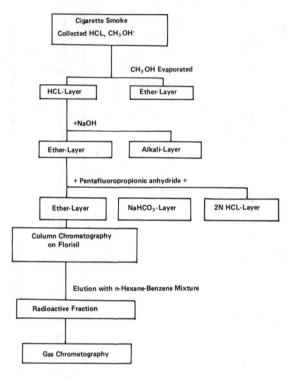

Figure 21. Analytical separation procedure for 1- and 2-naphthylamine from cigarette smoke [27,58].

smoke. The mass spectra of synthetic and isolated N-1- and N-2-naphthyl-pentafluoropropionamides and the retention times and retention volumes from two GLC systems served for the identification of 1- and 2-naphthylamines [27,58].

Sensitive chemical spot tests employing a "swipe" technique have been developed by Weeks et al. [59,61] for detecting a variety of carcinogenic primary aromatic amines and related compounds (e.g., those compounds which are readily transformable to aromatic amines, 4-nitrobiphenyl and 4-dimethylaminoazobenzene) on painted, metal and concrete surfaces. For most of the compounds and surfaces studied, limit of detection values were obtained at the level of less than 200 ng of material per cm^2 of surface. The tests in which fluorescent derivatives were formed were generally more sensitive than those relying upon highly colored substances. While chromogenic tests are frequently not as sensitive as the fluorogenic, positive chromogenic tests are obtained at concentration levels where quenching may obviate the fluorescence tests. By utilizing both chromogenic and fluorogenic derivatization techniques as complementary methods, the analytical confidence of a test series was enhanced. Figure 22 illustrates the relative detection range of chromogenic and fluorogenic reagents. While the fluorogenic detection limit is the lower of the two methods (e.g., of the order of ng/cm^2) it also has an upper limit due to fluorescence quenching and other secondary effects. Although the chromogenic test limit of detection values are generally of the order of tens or hundreds of ng/cm^2, there are no effective upper limits [60]. Figure 23 illustrates diagrammatically how these chromogenic and fluorogenic tests may be used to determine the presence or absence of primary amines. Only in the case when *both* the chromogenic and fluorogenic tests are negative can one suspect that the subject agents are *likely* absent at the respective limits of detection of the systems employed.

The most promising reagents employed by Weeks et al. [59,60] were Ehrlich's reagent (*p*-dimethylaminobenzaldehyde), fluorescamine and

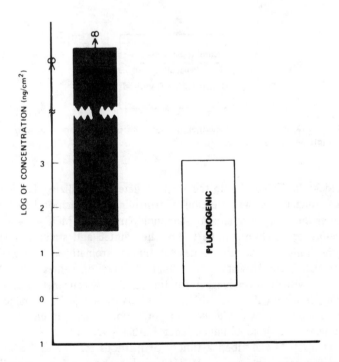

Figure 22. Typical relative detection range for chromogenic and fluorogenic reagents.

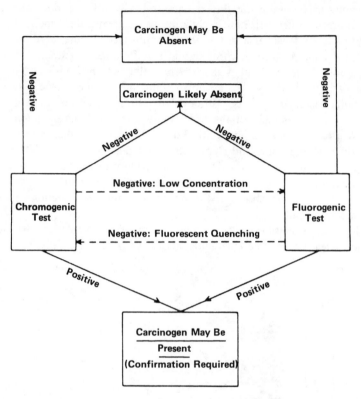

Figure 23. Flowchart depicting manner in which chromogenic and fluorogenic spot tests complement one another.

o-phthalaldehyde. Table II lists the limit of detection utilizing Ehrlich's reagent when utilized for the detection of benzidine, 3,3'-dichlorobenzidine, 1-naphthylamine, 2-naphthylamine, 4-aminobiphenyl and MOCA [4,4'-methylene-*bis*-(ortho-chloroaniline)]. For the painted and stainless steel surfaces, the limit of detection values for the six aromatic amines were all 150 ng or less. Table III lists typical limit of detection values using flourescamine as the visualization reagent for the six OSHA cancer-suspect agents shown. The detection limit for this reagent was of the order of nanograms or tens of nanograms of amine per cm^2 of surface. These levels are typically fivefold lower than those obtained using Ehrlich's reagent.

Linch et al. [61] described a variety of methods for the evaluation of hazards and exposure control of MOCA (methylene-*bis*-orthochloroaniline). MOCA is a commercially important curing agent for polymer and epoxy-resin systems containing isocyanates [62]. Production of MOCA in the U.S.

Table II. Limit of Detection (ng/cm) ρ-Dimethylaminobenzaldehyde
Visualization Reagent

Cancer-Suspect Agent	Filter Paper (Whatman 42) (Direct Technique)	Stainless Steel 316 (0.5-3.5 in.) (Leaching Technique)	Paint Machine Gray Glidden (Leaching Technique)
4,4'-Methylenebis(o-chloroaniline) [MOCA]	175	150	150
Benzidine	30	30	150
3,3'-Dichlorobenzidine	30	30	150
α-Naphthylamine	800	150	150
β-Naphthylamine	30	30	150
4-Aminobiphenyl	30	30	150

Table III. Limit of Detection (ng/cm) Fluorescamine Visualization

Cancer-Suspect Agent	Filter Paper (Whatman 42) (Direct Technique)	Stainless Steel 316 (0.5-3.5 in.) (Leaching Technique)	Paint Machine Gray Glidden (Leaching Technique)
4,4'-Methylenebis(2-chloroaniline)	3	6	15
Benzidine	3	6	15
3,3'-Dichlorobenzidine	3	6	15
α-Naphythylamine	30	30	30
β-Naphthylamine	3	6	15
4-Aminobiphenyl	3	6	30

was estimated at 3.3 million kg in 1972 when an estimated 10,000 people
were employed in either production or use of this compound [63]. The
production of MOCA has only recently been curtailed. The GLC procedure
which utilized flame-ionization detection and a column of 5% OV-101 on
80-100 mesh Chromosorb G (AW-1 MSC)HP operated isothermally at 260°C
was both sensitive and specific. The GLC procedure is capable of detecting
40 ppb of MOCA in urine or 10 $\mu g/m^3$ in air. Confirmatory colorimetric
and thin-layer methods were applied to the urine analysis as well. The
colorimetric procedure for total aromatic amines involved use of coupling
with N-1-naphthylethylene-diamine dihydrochloride. MOCA was extracted

from neutral urine with dichloromethane and separated from other urinary components by TLC on an alumina gel film with acetone: 1.0 N HCl. The separated MOCA was eluted and then measured colorimetrically. Since some absorbed MOCA is eliminated conjugated with glucuronic acid, preliminary hydrolysis of the glucuronides before extraction and separation is necessary. The monohydroxy metabolite of MOCA was detected by TLC.

The study of Linch et al. [61] disclosed relatively large differences in MOCA absorption rates and metabolism from one individual to another as well as wide variations in clearance rates. Skin absorption from direct contact was concluded to be the major source of worker absorption of MOCA.

There is a paucity of information that has appeared in the general published literature on the analysis of aromatic amines in air. Linch et al. [61] described a procedure for the determination of MOCA in air which involved adsorption on a Gas-Chrom S tube, desorption with acetone, and final analysis by flame-ionization gas chromatography utilizing a 30 cm x 30 mm o.d. (2.34 mm i.d.) stainless steel tube packed with 10% by weight of Dexsil 300 GC coated on 80/90 mesh ABS Anakrom, operated at column and inlet temperatures of 200 and 250°C, respectively. Within the concentration range of 2-150 $\mu g/m^3$, a relative standard deviation of 5% can be expected. A detection limit with a 1-μl aliquot of sample is 0.002 μg or about 2 $\mu g/m^3$ for a 500-liter air sample.

Rappaport and Morales [64] recently described a sampling and analytical method for the determination of airborne exposures to the carcinogen MOCA. The personal sample employs a filter to collect particulate MOCA followed by a bed of silica gel to remove the vapors. MOCA is extracted from the sampler stages with methanol, and a 10-μl aliquot is injected into an HPLC operating with a reverse-phase system. The UV detector (254 nm) permits quantitation of 3 ng of MOCA corresponding to 0.15 μg/sample. Precision levels were determined to be 9.2% at 1.5 μg/sample and 14% at 0.15 μg/sample. HPLC analysis utilized a Waters Model ALC 202/401. MOCA was eluted from the 4.0 mm x 30 cm μ-Bondapack C_{18} column in 4 min at a flowrate of 1.3 ml/min (1200 psi) of 8/2 (V/V) acetonitrile/water. The method developed by Rappaport and Morales [65] for the collection and analysis of MOCA in air has several suggested advantages over those previously reported. Primarily, the analysis is conducted at ambient temperature, hence minimizing the possibility of degradation of MOCA at gas chromatographic temperatures, and there is no requirement for derivatization. The sensitivity of the procedure is 3 to 10 times greater than that of Yasuda [65] or Lynch [61]. The quantitation of the method is 0.3 ng/μl or 150 ng/sample. Assuming that 48 liters of air are sampled (0.2 liter/min for 4 hr), the minimum air concentration that could be measured is 3 $\mu g/m^3$.

A relatively new technique, anodic differential pulse voltammetry (DPV), was suggested by Chey et al. [66] to have utility in the environmental analysis of several carcinogenic aromatic amines at the ppm to ppb level. Although benzidine, o-dianisidine, 1-naphthyl and 2-naphthylamines could be readily analyzed individually, these analyses in admixture would be difficult since benzidine and o-dianisidine are oxidized at identical Ep and the naphthylamine isomers would not be clearly separable. In cases where there are particular separation problems, preliminary TLC separations could be carried out followed by isolation of TLC spots and elution into small volumes for subsequent DPV analysis. An alternative procedure could involve HPLC resolution of aromatic amine mixtures with electrochemical detection [66].

AROMATIC DIAMINES IMPLICATED IN HAIR DYE TOXICITY, AND THEIR ANALYSIS

The focus of this review thus far has been on carcinogenic and mutagenic aromatic amines, azo dyes and related derivatives that are of concern principally from an occupational exposure standpoint. However, there is an increasing concern regarding aromatic diamines that may be in consumer products and hence of potential risk to a large population. Recent studies have implicated a broad spectrum of aromatic amines in hair dye toxicity, both of acute and chronic nature (e.g., mutagenic, carcinogenic and teratogenic effects in addition to delayed hypersensitivity and photo effects) [67,68]. The most common dyeing systems for coloring the hair, are: (1) permanent (oxidation) hair dyes, lasting for several months (except in areas of new growth); (2) the semipermanent (nonoxidation) hair dyes which last up to five weeks; and (3) the temporary (nonoxidation) hair dyes which can be rubbed off or removed with shampooing.

Most permanent dyes sold in the U.S. and probably elsewhere are the oxidation type. These are usually formulated with 7-12 aromatic intermediates. Some act as couplers, while others convert to colored substantive compounds on oxidation and polymerization in alkaline solution. The couplers are generally *meta*-aromatic diamines, hydroxylamines and diphenols; they are not themselves oxidized, but condense with the benzoquinone-imine derivatives that form in the oxidizing hair mixture. The intermediates are present at 0.1 to 4% concentration in an ammoniacal base that usually contains a detergent and a sequestering agent. The intermediates are diluted and oxidized by mixing with equal parts of 6% hydrogen peroxide [68]. Table IV lists substances that have been used as dye intermediates in permanent (oxidation) hair dyes.

Table IV.   Substances Which Have Been Used as Dye Intermediates in
Permanent (Oxidation) Hair Dyes

p-Phenylenediamine[a]	N-Phenyl-p-phenylenediamine[a]
o-Phenylenediamine	N-,N-Dimethyl-p-phenylenediamine
m-Phenylenediamine[a]	N,N-Diethyl-p-phenylenediamine
p-Aminophenol[a]	Resorcinol[a]
o-Aminophenol[a]	Hydroquinone[a]
O-Aminophenol[a]	1.5-Naphthalenediol
2.5-Toluenediamine	α-Naphthol[a]
2.4-Toluenediamine	Catechol
3.4-Toluenediamine	4.4-Methylenebis(N,N-dimethylaniline)
p-Methylaminophenol	4-Methoxy-m-phenylenediamine[a]
2.4-Diaminoanisole[a]	Amidodiphenylamine
4-Nitro-o-phenylenediamine[a]	p-Quinone
2-Nitro-p-phenylenediamine[a]	Hydroxyquinone
2-Amino-4-nitrophenol	Oxyhydroquinone
2-Amino-5-nitrophenol	Pyrogallol[a]
4-Amino-2-nitrophenol	Diaminodiphenylamine
Picramic acid	Phloroglucine
4-Chloro-o-phenylenediamine	1,2,4-Trihydroxybenzene
4-Chloro-m-phenylenediamine	1,4-Benzophenone
O-Anisidine	N,N-Bix(2-hydroxyethyl)-p-phenylenediamine[a]
p-Anisidine	4-Chlororesorcinol

[a]Products are components of formulations currently filed with the Division of
Cosmetics Technology/FDA under voluntary cosmetic registration program
(21CFR720).

Substances that have been used in semipermanent hair coloring products
are listed in Table V. These products penetrate and dye the hair directly
without oxidation. Some of the preparations used for semipermanent coloring contain toluene diamine or anthraquinone dyes or solvent-assisted nitro,
disperse and azo dyes. Certain oxidation colors are used as the main coloring components, but without an oxidizing agent. Among these are the
nitro derivatives such as 2-nitro-1,4-phenylenediamine, 4-nitro-1,2-phenylene-
diamine and 4-nitro-2-aminophenol [68].

It has been estimated that about 30% of U.S. women dye their hair,
often monthly and for many years. It was suggested by Ames et al.   [69]
that the possible risk of cancer and of genetic abnormalities appears sufficiently high and that large-scale epidemiology studies should be done to
determine any relationship between cancer incidence and years of hair
dyeing. There is evidence both from animal and human studies that constituents of semipermanent hair colorants, at concentrations found in
proprietary formulations, can be absorbed by the skin and appear in the
urine in appreciable amounts [67-72].

Table V.   Substances Which Have Been Used in Semipermanent
Hair Coloring Products

N$'$-Methyl-N$'$-bis(2-hydroxyethyl)2-nitrophenylenediamine
N$'$-Methyl-2-nitrophenylenediamine
N$'$-Tris(hydroxymethyl)-methyl-2-nitro-p-phenylenediamine
N$'$-N^4-Tris(2-hydroxyethyl)-2-nitro-p-phenylenediamine
N$'$-(2-Hydroxyethyl)-4-nitro-o-phenylenediamine
2-Nitro-p-phenylenediamine
N$'$-(2-Hydroxyethyl)2-amino-3-nitrobenzene
4-Nitro-o-phenylenediamine
2-Amino-4-nitrophenol
2-Amino-5-nitrophenol
Hydroxyethyl-2-amino-5-nitrophenol
N -(2-hydroxyethyl)-2nitro-p-phenylenediamine[a]
N -2(2-hydroxyethyl)-4-nitro-o-phenylenediamine
Fuchsin
C1-Disperse Violet #11[a]
Celliton Fast Navy Blue BRA
Amido Yellow EA
D&C Orange No 4
D&C Red No 33
Ext D&C Violet No 2
Ext D&C Yellow No 7
D&C Black No 1
Ext D&C Red No 13
D&C Yellow No 10
Bis(3-Aminopropyl)amine[a]
N,N-Bis(2-hydroxyethyl)-2-amino-5-nitrophenol[a]
Disperse Blue No 1[a]
N-(2-Hydroxyethyl)-2-nitroaniline[a]
C1 Disperse Black #9
2-Nitro-4 -hydroxydiphenylamine[a]

[a] Products are components of formulations currently filed with Division of
Cosmetics Technology/FDA under voluntary cosmetic registration program
(21CFR7201).

While we have stressed the utility and toxicity of the aromatic diamines
in hair dyes, it should also be noted that a number of these (e.g., isomeric
toluene and phenylene diamines; nitro- and chlorophenylene diamines and
2,4-diaminoanisole) are widely used in the production of dyes, pharmaceuticals, photographic chemicals and antioxidants [68]. Hence a large spectrum
of individuals both in the production stage and/or use applications are at
potential risk due to exposure to these agents.

A variety of analytical procedures including GLC, TLC, gel permeation
chromatography, spectrophotometric and nuclear magnetic resonance methods
have been employed for the detection and determination of the aromatic
diamines [67].

Boufford [73] described the separation and determination of the five isomeric diamino toluenes (3,4- 2,3-, 2,4-, 2,5- and 2,6-) by direct GLC. A Micro Tek Model 2500-R flame-ionization gas chromatograph was used with a 80 cm x 5 mm o.d. stainless steel column packed with 5% Bentone 34 and 15% Hyprose SP80 (Dow Chemical, octabis[2-hydroxypropyl] sucrose] on KOH-treated Chromosorb W; the column and detection temperatures were 170° and 220°C, respectively. The order of elution was 2,3-, 3,4-, 2,5-, 2,6- and 2,4-diamino toluenes. The isomeric diaminotoluenes have been determined by GLC employing a thermal conductivity detector, with an accuracy of ± 0.3% for 2,4-diaminotoluene [74]. GLC of isomeric diamino toluenes including the 2,4- and 2,5-isomers as their N-trifluoroacetyl derivative has been used for quality control in their production, with an accuracy of ± 0.45% [75].

TLC has been employed to separate primary aromatic amines including 2,4- and 2,5-diamino toluenes and phenylene diamines on silica gel followed by elution with methyl nitrite and absorbance measured at 855 nm, and on silica gel buffered with sodium acetate, using visualization with *para*-dimethylaminocinnamaldehyde [76].

The isomeric diamino toluenes, phenylene diamines and 4-nitro-1,2-phenylene diamines and 2,4-diaminoanisole have been separated on Polystyrene-based anion exchanges or on microcrystalline cellulose and Cellex D anion exchangers by Lepri et al. [77]. For example, AG1-X4(CH_3COO^-) and AG-1X4(ClO_4^-) polystyrene anoin exchangers were employed with eluents of: 0.1 M acetate buffer, 0.01 M acetic acid, and 1 M acetic acid. For a given compound, the R_f value of these aromatic amines increased as the pH of the eluent decreased. For isomers, The R_f sequence was the same as that of the pK_a values (e.g., the greater the pK_a, the higher is the R_f value) and hence it is possible to predict *a priori* the pH of the eluent at which the best separation of the isomers can be achieved [77].

REFERENCES

1. Clayson, D. B., and R. C. Garner. "Carcinogenic Aromatic Amines and Related Compounds," in: *Chemical Carcinogens*, C. E. Searle, Ed. (Washington, D.C.: American Chemical Society, 1973), pp. 366-461.

2. Arcos, J. C., and M. F. Argus. *Chemical Induction of Cancer*, *Vol. IIB*, (New York: Academic Press, 1974).

3. Arcos, J. C., and M. F. Argus "Molecular Geometry and Carcinogenic Activity of Aromatic Compounds, New Perspectives," *Adv. Cancer Res.* 11:305-471 (1968).

4. Miller, J. A., and E. C. Miller. "Chemical Carcinogenesis: Mechanisms and Approaches to Its Control," *J. Nat. Cancer Inst.* 47:V-XIV (1971).
5. Arcos, J. C. "Criteria for Selecting Chemical Compounds for Carcinogenic Testing: An Essay," *J. Environ. Pathol. Toxicol.* 1:433-458 (1978).
6. Miller, J. A., and E. C. Miller. "The Metabolic Activation of Carcinogenic Amines and Amides," *Prog. Exp. Tumor Res.* 11:273 (1969).
7. Miller, E. C., and J. A. Miller. "The Metabolism of Chemical Carcinogens to Reactive Electrophiles and Their Possible Mechanism of Action in Carcinogenesis," in: *Chemical Carcinogens*, C. E. Searle, Ed. ACS Monograph No. 173, (Washington, D.C.: American Chemical Society, 1976), pp. 737-762.
8. Miller, E. C., and J. A. Miller. "Mechanism of Chemical Carcinogenesis: Nature of Proximate Carcinogens and Interactions with Macromolecules," *Pharmacol. Res.* 18:805-838 (1966).
9. Kadlubar, F. F., J. A. Miller and E. C. Miller. "Hepatic Microsomal N-glucuronipation and Nucleic Acid Binding of N-hydroxylarylamines in Relation to Urinary Bladder Carcinogenesis," *Cancer Res.* 37:805-814 (1977).
10. Baetcke, K. "Aromatic Amines Program: Mechanistic Approaches to Carcinogenesis," National Center for Toxicological Research, Nov. 6 (1976).
11. Parkes, H. G. "The Epidemiology of the Aromatic Amine Cancers," in *Chemical Carcinogens*, C. E. Searle, Ed. (Washington, DC: American Chemical Society, 1976), pp. 462-480.
12. Case, R. A. M., M. E. Hosker, D. B. McDonald and J. T. Pearson. "Tumors of Urinary Bladder in Workmen Engaged in Manufacture and Use of Certain Dyestuffs Intermediates in British Chemical Industry," *Brit. J. Ind. Med.* 11:75 (1954).
13. Boyland, E. *The Biochemistry of Bladder Cancer* (Springfield, IL: Charles C. Thomas, Publisher (1963).
14. Scott, T. C. *Carcinogenic and Chronic Toxic Hazards of Aromatic Amines* (Amsterdam: Elsevier Publishing Co., 1962), p. 58.
15. U.S. Dept. of Labor. "Occupational Safety and Health Standards, Part 1910, Carcinogens," *Federal Register* 39(20):3756-3794 (1974).
16. Orjelick, R. "Research Finds Aromatic Amines Exposure Cause of Increased Number of Tumors," *Int. J. Occup. Health Safety* 44:46-47 (1975).
17. U.S. Tariff Commission. "Synthetic Organic Chemicals, U.S. Production and Sales, 1962," Government Printing Office (1963).
18. U.S. Tariff Commission. "Synthetic Organic Chemicals, 1948," *Report on Synthetic Organic Dyes*, Series 6-2, Washington, D.C.
19. U.S. Tariff Commission. "United States Production and Sales, 1971, Synthetic Organic Chemicals," Washington, D.C. (1973).

20. Shriner, C. R., J. S. Drury, A. S. Hammons, L. E. Towill, E. B. Lewis and D. M. Opresko. "Reviews on the Environmental Effects of Pollutants: II Benzidine," ORNL/EIS-86; EPA-600/1-78-024 (1978).

21. "NIOSH/NCI Joint Current Intelligence Bulletin No. 24: Direct Black 38, Direct 6, and Direct Brown 95 Benzidine-Derived Dyes," DHEW (NIOSH) No. 78-148; U.S. Dept. HEW; Washington, D.C., April 18 (1978).

22. Takemura, N., T. Akiyama and C. Nakajima. "A Survey of the Pollution of the Sumida River, Especially on the Aromatic Amines in the Water, *Int. J. Air Water Pollut.* 9:665-670 (1965).

23. NIOSH. "Current Intelligence Bulletin; Metabolic Precursors of a Known Human Carcinogen, beta-Naphthylamine," U.S. Dept. HEW, Rockville, MD (1976) pp. 1-3.

24. IARC. *Monographs on the Evaluation of Carcinogenic Risk of Chemicals to Man, Vol. 16* (Lyon: International Agency for Research on Cancer, 1978).

25. Masuda, Y., K. Mori and M. Kuratsune. "Studies on Bladder Carcinogens in the Human Environment. I. Naphthylamines," *Int. J. Cancer* 2:489-493 (1967).

26. Battye, R. "Bladder Carcinogens Occurring During the Production of "Town" Gas by Coal Carbonization," *Trans. 15th Int. Congr. Ind. Health* 3:156 (1966).

27. Hoffmann, D., Y. Masuda and E. L. Wynder. "1-Naphthylamine and 2-Naphthylamine in Cigarette Smoke," *Nature* 221:254 (1969).

28. Hammond, E. C., and D. J. Horn. "Smoking and Death Rates–Report of 44 Months of Follow-up of 187,783 Men," *J. Am. Med. Assoc.* 166:1159, 1294 (1958).

29. Karasek, F. W. "Detection Limits in Instrumental Analysis," *Res. Develop.* 26:20-24 (1975).

30. Yllo, M. S. "Analytical Techniques for Ecological and Toxicological Monitoring," *Analytical Chemistry of Synthetic Dyes*, K. Venkataraman, Ed. (New York: John Wiley & Sons, Inc., 1977), pp. 571-580.

31. Baker, R. K., and J. G. Deighton. "Metabolism of Benzidine in the Rat," *Cancer Res.* 13:529-531 (1953).

32. Sciarini, L. J., and J. W. Meigs. "The Biotransformation of Benzidine," *Arch. Ind. Health* 18:521-530 (1958).

33. Elson, L. A., F. Goulden and F. L. Warren. "The Metabolism of Aromatic Amines in Relation to Carcinogenesis," *Brit. J. Cancer* 12:108-115 (1958).

34. El-Dib, M. A. "Colorimetric Determination of Aniline Derivatives in Natural Waters," *J. Assoc. Offic. Anal. Chemists* 54:1383-1387 (1971).

35. Meigs, J. W., R. M. Brown and L. J. Sciarini. "A Study of Exposure to Benzidine and Substituted Benzidines in a Chemical Plant," *Arch. Ind. Hyg.* 4:540-553 (1951).

36. Butt, L. T., and N. Stafford. "Papilloma of the Bladder in the Chemical Industry—Analytical Methods for Determination of Benzidine," *J. Appl. Chem.* 6:525-539 (1956).
37. Sciarini, L. J., and J. A. Mahew. "Rapid Technique for Estimating Benzidines in Industrial Exposure," *Arch. Ind. Health* 11:420-421 (1955).
38. Glassman, J., and J. W. Meigs. "Benzidine (4,4'-diaminobiphenyl) and Substituted Benzidines, a Microchemical Screening Technique for Estimating Levels of Industrial Exposure from Urine and Air Samples," *Arch. Ind. Hyg. Occup. Med.* 4:519 (1951).
39. Dangwal, S. K., V. T. Kadam and B. M. Jethani. "Modified Method for Determination of Urinary Benzidine," *Am. Ind. Hyg. Assoc. J.* 39:1019-1022 (1978).
40. "Method for Benzidine and Its Salts in Waste Water," Methods Development and Quality Assurance Research Laboratory, National Environmental Research Center, U.S. Environmental Protection Agency, Cincinnati, Ohio (1975).
41. Jenkins, R. L., and R. B. Baird. "The Determination of Benzidine in Wastewaters," *Bull. Env. Contam. Toxicol.* 13:436-442 (1975).
42. Jenkins, R. L., J. E. Haskins, L. G. Carmona and R. B. Baird. "Chlorination of Benzidine and Other Aromatic Amines in Aqueous Environments," *Arch. Environ. Contam. Toxicol.* 7:301-315 (1978).
43. Bowman, M. C., J. R. King and L. C. Holder. "Benzidine and Congeners: Analytical Chemical Properties and Trace Analysis in Five Substrates," *Int. J. Environ. Anal. Chem.* 4:205-233 (1976).
44. Bowman, M. C., and J. R. King. "Analysis of 2-acetylaminofluorene: Residues in Laboratory Chow and Microbiological Media," *Biochem. Med.* 9:390-401 (1974).
45. Holder, C. L., J. R. King and M. C. Bowman. "4-Aminobiphenyl, 2-Naphthylamine and Analogs: Analytical Properties and Trace Analysis in Five Substrates," *J. Toxicol. Env. Health,* 2:111-129 (1976).
46. Nony, C. R., E. J. Treglown and M. C. Bowman. "Removal of Trace Levels of 2-acetylaminofluorene (2-AAF) from Wastewater," *Sci. Total Environ.* 4:155-163 (1975).
47. Bowman, M. C., and L. G. Rushing. "Trace Analysis of 3,3'-dichloro-benzidine in Animal Chow, Waste Water and Human Urine by Three Gas Chromatographic Procedures," *Arch. Environ. Contam. Toxicol.* 6:471-482 (1977).
48. Bowman, M. C. "Trace Analysis: A Requirement for Toxicological Research with Carcinogens and Hazardous Substances," *J. Assoc. Offic. Anal. Chem.* 61-1253-1262 (1977).
49. Nony, C. R., and M. C. Bowman. "Carcinogens and Analogs: Trace Analysis of Thirteen Compounds in Admixture in Waste Water and Human Urine, *Int. J. Environ. Anal. Chem.* (in press)

50. Mancy, K. H. "Elements of Instrumental Analysis," in *Instrumental Analysis for Water Pollution Control,* K. H. Mancy, Ed. (Ann Arbor, Michigan: Ann Arbor Science Publishers, Inc., 1971) p. 70.

51. Gutman, H. R. "Isolation and Identification of the Carcinogen N-hydroxy-2-fluorenylacetamide and Related Compounds by Liquid Chromatography," *Anal. Biochem.* 58:469-478 (1974).

52. Fullerton, F. R., and C. D. Jackson. "Determination of 2-Acetylaminofluorene and its Metabolites by High Pressure Liquid Chromatography," *Biochem. Med.* 16:95-103 (1976).

53. Thorgeirsson, S. S., and W. L. Nelson. "Separation and Quantitative Determination of 2-acetylaminofluorene and its Hydroxylated Metabolites by High Pressure Liquid Chromatography," *Anal. Biochem.* 75: 122-128 (1976).

54. Mefford, I., R. W. Keller, R. N. Adams, L. A. Sternson and M. S. Yllo. "Liquid Chromatographic Determination of Picomole Quantities of Aromatic Amine Carcinogens," *Anal. Chem.* 49:683 (1977).

55. Stanley, J. W., G. D. Newport, C. C. Weis and R. W. West. "An Analytical Approach to Metabolic Profiling of Aromatic Compounds Using Liquid Chromatography," *J. Liquid Chromatog.* 1:305-325 (1978).

56. Riggin, R. M., and C. C. Howard. "Determination of Benzidine, Dichlorobenzidine and Diphenylhydrazine in Aqueous Media by High Performance Liquid Chromatography," *Anal. Chem.* 51:210-214 (1979).

57. Banerjee, S., H. C. Sikka, R. Gray and C. M. Kelly. "Photodegradation of 3,3'-dichlorobenzidine," *Environ. Sci. Technol.* 12:1425-1427 (1978).

58. Masuda. Y., and D. Hoffman. "Quantitative Determination of 1-naphthylamine and 2-naphthylamine in Cigarette Smoke," *Anal. Chem.* 41:650-652 (1969).

59. Weeks, R. W., Jr., B. J. Dean and S. K. Yasuda. "Detection Limits of Chemical Spot Tests Toward Certain Carcinogens on Metal, Painted, and Concrete Surfaces," *Anal. Chem.* 48:2227-2233 (1976).

60. Weeks, R. W., Jr., B. J. Dean and S. K. Yasuda. "Tests Monitor Carcinogenic Aromatic Amines, Aid in Work Decontamination," *Occup. Health Safety* (March/April 1977), pp. 19-23.

61. Linch, A. L., G. B. O'Connor, J. R. Barnes, and A. S. Killian, Jr. "Methylene-bis-ortho-chloroaniline (MOCA): Evaluation of Hazards and Exposure Control," *J. Am. Ind. Hyg. Assoc.* 32:802-819 (1971).

62. Ryan, J. D. "Moca a Diamine Curing Agent for Isocyanate-containing Polymers," DuPont Chemicals for Elastomers, Trade Bulletin, Wilmington, DE (1971).

63. "Final Rules Set for Carcinogens," *Chem. Eng. News.* 52:12 (1974).

64. Rappaport, S. M., and R. Morals. "Air-sampling and Analytical Method for 4,4'-methylenebis(2-chloroaniline)," *Anal. Chem.* 51:19-23 (1979).

65. Yasuda, S. K. "Determination of 3,3'-dichloro-4,4'-diamino-diphenylmethane in Air," *J. Chromatog.* 104:283-290 (1975).

66. Chey, W. M., R. N. Adams and M. S. Yllo. "Anodic Differential Pulse Voltammetry of Aromatic Amines and Phenols at Trace Levels," *J. Electroanal. Chem.* 75:731-738 (1977).

67. *Monographs on the Evaluation of the Carcinogenic Risk of Chemicals to Man, Vol. 16, Some Aromatic Amines and Related Nitro Compounds—Hair Dyes, Colouring Agents and Miscellaneous Industrial Chemicals* (Lyon: International Agency for Research on Cancer, 1978).

68. Marzulli, F. N., S. Green and H. I. Maibach. "Hair Dye Toxicity—A Review," *J. Env. Pathol. Toxicol.* 1:509-530 (1978).

69 Ames, B. N., H. O. Kammen and E. Yamasaki. "Hair Dyes Are Mutagenic: Identification of a Variety of Mutagenic Ingredients," *Proc. Nat. Acad. Sci.* 72:2423-2427 (1975).

70. Blijleven, W. G. H. "Mutagenicity of Four Hair Dyes in *Drosophila melanogaster*," *Mutation Res.* 48:181-186 (1977).

71 Palmer, K. A., A. Denunzio and S. Green. "The Mutagenic Assay of Some Hair Dye Components Using Thymidine Kinase Locus L5178Y Mouse Lymphoma Cells," *J. Environ. Pathol. Toxicol.* 1:87-91 (1977).

72. Wernick, T., B. M. Lanman and J. L. Fraux. "Chronic Toxicity, Teratologic and Reproductive Studies with Hair Dyes," *Toxicol. Appl. Pharmacol.* (in press).

73. Boufford, C. E. "Determination of Isomeric Diamino Toluenes by Direct Gas Chromatography," *J. Gas Chromatog.* 6:438-440 (1968).

74. Willeboordse, F., Q. Quick and E. T. Bishop. "Direct Gas Chromatographic Analysis of Isomeric Diaminotoluenes," *Anal. Chem.* 40:1455-1458 (1968).

75. Brydia, L. E., and F. Willeboordse. "Gas Chromatographic Analysis of Isomeric Diaminotoluenes," *Anal. Chem.* 40:110-113. (1968)

76. Bassl, A., H. J. Heckemann and E. Baumann. "Thin-layer Chromatography of Primary Aromatic Amines," *J. Prakt. Chem.* 36:265-273 (1967).

77. Cepri, L., P. G. Desideri and V. Coas. "Chromatographic and Electrophoretic Behavior of Primary Aromatic Amines on Anion-Exchanges Thin-layers," *J. Chromatog.* 90:331-339 (1974).

CHAPTER 13

USE OF HUMAN BIOLOGICAL MONITORING FOR RISK ASSESSMENT OF MUTAGENESIS AND CARCINOGENIC EFFECT

D. Jack Kilian

University of Texas Health Science Center
School of Public Health
Houston, Texas

Department of Preventive Medicine
and Community Health
University of Texas Medical Branch
Galveston, Texas

INTRODUCTION

Almost daily, new compounds are identified as mutagenic in bacterial, *Drosophila* and mammalian, or various in vitro test systems. These test systems cannot quantitatively define the risk of mutation in the exposed human population, but they can provide valuable clues and help us prioritize which compounds should undergo further testing and evaluation of human exposure.

There are compelling reasons to develop capabilities for the assessment of genetic effects from environmental or work-related situations. In her excellent review paper on chemical agents that damage human chromosomes, Shaw [1] states, "Man's most precious possession is his genetic heritage. If, in the short time we are allowed to store the genes for future generations, we carelessly squander our resources and poison our germ plasm with devastating mutations, then our heirs will be the losers." Methodology and validation of several genetic monitoring tests has progressed to a point where meaningful interpretations can be made to identify conditions that may pose a threat to the human genetic system. Germinal or reproductive genetic effects would most likely manifest themselves as fetal wastage or spontaneous abortions, but the possibility of surviving heritable problems exists. Somatic mutation may result in increased cancer risk. Knudson [2] points out that carcinogenesis in man may involve the interaction of genetic and environmental forces and that mutations, whether germinal or somatic, seem to be involved in the origin of many, or perhaps, all cancers. Bridbord et al. [3] state that nearly 90% of chemicals established to be carcinogens by animal or human data give positive test results in one or more of the in vitro mutagenic test systems.

At this time, one cannot scientifically predict which industrial chemicals or drugs will be human carcinogens on the basis of mutagenic test systems. However, the close correlation between mutagenesis and carcinogenesis requires careful consideration of the data generated in these areas as a valuable resource in safety evaluation. Extrapolation of results from bacterial test systems to the human species is a giant step which most scientists are unwilling to take, but human genetic monitoring of exposed populations can provide essential information to confirm or deny evidence of an effect on the human genetic system. The enlightened occupational physician will recognize the need to provide definitive answers regarding genetic effect in humans exposed to compounds judged to be positive in the in vitro mutagenic test systems.

Practical methods will be presented in this chapter that can be utilized to help define the genetic risk of environmental factors such as radiation, drugs or chemicals. Many experts [4] estimate that at least 25% of our health burden is of genetic origin which will ultimately increase to an even larger proportion as we control infectious and degenerative disease. Table I outlines some of the problems in human genetics.

Table I. Problems in Human Genetics

15 Million Americans today have birth defects of varying severity.
12 Million of this group or 80% carry true genetic diseases.
40% of all infant mortality results from genetic factors.
33% of all admissions to hospital pediatric wards are for genetic reasons.
3% of all married couples will have a genetically defective child.
30% of all human conceptions end as spontaneous abortions.

Useful human genetic monitoring tests that have been validated and incorporated into the medical literature are presented in Table II. There are several other test systems, such as the sister chromatid exchange and HGPRT somatic mutation test, that show great promise. Time and experience will probably establish their usefulness along with those reported in this chapter.

Table II. Human Genetic Monitoring Test Data

Test	Approx. Cost per Person	Persistence of Mutagenic Effect Detected
1. Cytogenetics	$200	Up to 20 yr (radiation)
2. Body Fluid Analysis	$50-300	2 hr to a wk
3. YF Body	$50	7-10 wk
4. Epidemiology	$100	?

CYTOGENETICS

Cytogenetic monitoring becomes a reliable and objective method of evaluating change in the human genetic material when there is a sizeable population under competent medical surveillance, when the workforce is relatively stable and healthy, and when there is known exposure to diverse chemical compounds [5]. Cytogenic or chromosome analysis of number or structural rearrangement of the genetic material in peripheral lymphocytes is a well-established system that yields precise and objective data that are useful in statistical evaluation. A collaborative study [6] by six expert laboratories to measure interlaboratory variation of cytogenetic results revealed far better correlations than conventional toxicological techniques such as chemically induced animal eye and skin irritation.
To perform the cytogenetic test, a few drops of whole blood are seeded into a tissue culture system to encourage mitosis and replication of the lymphocytes from peripheral blood. The chromosomes are arrested in metaphase after 48-72 hours of culture, after which the cells are harvested, placed on a microscope slide, and stained after some special procedures to encourage spreading of the chromosomes. Details of the techniques are outlined in a publication by Kilian and Picciano [7]. Scoring is done by trained observers using microscopes with excellent optics. Cytogenetic aberrations in 100-200 cells are usually scored on each case, the data summarized and then compared to a suitable control population. Table III, taken from a paper by Picciano et al. [8], indicates how such data are gathered and utilized.

Table III. Vinyl Chloride Exposure Studies

Cytogenetic Study of 209 Workers Exposed to Vinyl Chloride

No. of Cultures	209	295
No. of Cells	10,483	14,761
Chromatid Breaks	2.4%	3.6%
Chromosome Breaks	1.0%	1.1%
Rings, Dicentrics and Exchanges	0.4%	0.2%
Abnormal Cells	3.7%	4.5%

Distribution of Chromatid Aberrations Related to Vinyl Chloride (VC) Exposure

	No. in Group	% of Group with 0-5% Aberrations	% of Group with >5% Aberrations
Exposure to VC[a]	209		
<1 ppm	70	90	10
1-5 ppm	98	77	23
>5 ppm	41	80	20
Controls	295	75	25
		χ^2(3) = 7.75 (P $\cong$ 0.06)	

[a]Exposure levels are estimates based on calculations for specific job classifications; prior exposure for individuals may have been higher or lower; exposure levels for individuals are known to vary within job classifications.

Distribution of Chromosome Aberrations Related to Vinyl Chloride (VC) Exposure

	No. in Group	% of Group with 0-5% Aberrations	% of Group with >5% Aberrations
Exposure to VC	209		
<1 ppm	70	96	4
1-5 ppm	98	94	6
>5 ppm	41	95	5
Controls	295	94	6
		χ^2(3) = 0.355 (P $\cong$ 0.95)	

Distribution of Abnormal Cells Related to Vinyl Chloride (VC) Exposure

	No. in Group	% of Group with 0-5% Aberrations	% of Group with >5% Aberrations
Exposure to VC	209		
<1 ppm	70	84	16
1-5 ppm	98	71	29
>5 ppm	41	73	27
Controls	295	70	30
		χ^2(3) = 5.97 (P $\cong$ 0.12)	

At this point in time, cytogenetic analysis is the best tool available for the detection of genetic injury at a stage when corrective action can be taken for the benefit of the individuals involved. Since various environmental forces such as radiation, viral infection, drugs and chemicals can cause increased cytogenetic aberration rates, it is essential that such studies be planned with sound epidemiological principles to minimize variables that may affect the result.

BODY FLUID ANALYSIS

Legator et al. [9] demonstrated the practicality of utilizing the *Salmonella* bacterial test systems to detect the presence of mutagenic substances in blood and urine. Figure 1 from this study reveals the substantial increase in bacterial mutagenic activity in urine of six patients treated with the commonly prescribed drug, metronidazole. It must be

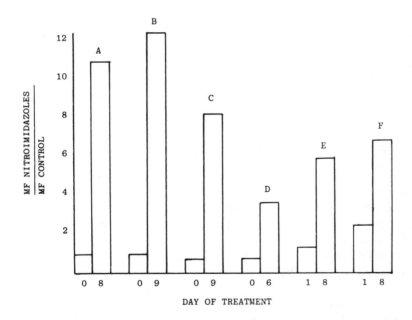

Figure 1. Mutagenic activity detected with *S. typhimurium* (TA 1535) in urine samples of six patients treated with metronidazole. Patients received 750 mg/day, and the urine was collected 1 hr after the morning dose on the day indicated. Each letter represents a separate patient, and "O" indicates a control sample taken 1 day prior to therapy. Urine samples were concentrated fivefold by lyophilization, and 0.1 ml of concentrated urine was added per plate.

understood, however, that a positive in this system indicates mutagenic activity of the bacteria and does not necessarily indicate damage to genetic material within the person from which the sample was obtained. It serves as a valuable tool, however, to quantitate how much drug or chemical is needed to exceed the normal metabolic pathways to detoxify most of these compounds. In some instances, it is the metabolite which is activated into a mutagen; in this case, a positive result gives us valuable clues as to how that individual metabolizes a particular compound. This is something that no laboratory animal or in vitro test system can do.

Kilian et al. [10] demonstrated the practicality of this system in the industrial setting by measuring the mutagenic activity in the urine of workmen exposed to various levels of epichlorohydrin. In this study there was no evidence of mutagenic activity in the urine to levels of exposure below 4 ppm TWA. This information was accepted by NIOSH and placed in the criteria document for epichlorohydrin.

One great advantage of this test system is that it is inexpensive and fairly rapid to run. Although definitive answers regarding genetic damage to the host are not there, it can serve as a valuable tool to quantitate a mutagenic threshold of a variety of environmental situations. Thus, it becomes valuable as another piece of evidence to improve our decision-making in this difficult but most important area of genetic effect. No one test system has a definitive answer, and only through gathering information from a variety of procedures can one arrive at a logical and accurate appraisal of effect.

FLUORESCENT Y BODY IN HUMAN SPERM CELLS

All of the normal somatic cells in the body carry 46 chromosomes, two of which are the sex-determining chromosomes. The normal male has an XY sex chromosome complement, and a normal female has an XX complement. One extremely important new mutagenic test system that allows us to look directly at the human germ cells has been reported by Kapp [11] and Kapp et al. [12,13]. Normal human sperm carries either one male-determining (Y) chromosome or one female-determining (X) chromosome. It has been known for a number of years that the Y chromosome stains much brighter with quinacrine mustard stain when viewed through a microscope under ultraviolet fluorescing conditions. Some sperm cells, however, carry two Y chromosomes, which is abnormal; they have the ability to fertilize the ovum in human reproduction, as we know that approximately 1 out of every 1250 live births results in an abnormal XYY offspring. This is a significant problem within the human race, and, now, for the first time, we have the tools to evaluate environmental conditions that increase the number of extra Y chromosomes in sperm cells. The articles by Kapp and Kapp et al. fully describe the techniques and the effects from exposure to chemicals, drugs and radiation, all of which have produced an increase in the double Y chromosome complement. An "ideal" mutagenic test system is one where human germinal material is easily obtained and can be processed rapidly at a modest cost, and where the "positive" result is known to produce an abnormal heritable effect. From the data gathered by Kapp and Kapp et al. thus far, this test system would appear to satisfy these criteria.

EPIDEMIOLOGY

It would seem that the most important and meaningful mutagenic test system would be epidemiology, as it reveals final results in the human species. Such a study could best be labeled reproductive epidemiology. At this point in time, there have been very few efforts in this area. Infante et al. [14] studied a group of vinyl chloride workmen and concluded that there was a genetic effect, but this study has been challenged repeatedly. A study of anesthesiologists and operating room personnel revealed evidence of fetal wastage and increased birth defects [15], but this was later refuted by another study [16]. We are at a stage of development in reproductive epidemiology where our tools are being sharpened and our shortcomings recognized. There are many conflicting factors to be considered in such studies, as people have multiple environmental exposures plus the ever-present background of recessive genetic diseases that complicate such studies. However, the future will bring greater understanding of accurate methodology with the resulting benefit to our society.

RELATIONSHIP OF HUMAN GENETIC MONITORING
TO HUMAN CARCINOGENESIS

Studies on the relationship of animal carcinogens to positive mutagenic test systems show a remarkably high relationship [17]; different investigators place it at 50-90%. A review of our most reliable human genetic test system at this time—cytogenetics—also reveals an excellent correlation with human carcinogenesis and provides us with a valuable tool for carcinogenic risk assessment from exposure to various environmental situations, such as radiation, viruses or chemicals.

More than 60 years ago Boveri advanced the hypothesis that malignancy was caused by chromosomal imbalance but that better techniques would be necessary for study [18]. The advances in the preparation of chromosome spreads, the banding of chromosomes, and the sister chromatid exchange procedure have, in part, verified the prophetic words of Boveri; the next few years will see exciting developments in correlating these systems with human cancer epidemiology studies.

At the present time, we know that a number of diseases such as ataxia telangiectasia, Fanconi's anemia, and Bloom's syndrome have two things in common—high risk of cancer and excess chromosomal breaks. Individuals with an extra chromosome in all their cells—such as Mongolism (47 chromosomes instead of 46)—have an extremely high risk of leukemia. The risk of breast cancer in Klinefelter's syndrome (extra X sex chromosome) is about 66 times the risk in normal men. There are many other examples of malignant conditions associated with loss or too much chromosome material in the basic cell constituents [9]. Miller, [20] from the National Cancer Institute states, "Thus, from rare conditions, we appear to be developing a generalization concerning leukemogenesis, namely, that the myelocytic form of the neoplasm is caused or accompanied by cytogenetic abnormality." It is interesting to note that high levels of exposure to benzene in humans have led to the myelocytic type of leukemia and that increased incidence of chromosome aberrations under similar conditions has amply been demonstrated by others [21-25].

A review of the medical literature (Table IV) reveals a significant correlation between increased cancer risk to various environmental conditions as defined by human epidemiology studies and human chromosome studies. More details and references to these studies will be included in the forthcoming book *Prevention of Occupational Cancer* edited by Dr. Charles Shaw and published by the Chemical Rubber Company.

It is a universal goal to develop early warning systems that signify increased cancer risk. Table V illustrates techniques available to us at this time. Epidemiology and medical surveillance for the early detection of the disease represent our main efforts; but, unfortunately, a "positive" means cancer is already present. Risk assessment may involve animal toxicology, cell transformation studies, mutagenic test systems or structure analogy. All of these have problems of extrapolation to the human species. In 1734 Alexander Pope stated, "The proper study of mankind is man." Cytogenetics with its newer expanded techniques shows great promise in helping to identify human carcinogens through the utilization of this practical clinical test system in man himself.

Cohen and Bloom [26], both physicians and human geneticists, state "It is safe to point out at this stage of our information-gathering that groups of individuals that have been exposed to chromosomolytic agents, or that have an increased incidence of breaks on a congenital basis, tend to have more neoplastic disease than those not so exposed. Thus, the relationship between induced chromosomal aberrations in

Table IV. Carcinogenic-Cytogenetic Relationships

	Increased Cancer Incidence from Human Epidemiology Studies	Increased Chromosomal Aberration Rates from Human Cytogenetic Studies
Therapeutic Radiation for Ankylosing Spondylitis	+ Leukemia	+ (Dose Related)
A-Bomb Survivors	+ Thyroid + Leukemia	+ (Dose Related)
Thorotrast Administration	+ Liver	+ (Dose Related)
Radium Dial Painters	+ Osteogenic Sarcoma	+ (Dose Related)
Uranium Miners	+ Lung	+ (Dose Related)
Plutonium Workers		+ (Dose Related)
Benzene	+ Leukemia	+ (Dose Related)
Vinyl Chloride	+ Angiosarcoma	+ (Dose Related)
Epichlorohydrin	(?) + Lung	+ (Dose Related)
Methotrexate RX for Psoriasis	+ Leukemia	+
Cytoxan for Rheumatoid Arthritis	+ Leukemia	+
Chloramphenicol	+ Leukemia	+

Table V. Warning Systems for Neoplasia

Human Clinical Monitoring

Epidemiology
Medial Surveillance
Cytology Studies   } Neoplasia Already Present
Cea and Alpha-Fetoprotein
Cytogenetics

Risk Assessment

Animal Toxicology
Mutagenic Test Systems
Cell Transformation Systems
Structure Analogy

somatic cells and the increased incidence of tumors in persons with such aberrations . . . is becoming well established." D. G. Harnden [27] from the Department of Cancer Studies, University of Birmingham in England, further points out, "It would seem wise, by analogy with ionizing radiation, to assume that increasing (chromosome) damage at higher dose levels (of chemicals) indicates higher risk (of malignancy). Cytogenetic studies may therefore play an important part in screening for environmental carcinogens, and may be useful in recognizing especially susceptible individuals."

Chromosome studies of chemically exposed workmen are common in Europe but rare in the United States. Occupational physicians, management and union officials in this country need to be aware that this valuable resource for the protection of our workmen is not being implemented in a reasonable manner.

ACKNOWLEDGMENTS

Grateful acknowledgment is hereby accorded to my secretary, Janice McKee, whose great motivation for organization and precision has been an invaluable aid to this somewhat disorganized physician.

REFERENCES

1. Shaw, M. W. "Human Chromosome Damage by Chemical Agents," *Am. Rev. Med.* 21:409-432 (1970).
2. Knudson, A. G., Jr. "Environmental Carcinogens and Genetic Variability in Man," in *Human Genetics,* S. Armendares and R. Lisker, Eds. (Amsterdam: Excerpta Medica, 1977), pp. 404-408.
3. Bridbord, K., Wagoner, J. K. and H. P. Bleier. "Chemical Carcinogens," in *Occupational Diseases: A Guide to Their Recognition,* M. M. Key et al., Eds. (Washington, DC: U.S. Dept. of Health, Education, and Welfare, 1977), pp. 443-450.
4. Merz, T. "Radiation, Clastogenic Agents, and Health," in *Genetic Issues in Public Health and Medicine,* B. H. Cohen et al., Eds. (Springfield, IL: Charles C. Thomas, Publisher, 1978), pp. 60-82.
5. Kilian, D. J., D. J. Picciano and C. B. Jacobson. "Industrial Monitoring: A Cytogenetic Approach," *Ann. N.Y. Acad. Sci.* 269:4-11 (1975).
6. Kilian, D. J., F. Moreland, M. Genge, M. S. Legator and E. B. Whorton, Jr. "A Collaborative Cytogenetics Study to Measure and Minimize Interlaboratory Variation," *Mut. Res.* 44:97-104 (1977).
7. Kilian, D. J., and D. J. Picciano. "Cytogenetic Surveillance of Industrial Population," in *Chemical Mutagens,* Alexander Hollaender, Ed. (New York: Plenum Publication Corp., 1976), pp. 321-339.

8. Picciano, D. J., R. E. Flake, P. C. Gay and D. J. Kilian. "Vinyl Chloride Cytogenetics," *J. Occup. Med.* 19(8):527-530 (1977).
9. Legator, M. S., T. Connor and M. Stoeckel. "The Detection of Mutagenic Substances in the Urine and Blood of Man," *Ann N.Y. Acad. Sci.* 269:16-20 (1975).
10. Kilian, D. J. "Criteria for a Recommended Standard for Occupational Exposure to Epichlorohydrin," HEW Publication No. (NIOSH) 76-206 (1976), pp. 79-80.
11. Kapp, R. W., Jr. "Detection of Aneuploidy in Human Sperm," *Environ. Health Persp.* (in press).
12. Kapp, R. W., Jr., M. C. Benge, D. J. Picciano, D. J. Kilian, M. S. Legator and C. B. Jacobson. "Monitoring Y Chromosomal Nondisjunction in Humans with the YFF Sperm Test," *J. Toxicol. Environ. Health Supp.* (in press).
13. Kapp, R. W., Jr., D. J. Picciano and C. B. Jacobson. "Y-Chromosomal Nondisjunction in Dibromochloroporpane Exposed Workmen," *Mut. Res.* 64(1):47-51 (1979).
14. Infante, P. F., J. K. Wagoner, A. J. McMichael, R. J. Waxweiler and H. Falk. "Genetic Risks of Vinyl Chloride," *Lancet* 1:734-735 (1970).
15. Ad Hoc Committee on the Effect of Trace Anesthetics on the Health of Operating Room Personnel. "Occupational Disease Among Operating Room Personnel," *Anesthesiology* 41(4):321-340 (1974).
16. Walts, L. F., A. B. Forsythe and G. Moore. "Critique: Occupational Disease Among Operating Room Personnel," *Anesthesiology* 42(5):608-611 (1975).
17. Purchase, I. F. H., E. Longstaff, J. Ashby, J. A. Styles, G. Anderson, P. A. Lefevre and F. R. Westwood. "Evaluation of Six Short-Term Tests for Detecting Organic Carcinogens and Recommendations for Their Use," *Nature* 264:624-627 (1976).
18. Boveri, T. *Zur Frage der Entsehung maligner Tumoren* (Jena: Gustav Fischer, 1914).
19. Mulvihill, J. J. "Congenital and Genetic Diseases," in *Persons at High Risk of Cancer,* J. F. Fraumeni, Jr., Ed. (New York: Academic Press, Inc., 1975), pp. 3-35.
20. Miller, R. W. "Overview: Host Factors," in *Persons at High Risk of Cancer,* J. F. Fraumeni, Jr., Ed. (New York: Academic Press, Inc., 1975), pp. 121-127.
21. Forni, A., and L. Moreo. "Cytogenetic Studies in a Case of Benzene Leukaemia," *Eur. J. Cancer* 3:251-55 (1967).
22. Forni, A., and L. Moreo. "Chromosome Studies in a Case of Benzene-Induced Erythroleukaemia," *Eur. J. Cancer* 5:459-63 (1969).
23. Pollini, G., and R. Colombi. "Medullary Chromosome Damage in Aplastic Anemia Caused by Benzol," *Med. Lavoro* 55:241-55 (1964).
24. Forni, A. M., A. Cappellini, E. Pacifico and E. C. Vigliani. "Chromosome Changes and Their Evolution in Subjects with Past Exposure to Benzene," *Arch. Environ. Health* 23:385-91 (1971).

25. Tough, I. M., P. G. Smith, W. M. Court-Brown and D. G. Harnden. "Chromosome Studies on Workers Exposed to Atmospheric Benzene, The Impossible Influence of Age," *Eur. J. Cancer* 6:49-55 (1970).

26. Cohen, M. M., and A. D. Bloom. "Monitoring for Chromosomal Abnormality in Man," in *Monitoring, Birth Defects and Environment*, E. B. Hook et al., Eds. (New York: Academic Press, Inc., 1971), pp. 249-272.

27. Harnden, D. G. "Cytogenetics of Human Neoplasia," in *Genetics of Human Cancer*, J. J. Mulvihill et al., Eds. (New York: Raven Press, 1977), pp. 87-104.

CHAPTER 14

IMMUNOLOGIC ASSESSMENT OF PATIENTS
WITH PULMONARY METAPLASIA
AND NEOPLASIA

Robert Lester Gross, David Marshall Smith and
Robert Glenn Thomas
    Mammalian Biology Group
    University of California
    Los Alamos Scientific Laboratory
    Los Alamos, New Mexico

Geno Saccomanno and Richard Saunders
    Department of Pathology
    St. Mary's Hospital
    Grand Junction, Colorado

INTRODUCTION

A vast and often conflicting literature has appeared in recent years concerned with the interactions between host immune systems and developing or established neoplasms. Much of this work in tumor immunology resulted from the theory of immunosurveillance which originally proposed that host immunocompetent cells are capable of recognizing and reacting to neoantigens expressed by developing neoplastic cells, with the resultant elimination of the malignant cells [1]. Although in the light of recent advances in the understanding of basic immunologic processes the theory per se appears oversimplistic [2], it is clear that host immunologic reactivity against tumors can and does occur. Despite this capability, tumor-specific immune responses and general immunocompetence are usually depressed when neoplasms are clinically evident and become progressively more abnormal as the neoplasm increases in size.

Much research today is directed toward determining when and why immunologic capacity is lost in cancer patients and how it might be restored. Underground uranium miners represent one human population of particular interest in this regard. In this population group exposure to radon, the environmental carcinogen associated with uranium mining, and cigarette smoking results in a synergistic or co-carcinogenic effect leading to a markedly increased incidence of lung cancer. This population has also been extensively studied by Saccomanno and colleagues [3,4] who have utilized sputum cytologic examination to describe the progressive changes in the respiratory tract that occur during the development of lung cancer. Following exposure to inhaled carcinogens, the bronchial epithelium undergoes a series of gradual changes from squamous metaplasia to progressively more atypical metaplasias charcterized as mild, moderate and marked, leading to noninvasive carcinoma in situ and finally invasive, clinical lung cancer. Similar delayed progressive development of cells in the bronchial tree has been demonstrated by Schreiber in hamsters [5] and by Hayata in the dog [6] after carcinogen exposure. Of particular interest and importance in the study of uranium miners was the finding that individuals may exfoliate markedly atypical metaplastic cells or cells representing carcinoma in situ for long periods of time (4-5 years) before progression to invasive carcinoma occurs, making early detection a real possibility. Such a well-defined population of individuals with identifiable premalignant cytologic changes also provides the long sought after opportunity to study the timing, type and extent of immunologic changes that occur in the early stages or premalignant stages of lung cancer development.

Our specific interest in the immunologic evaluation of lung cancer dates back to an earlier study [7]. In this study it was found that circulating thymus-dependent lymphocytes (T cells) as measured by spontaneous rosette formation with sheep red blood cells (SRBC) [8] were significantly depressed in a group of patients with localized stage I lung cancer. Of further interest was the observation that a newer test involving the inhibition of rosette formation by antilymphocyte globulin [9] was profoundly depressed and represented a much more sensitive measure of immune status than T cell levels alone. These results suggested that with the appropriate test one might detect immunologic changes prior to the development of clinically detectable cancer. Other investigators have studied immune function in patients with different clinical stages of lung cancer with a variety of different immunologic techniques [10-14]. Although most report detection of abnormalities in a high proportion of lung cancer patients, the results do not provide information about early lung cancer, or give any indication of which test is most appropriate for the clinical evaluation of cancer patients. The available literature on lung cancer has recently been reviewed [15].

The present study attempts to answer many of these questions. We have performed a battery of immunologic tests on uranium miners in whom various stages of preneoplastic and neoplastic changes have been identified by sputum cytologic exam as well as performing an immuno-profile on patients with known lung cancer. We have attempted to answer several important questions including: can changes in immunologic function be detected in individuals with preneoplastic lesions of the respiratory tract; and do these changes help identify those individuals most likely to progress and develop invasive lung cancer? Which immunologic test is most sensitive in detecting abnormalities in this high risk population group? Can one determine the relative contributions of the environmental carcin-ogens involved, i.e., radon exposure from uranium mining and tobacco smoking, to changes in immune function?

MATERIALS AND METHODS

Study Populations

The study populations comprised three general groups including healthy, age- and sex-matched controls; uranium miners; and patients with known lung cancers. The healthy controls were volunteers living in the same geographic area (western slope of Colorado) as the individuals in the other two groups, and with no history of uranium mining. The controls were further subdivided according to smoking history with nonsmokers; light smokers (defined as less than 10 pack-years cigarettes); moderate smokers (10-20 pack-years cigarettes); and heavy smokers (greater than 20-pack-years cigarettes).

The uranium miner group consisted of individuals with at least six months of underground uranium mining experience. This group was further subdivided on the basis of sputum cytologic findings (see below) into a control uranium miner group (UGU) with normal or mildly atypical cy-tology, and groups with moderate atypica, moderate-marked atypica, marked atypia, and carcinoma in situ. The moderate-marked group in-cluded miners with changes in sputum cytology from moderate to marked or vice versa on the most recent cytologic exam, and many represent those individuals in transition to higher or lower degrees of respiratory tract abnormalities. The control UGU group was also subdivided on the basis of smoking history as was done for normal controls.

The lung cancer group consisted of patients with known lung cancer, diagnosed either histologically or by sputum cytology. The majority of these patients were studied during their initial hopsitalization for diagnostic workup, and represented patients with localized disease without previous treatment. Patients with known metastatic disease or those undergoing treatment were excluded.

For all groups, individuals with recent histories of infection or those on medications known to interfere with immune function were excluded.

SAMPLE COLLECTIONS

Sputum, Collection and Cytology

The sputum was collected and prepared by the Saccomanno method [16] and stained with Papanicolaou stain. Figure 1 shows these cell patterns in each category.

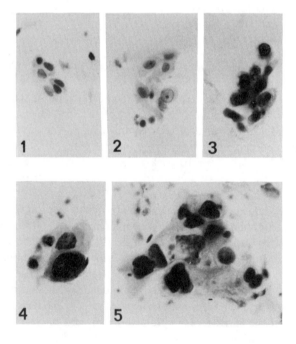

Figure 1.   Development of epidermoid carcinoma of the lung. Progressive cytological atypia in development of cancer from (1) mild; (2) moderate; (3) marked;
(4) CIS; and (5) invasive carcinoma.

Peripheral Blood

Twenty milliliters of peripheral blood was collected by venipuncture into sterile, heparinized containers. For the uranium miner group, blood samples were obtained at the same time as sputum cytology specimens. A complete blood count including white blood cell count and differential were done on all samples.

IMMUNOLOGIC STUDIES

Lymphocyte Preparation

Lymphocytes were separated from whole blood by centrifugation through a Ficoll/sodium diatrizoate gradient (LSM medium, Litton Bionetcs, Kensington, MD) according to the method described by Boyum [17]. Lymphocytes recovered from the gradient interface were washed twice with Hanks' balanced salt solution (HBSS, Microbiological Associates, Bethesda, MD) and divided into two equal portions. After a third wash, one lymphocyte sample was resuspended in HBSS supplemented with 20% fetal calf serum (FCS) at a concentration of 2×10^6 cells per milliliter. This sample was prepared for use in the rosette assays and rosette inhibition test (see below) by incubation with latex particles to identify contaminating phagocytic mononuclear cells. The lymphocyte suspension (0.1 ml) was added to 0.1 ml of 1% latex particles (0.801 μm-diameter particles, 10%, Dow Chemical Co., Indianapolis, IN) and the mixture incubated at 37°C for 30 min. The mixture was layered on 1-ml FCS and centrifuged at 200 x g for 5 min to remove free latex particles. The lymphocytes were washed once with HBSS and resuspended in HBSS to a final concentration of 1×10^6/ml.

The second aliquot of lymphocytes was resuspended in complete medium consisting of RPMI 1640 culture medium with 25 mM Hepes buffer (Microbiological Assoc., Bethesda, MD) supplemented with 10% fetal calf serum (GIBCO, Grand Island, NY), 2 mM L-glutamine (GIBCO) and 100 μg penicillin, 1 μg streptomycin, and 0.25 μg fungizone per 100 ml (Microbiological Associates). A final concentration of 2×10^6 cells/ml in complete medium was made for use in the mitogen studies.

Total Lymphocyte Count

A white blood count and differential was performed on each blood sample.

T Cell Enumeration

T cells were identified by their ability to bind to sheep red blood cells (SRBC) [8,18]. Fresh SRBC were obtained weekly and stored in Alsever's solution. Before use, they were washed three times in HBSS, counted and diluted to concentrations of 2.5% and 0.5% in HBSS.

Total T Lymphocytes

The lymphocyte suspension in HBSS (0.1 ml) was incubated for 5 min at 37°C, then 0.1 ml of the 2.5% SRBC suspension added giving a SRBC: lymphocyte ratio of approximately 40:1. The mixture was centrifuged at 200 x g for 5 min, then incubated 18 hr (overnight) at 4°C. The cell pellet was then gently resuspended and a sample placed on a hemocytometer. The proportion of rosette-forming cells (RFC) defined as any lymphocyte binding three or more SRBC was determined by counting 200 cells. Phagocytic cells containing latex particles were excluded. Lymphocyte viability was determined by new methylene blue dye uptake, and nonviable cells were excluded. Total T cells per mm^3 was calculated by multiplying the percentage of RFC by the total lymphocyte count.

Early Rosette-Forming Cells

By limiting the number of SRBC available for binding and the amount of time lymphocytes are in contact with SRBC, presumably one can identify more "active" rosette-forming cells (RFC).

The determination of the proportion of these "early" or active RFC may identify the subpopulation of T cells with high-affinity receptors for SRBC. Early RFC were measured by the method described by Wybran and Fudenberg [19]. The lymphocyte suspension (0.1 ml HBSS) was preincubated at 37°C for 60 min and then 0.1 ml of the 0.5% SRBC suspension was added to give a final SRBC lymphocyte ratio of 8:1. The mixture was centrifuged for 5 min at 200 x g, the cells were gently resuspended and the proportion of RFC counted immediately. Total early RFC/mm^3 peripheral blood was calculated by multiplying the percentage early RFC by the total lymphocyte count per mm^3.

B Cell Enumeration

B cells were determined using an EAC (erythrocyte-antibody-complement) technique which identifies cells with receptors for activated C3 component of complement. Antibody- and complement-coated SRBC were prepared by incubating 10 ml of a 5% suspension of SRBC with an equal volume of 1:5000 dilution of rabbit IgM anti-SRBC antibody (Cappel Labs, Cochranville, MD) for 30 min at 37°C. The antibody-coated SRBC (EA) were washed twice in HBSS, and a 5% suspension in Veronal buffer (Microbiological Assoc.) was made.

An equal volume of fresh guinea pig complement (Cappel Labs) diluted 1:10 in Veronal buffer was added and the mixture incubated for 45 min at 37°C. The antibody and complemented SRBC (EAC) were washed three times in HBSS and resuspended in HBSS to a 1% concentration. EAC rosette formation was determined by mixing 0.1 ml of the lymphocyte suspension (HBSS) with 0.1 ml of the 1% EAC, contrifuging 5 min at 200 x g incubating mixture for 20 min at 37°C. The cells were gently resuspended and %RFC counted as described above. Total peripheral B cells was calculated by multiplying the percent EAC–RFC by the total lymphocyte count per mm^3.

Rosette Inhibition Test

Inhibition of T cell-SRBC rosette formation was determined using a horse antihuman thymocyte serum (ATS) kindly provided by Dr. Barbara Loughman, Upjohn Co., Kalamazoo, MI. Although the exact mechanism of action of ATS on T cells is unknown, the rosette inhibition test provides a measure of the strength of lymphocyte-SRBC interaction, presumably an indirect measure of T cell functional competence. The rosette inhibition test was performed by a modification of the technique previously described [7,9]. Serial double dilutions of ATS in HBSS, 1:100 to 1:12,800, were prepared and 0.1 ml of each dilution added to 12 x 75 mm culture tubes. Added to each tube was 0.1 ml of the lymphocyte suspension in HBSS; 0.1 ml lymphocytes in 0.1 ml HBSS served as control tubes. All dilutions and controls were tested in duplicate. The ATS-lymphocyte mixtures were incubated at room temperature for 30 min. then 0.2 ml fetal calf serum (previously absorbed with SRBC) and 0.1 ml of 2.5% SRBC were added. The cells were pelleted by centrifugation at 200 x g for 5 min, then incubated a further 2 hr at room temperature. After the 2-hr incubation, the cells were gently resuspended and the percentage of RFC determined for each dilution as described above. The percent inhibition was then calculated for each dilution by dividing the percent RFC obtained in the ATS tube by the percent RFC in the control tubes. The 25% inhibitory titer was determined graphically by graphing % inhibition versus ATS titer. The result was expressed as the reciprocal of the dilution. In interpreting the results of the rosette inhibition test, the lower the dilution producing 25% inhibition, the more antibody required, and thus the more functional the lymphocytes.

In Vitro Lymphocyte Transformation to Mitogens

Certain plant lectins are capable of inducing blastogenesis in lympho-cytes, an event analogous to what occurs when sensitized lymphocytes encounter antigen and initiate an immune response. Though indirect, the ability of lymphocytes to undergo blastogenesis in response to mitogens has been utilized as a measure of functional competence of the cellular immune system. The degree of response to mitogen stimulation is mea-sured by the amount of ^{3}H-thymidine incorporated into DNA by the stimulated lymphocytes.

The three mitogens used were phytohemagglutinin (PHA), concanavalin A (Con A) and pokeweed mitogen (PWM). PHA and Con A are considered primarily T cell mitogens, although they apparently stimulate different subpopulations of T cells [20]. PWM, on the other hand, induces blasto-genesis primarily in B cells. This response, however, depends on T cell helper function [21].

Multiple dilutions of each mitogen were made in complete medium. Stock PHA solution (Burroughs Wellcome, Research Triangle Park, NC) was diluted 1:40, 1:80, 1:160 and 1:320 for testing. Con A (Sigma Chemical Co., St. Louis, MO) was diluted in complete medium to final concentrations of 2.5, 5.0, 10.0 and 25.0 $\mu g/ml$ for use. Dilutions of 1:10, 1:20, 1:50 and 1:100 of stock PWM solution (GIBCO) in complete medium were used.

All samples were cultured in triplicate in sterile, flat-bottom Microtest II microtiter plates (Falcon Plastics, Oxnard, CA). To each culture 0.1 ml lymphocyte suspension (2×10^6 cells per ml) and 0.1 ml of the appro-priate mitogen dilutions were added. Triplicate control or unstimulated cultures consisted of 0.1 ml of the lymphocyte suspension plus 0.1 ml of culture medium alone. Cultures were incubated for 72 hr at 37°C in a humidified atmosphere of 5% CO_2 in air. Eighteen hours prior to harvesting, each culture was pulsed with 1 μCi of methyl-^{3}H-thymidine (Sp. act. 6.7 Ci/mM, New England Nuclear, Bedford, MA) and subsequently harvested onto glass fiber filters with a semiautomated multiple culture harvester (Otto Hiller Co., Madison, WI). The samples were dried, then placed in glass scintillation vials containing 10 ml of Aquasol-2 (New England Nuclear) and counted in a Packard Tri-Carb-Liquid Scintillation Spectrometer. Results are expressed as counts per minute (CPM), or as stimulation index (SI) which is calculated as:

$$SI = \frac{CPM \text{ Stimulated Cultures}}{CPM \text{ Unstimulated Cultures}}$$

Statistical analysis was performed using the student's t test. For analysis of the rosette inhibition data, the log of the reciprocal titer was used because of the nonlinearity of the test results.

RESULTS

Effect of Smoking on Immune Function

A total of 57 normal controls were studied; 32 were nonsmokers and 25 were smokers. Results of the immunologic testing in this group are presented in Table I. Total T cells and rosette inhibition titers were slightly elevated in the smoking controls compared to nonsmokers, though these differences were not statistically significant. All other tests showed no differences between the two groups.

Table I. Immunologic Parameters in Normal Controls

Test N =	Nonsmokers 32	Smokers[a] 25	Total 57
% T Cells	65.3 ± 4.6	65.3 ± 7.1	65.3 ± 5.8
Total T Cells/mm^3	1438 ± 382	1542 ± 483	1483 ± 429
% B Cells	24.2 ± 3.3	23.1 ± 3.2	23.1 ± 3.0
Total B Cells	505 ± 138	536 ± 163	519 ± 149
% Early T Cells	26.5 ± 2.9	25.3 ± 3.1	26.0 ± 3.0
Total Early T Cells	581 ± 151	591 ± 190	586 ± 168
R.I. Titer (Reciprocal)	325 ± 121	404 ± 226	361 ± 179
PHA Response			
CPM	115,816 ± 18,535	112,132 ± 14,933	114,327 ± 17,017
SI	221 ± 65	217 ± 59	219 ± 62
Con A Response			
CPM	67,878 ± 20,092	65,057 ± 20,933	66,669 ± 20,289
SI	124 ± 36	122 ± 39	123 ± 37
Pokeweed Mitogen			
CPM	37,264 ± 8881	37,147 ± 11,110	37,215 ± 9758
SI	70 ± 20	73 ± 29	71 ± 25

[a]No significant differences were noted between smoking and nonsmoking groups for any of the tests.

When the 25 smokers were further subdivided according to amount of smoking, an interesting pattern emerged. As can be seen in Table II, there is no difference for any of the tests between the light and moderate smokers. However, in the heavy smoker group total T cells, total early % cells and total B cells are elevated compared to nonsmokers, light and moderate smokers, with the differences almost reaching statistical significance (p = 0.08). Contrary to these observed increases in quantitative T and B cell numbers, however, functional parameters including rosette inhibition titer, PHA, Con A and PWM responses are slightly depressed in the heavy smokers compared to nonsmokers and light smokers. These differences were not statistically significant.

Table II. Immunologic Parameters in Normal Controls According to Smoking History

	Smoking History			
	Nonsmokers	Light	Moderate	Heavy
Test N =	32	6	7	12
% T Cells	65.3 ± 4.6	67.1 ± 7.3	66.6 ± 7.9	63.7 ± 6.9
Total T Cells/ mm^3	1438 ± 382	1342 ± 506	1413 ± 455	1717 ± 462
% Early T Cells	26.5 ± 2.9	24.5 ± 2.1	26.6 ± 2.8	25.0 ± 3.7
Total Early T Cells/mm^3	581 ± 151	510 ± 179	561 ± 176	660 ± 193
R.I. Titer (Reciprocal)	325 ± 121	364 ± 166	361 ± 143	449 ± 289
Phytohemagglutinin Response CPM	115,816 ± 18,535	112.411 ± 13,667	116,904 ± 20,443	108,771 ± 12,205
Pokeweed Mitogen Response CPM	37,264 ± 8,881	37,290 ± 10,817	34,222 ± 6,808	33,008 ± 3,682

Effect of Uranium Mining Exposure on Immune Function

Thirty-two individuals with at least six months history of uranium mining and normal sputum cytology were studied. Of these, 10 were nonsmokers and 22 smokers. The results for this group are presented in Table III. The effect of uranium mining exposure alone was evaluated by comparing nonsmoking miners with nonsmoking controls. Comparing these two groups, there were no observable differences for any of the tests.

Table III. Immunologic Parameters in Underground Uranium Miners with
Normal Respiratory Cytology

Test N =	Nonsmokers 10	Smokers 22	Total 32
% T Cells	62.5 ± 5.2	63.4 ± 4.8	63.1 ± 4.9
Total T Cells/mm^3	1400 ± 378	1378 ± 416	1385 ± 397
% Early T Cells	25.1 ± 2.7	25.5 ± 2.7	25.4 ± 2.6
Total Early T Cells/mm^3	565 ± 110	548 ± 134	554 ± 125
% B Cells	23.3 ± 3.2	23.7 ± 2.6	23.5 ± 2.8
Total B Cells/mm^3	513 ± 111	505 ± 126	508 ± 119
R.I. Titer (Reciprocal)	371 ± 73	441 ± 155	420 ± 138
PHA Response	+		
CPM	117,574 ± 17,160	109,606 ± 13,638	112,075 ± 15,021
SI	215 ± 39	186 ± 42	195 ± 43
Con A Response			
CPM	62,793 ± 22,443	63,007 ± 19,914	62,940 ± 20,369
SI	114 ± 16	109 ± 33	110 ± 29
Pokeweed Mitogen			
CPM	37,563 ± 11,300	37,796 ± 10,432	37,723 ± 10,527
SI	67 ± 13	63 ± 20	65 ± 18

When the 10 nonsmoking uranium miners were compared to the 22 miners who smoked, no differences in quantitative T and B cells were noted. Functionally, though, slight abnormalities were noted with the rosette inhibition titer slightly increased and the PHA response slightly decreased in the smoker subgroup. When the amount of smoking is taken into account, several suggestive changes **are noted** (Table IV). Total T cells are decreased in the **light**, moderate and heavy smokers when compared to the corresponding groups in the normal controls. For the uranium miners, heavy smokers have elevated total T cells compared to nonsmokers, light and moderate smokers, a similar pattern to that seen in the normal controls. However, the smoking effect is considerably blunted in the miner group, total T cells being 1526/mm^3 in the heavy smoking miners compared to 1717/mm^3 for heavy smoking normal controls. The same pattern, though less pronounced, was seen for total early T cells and total B cells.

Functional parameters including rosette inhibition titer **and** mitogen responses are slightly though not significantly depressed in the smoking miners compared to nonsmoking miners. The abnormalities increase

Table IV. Immunologic Parameters in Uranium Miners with Normal Respiratory
Cytology According to Smoking History

	Smoking History			
	None	Light	Moderate	Heavy
Test N =	10	5	7	10
% T Cells	62.5 ± 5.2	64.0 ± 3.9	60.7 ± 4.0	65.2 ± 5.3
Total T Cells/ mm^3	1400 ± 378	1244 ± 274	1283 ± 363	1526 ± 502
% Early T Cells	25.1 ± 2.7	26.8 ± 2.0	24.6 ± 3.1	25.6 ± 2.6
Total Early T Cells/mm^3	565 ± 110	534 ± 115	514 ± 129	582 ± 154
R. I. Titer (Reciprocal)	371 ± 73	420 ± 74	422 ± 151	487 ± 194
Phytohemagglutinin Response CPM	117,574 ± 17,160	115,918 ± 7764	112,097 ± 11,804	104,571 ± 16,098
Pokeweed Mitogen Response CPM	37,563 ± 11,300	43,024 ± 9613	38,094 ± 11,076	34,973 ± 10,343

gradually as the amount of smoking increases. Comparing uranium miners
to normal controls, for equivalent smoking histories—nonsmoker to heavy
smoker—the rosette inhibition titer, PHA and Con A responses are abnormal, though not significantly in the uranium miner groups.

For all the tests discussed below statistical analysis was carried out
comparing results for each atypia and carcinoma group to the control
groups (normal and UGU) as a whole, and to the smoking subgroups of
the control groups. The analysis is expressed as one p value unless dis-
crepancies occurred.

Peripheral Blood T Cell Percentage

The percentage of peripheral blood lymphocytes identifiable as T cells
for each group is presented in Table V. As can be seen, there was no
difference between the normal control and underground uranium miner
control (UGU) groups. In individuals with atypical metaplastic changes,
however, the percent T cells was significantly reduced. A progressive decrease in percent T cells was noted from control levels of 65.3 ± 5.8% and
63.1 ± 4.7% to 56.8 ± 9.4% for the moderate atypia group (p < 0.02),

Table V. Peripheral Blood T Cell Levels in Pulmonary Metaplasia/Neoplasia

| Group | N | Patients | |
		Percent T Cells $\pm$ SD	T Cells/mm^3 $\pm$ SD
Controls	57	65.3 $\pm$ 5.8	1494 $\pm$ 482
UGU	32	63.1 $\pm$ 4.9[a]	1374 $\pm$ 381[a]
Moderate Atypia	37	56.8 $\pm$ 9.4[b]	1329 $\pm$ 431[a]
Moderate-Marked Atypia	11	48.9 $\pm$ 6.9[c]	1135 $\pm$ 388[b]
Marked Atypia	10	44.4 $\pm$ 8.0[c]	674 $\pm$ 382[c]
Carcinoma in situ	9	45.0 $\pm$ 9.1[c]	790 $\pm$ 138[c]
Invasive Carcinoma	50	45.7 $\pm$ 11.9[c]	609 $\pm$ 424[c]

[a]No significant difference from controls.
[b]Significantly different from controls (smoking and nonsmoking) with $p < 0.02$
[c]Significantly different from controls with $p < 0.001$.

and 48.9 $\pm$ 6.9% for the moderate-marked atypia ($p < 0.001$). T cell levels for the marked atypias and carcinoma in situ groups were indistinguishable from the clinical lung cancer group ($p < 0.001$).

Total Peripheral Blood T Cells/mm^3

Total T cells were decreased in the moderate atypia group but not significantly compared to control groups (Table V). A marked reduction in total T cells was observed in the moderate-marked atypia group, which was significantly different from controls ($p < 0.02$). Profound decreases were seen in the marked and carcinoma in situ groups to less than 50% of controls ($p < 0.001$), a level observed in the lung cancer group.

Peripheral Blood "Early" T Cell Percentage

No significant differences were observed for the percent early T cells in control, UGU and moderate atypia groups (Table VI). Early T cell percentage was significantly decreased in the moderate atypia group at 21.0 $\pm$ 3.2% ($p < 0.005$). More marked depression was observed in the marked atypia and carcinoma in situ groups at 17.5 $\pm$ 2.6% and 18.0 $\pm$ 2.7%, respectively ($p < 0.001$), a level identical to that seen in the invasive carcinoma group (17.6 $\pm$ 4.8%, $p < 0.001$).

Table VI. "Early" T Cell Percentage in Peripheral Blood of Pulmonary Metaplasia/Neoplasia Patients

Group	N	% Early T Cells ± SD	Total Early T Cells/mm^3 ± SD
Control	57	26.3 ± 3.0	596 ± 186
UGU	32	25.8 ± 2.6[a]	559 ± 128[a]
Moderate Atypia	37	24.1 ± 3.7[a]	556 ± 159[a]
Moderate-Marked Atypia	10	21.0 ± 3.2[b]	473 ± 183[a]
Marked Atypia	11	17.5 ± 2.6[c]	310 ± 163[c]
Carcinoma in situ	9	18.0 ± 2.7[c]	321 ± 67[c]
Invasive Carcinoma	50	17.6 ± 4.8[c]	237 ± 160[c]

[a]No significant difference from control.
[b]Significantly different from controls (smokers) with $p < 0.005$.
[c]Significantly different from controls with $p < 0.001$.

Total Early T Cells/mm^3 in Peripheral Blood

Less prominent changes were noted for total early T cells. No differences were observed between normal controls, UGU and moderate atypia groups (Table VI). Total T cells were decreased in the moderate-marked atypia group, but the difference was not statistically significant. Total T cells were profoundly decreased in the marked atypia and carcinoma in situ groups to approximately 50% of control values ($p < 0.001$). A further decrease was observed in the invasive carcinoma group with only 237 ± 160/mm^3 compared to control levels of 596 ± 186/mm^3 ($p < 0.001$).

Peripheral Blood B Cell Percentage

No significant differences were noted for the percentage of peripheral blood lymphocytes identifiable as B cells (EAC rosettes) between controls, atypias and lung cancer groups (Table VII).

Total Peripheral Blood B Cells/mm^3

Decreased total B cells were observed in the marked and carcinoma in situ groups, but the differences were not statistically significant compared to controls. Total B cells were significantly decreased in the invasive carcinoma group with $p < 0.001$ (Table VII).

Table VII. Percentage and Total Peripheral Blood B Cells in Pulmonary
Metaplasia/Neoplasia Patients

Group	N	% B Cells ± SD	Total B Cells/mm^3 ± SD
Control	57	23.5 ± 3.1	526 ± 160
UGU	32	23.7 ± 2.9	509 ± 116
Moderate Atypia	37	24.6 ± 3.5	581 ± 219
Moderate-Marked Atypia	10	23.1 ± 2.7	529 ± 165
Marked Atypia	11	24.3 ± 2.7	440 ± 237
Carcinoma in situ	9	25.0 ± 2.7	456 ± 144
Invasive Carcinoma	50	24.2 ± 4.1	312 ± 186[a]

[a]Significantly different from controls with p < 0.001. All other groups were not significantly different from controls.

Rosette Inhibition by Antithymocyte Serum

Results for the rosette inhibition test are expressed as the reciprocal of the dilution of ATS resulting in 25% or greater inhibition of rosette formation. These results are presented in Table VIII and depicted graphically in Figure 2.

The mean reciprocal inhibition titer for 57 normal controls was 352 ± 161, with 56 of 57 having titers of 640 or less. The mean reciprocal inhibition titer for the UGU control group was slightly increased at 427 ± 133, though this difference was not significant statistically. The narrow range over which values for inhibition titers occur for these two controls groups is clearly depicted in Figure 2. In the absence of respiratory cytopathology rosette inhibition titers occur in a tight distribution.

The mean inhibition titer for the 37 persons with moderate atypia was significantly increased compared to controls being 1024 ± 931 (p < 0.001). As can be seen in Figure 2, there was a wide scatter of values in this group compared to the control distribution. One of the striking features of this wide distribution was the large degree of overlap with the control population. This observation was used to evaluate the moderate atypia group as two distinct populations, a large population with normal inhibition titers, and a smaller population with very abnormal inhibition titers. The division into two separate populations was done empirically from the scattergram (Figure 2) with an arbitrary division being made at a reciprocal titer of approximately 800 (UGU mean plus two standard deviations). As shown in Table VIII, subgroup A consisted of 22 individuals with a mean inhibition titer of 517 ± 173. This was not significantly different from the control groups. Subgroup B consisted of 15 individuals with a

Table VIII. Rosette Inhibition by Antithymocyte Serum in Pulmonary
Metaplasia/Neoplasia Patients

Group	N	Inhibition Titer (Reciprocal) ± SD	Range
Control	57	352 ± 161	120-853
UGU	32	427 ± 133[a]	157-864
Moderate Atypia			
Total	37	1024 ± 931[b]	235-4400
A	22	517 ± 173[a]	235-827
B	15	1766 ± 1090[b]	933-4400
Moderate-Marked Atypia	10	1439 ± 1140[b]	306-3931
Marked Atypia	11	1839 ± 706[c]	800-2950
Carcinoma in situ	9	1826 ± 580[c]	960-2810
Invasive Carcinoma	50	2808 ± 1741[c]	421-6826

[a]No significant difference from controls.
[b]Significantly different from controls with p < 0.001.
[c]Significantly different from controls with p < 0.0001.

mean inhibition titer of 1766 ± 1090 which was significantly increased compared to control (p < 0.001). As seen in Figure 2, subgroup B contained several individuals with markedly abnormal inhibition titers.

The mean inhibition titer for the 10 individuals in the moderate-marked atypia group was 1439 ± 1140 which was significantly increased compared to controls (p < 0.001). The large standard deviation for this group results primarily from several individuals with markedly abnormal inhibition titers (5 with titers of 1800 to 3931).

The mean inhibition titers for the 11 persons with marked atypia and 9 with carcinoma in situ were virtually identical at 1839 ± 706 and 1826 ± 580, respectively. These means were very highly statistically significant compared to control (p < 0.0001). Figure 2 demonstrates no overlap between these two groups and controls, with most individual values being markedly elevated over controls.

The mean inhibition titer for the 50 patients in the lung cancer group was markedly abnormal at 2808 ± 1741 compared to controls (p < 0.0001). Figure 2 shows that the large majority of individual values were markedly abnormal, with only 5 of 50 with titers less than 1000.

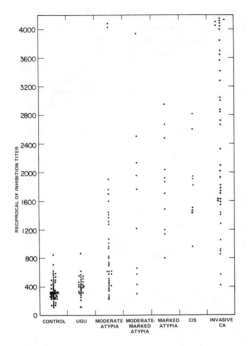

Figure 2. Reciprocal of the rosette inhibition titers for controls, uranium miners with pulmonary metaplasia, and lung cancer patients. Each point represents one individual.

Phytohemagglutinin Response of Peripheral Blood Lymphocytes

Lymphocyte transformation to PHA was measured by ^{3}H-thymidine incorporation into DNA. The absolute response was expressed as CPM. Relative proliferative capacity was determined with the stimulation index which compares incorporation of stimulated cells with incorporation by resting cells. Results are presented in Table IX and depicted graphically in Figure 3.

No significant difference was noted between normal controls and UGU. The mean CPM for the moderate atypia group was significantly depressed at 96,390 ± 13,822 compared to controls (p < 0.05). Further, progressive decreases were observed for the moderate-marked atypia, marked atypia and carcinoma in situ groups (p < 0.005). Though the mean values for these groups are very significantly different compared to controls, there is a wide range of values within each group as is reflected in the large standard deviations. This is graphically depicted in Figure 3, a scattergram of each individual PHA response. As can be seen, although the populations

Table IX. Response of Peripheral Blood Lymphocytes to Phytohemagglutinin as Measured by ^{3}H-Thymidine Incorporation into DNA in Pulmonary Metaplasia/Neoplasia Patients

Group	N	Counts per Minute (CPM) ± SD	Stimulation Index (SI) ± SD
Control	57	115,816 ± 18,535	221 ± 65
UGU	32	112,075 ± 15,021[a]	195 ± 43
Moderate Atypia	37	96,390 ± 13,822[b]	176 ± 42
Moderate-Marked Atypia	10	76,219 ± 20,739[c]	138 ± 52
Marked Atypia	11	63,911 ± 27,843[c]	112 ± 43
Carcinoma in situ	9	62,010 ± 40,560[c]	84 ± 54
Invasive Carcinoma	50	43,302 ± 28,580[d]	83 ± 52

[a]No significant difference from controls.
[b]Significantly different from controls with $p < 0.05$.
[c]Significantly different from controls with $p < 0.005$.
[d]Significantly different from controls with $p < 0.0001$.

as a whole become progressively depressed compared to controls, individuals within each group overlap with the control populations. This is particularly true for the moderate atypia group.

The PHA responses in the invasive cancer group are profoundly depressed at 43,302 ± 28,580 CPM compared to controls 115,816 ± 18,535 CPM ($p < 0.0001$). Figure 3 shows, however, that even in this group there is a wide range of responses with some overlap with controls.

The stimulation index follows a similar pattern to the absolute CPM with a progressive decline with progressive cytologic abnormalities.

Concanavalin A Response of Peripheral Blood Lymphocytes

As can be seen in Table X, a similar progressive decline in Con A response occurred with increasing cytopathology. The moderate atypia group was significantly depressed at 52,739 ± 15,002 CPM compared to controls 66,660 ± 20,289 CPM ($p < 0.02$). A more marked depression to 36,284 ± 16,121 was observed for the moderate-marked atypia group ($p < 0.001$), a level similar to that observed for the marked atypia group. The Con A response was depressed to only 40% of control level in the carcinoma in situ group ($p < 0.001$), while the invasive carcinoma group mean response was less than one-third normal at 21,485 ± 16,539 CPM ($p < 0.001$).

The stimulation index followed a similar pattern with significant decrease observed in the moderate atypia group; more marked decreases in the moderate-marked and marked atypia groups; and the greatest depression in the carcinoma in situ and invasive carcinoma groups where the stimulation index was depressed equivalent amounts.

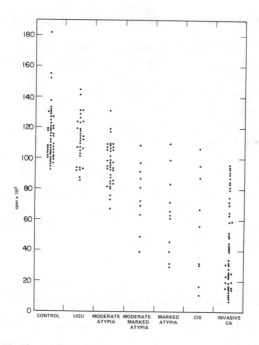

Figure 3. Phytohemagglutinin response (CPM) in controls, uranium miners with metaplasia and patients with lung cancer. Each point represents one individual.

Table X. Response of Peripheral Blood Lymphocytes to Concanavalin A as Measured by ^{3}H-Thymidine Incorporation into DNA in Pulmonary Metaplasia/Neoplasia Patients

Group	N	Counts per Minute (CPM) ± SD	Stimulation Index (SI) ± SD
Control	57	66,660 ± 20,289	123 ± 37
UGU	32	62,940 ± 20,369[a]	110 ± 29
Moderate Atypia	37	52,739 ± 15,002[b]	96 ± 25
Moderate-Marked Atypia	10	36,284 ± 16,121[c]	65 ± 28
Marked Atypia	11	33,707 ± 22,903[c]	58 ± 30
Carcinoma in situ	9	27,219 ± 19,054[c]	35 ± 21
Invasive Carcinoma	50	21,485 ± 16,539[c]	41 ± 27

[a]No significant difference from controls.
[b]Significantly different from controls with p < 0.02.
[c]Significantly different from controls with p < 0.001.

Pokeweed Mitogen Response of Peripheral Blood Lymphocytes

Abnormalities in PWM responsiveness can result from either abnormal B cell proliferative capacity, or from loss of T cell helper function, or a combination of both.

No differences were observed between normal controls, UGU and moderate atypia groups (Table XI). A significant decrease was observed for the moderate-marked atypia group with a mean value of 25,571 ± 15,944 compared to controls 37,723 ± 10,527 (p < 0.05). A further decrease was noted for the marked atypia and carcinoma in situ groups, both being depressed to similar levels (p < 0.02). Marked depression of PWM response was observed for the invasive carcinoma group (p < 0.001).

The stimulation index cahnges paralleled those seen for absolute CPM with the exception that the indices for the carcinoma in situ and invasive carcinoma groups were closely similar.

Table XI. Response of Peripheral Blood Lymphocytes from Pulmonary Metaplasia/ Neoplasia Patients to Pokeweed Mitogen as Measured by Incorporation of ^{3}H-Thymidine into DNA

Group	N	Counts per Minute (CPM) ± SD	Stimulation Index (SI) ± SD
Control	57	37,215 ± 9,758	70 ± 20
UGU	32	37,723 ± 10,527[a]	65 ± 18
Moderate Atypia	37	36,304 ± 8,940[a]	67 ± 18
Moderate-Marked Atypia	10	25,571 ± 15,944[b]	45 ± 25
Marked Atypia	11	20,981 ± 12,299[c]	38 ± 27
Carcinoma in situ	9	21,963 ± 16,096[d]	28 ± 17
Invasive Carcinoma	50	14,610 ± 11,517[c]	27 ± 18

[a]No significant difference from controls.
[b]Significantly different from controls with p < 0.05.
[c]Significantly different from controls with p < 0.001.
[d]Significantly different from controls with p < 0.02.

Evaluation of Moderate Atypia Subgroups

Although the subdivision of the moderate atypia group into two subgroups was arbitrarily based solely on rosette inhibition titers, the striking differences between the subgroups suggests that the division has validity. Table XII presents all the immunologic data for the moderate atypia group as a whole and broken down into subgroups A and B. As can be seen in many instances, mean values for a given test for the moderate group as a whole were not significantly different from controls. However, when sub-divided into subgroups A and B, it is clear that 60% of the moderates (subgroup A) did not differ from the controls, while 40% (subgroup B) were significantly different. This was the case for total T cells, total early T cells and rosette inhibition titer.

Table XII. Immunologic Parameters in Patients with Moderate Atypia

Test N =	Subgroup A 22		Subgroup B 15		Total 37	
% T Cells	59.8	6.9	52.5	11.0	56.8	9.4
Total T Cells/mm^3	1467	431	1126	353	1329	431
% Early T Cells	24.8	3.0	22.9	4.3	24.1	3.7
Total Early T Cells/mm^3	601	170	497	122	559	159
% B Cells	24.7	3.6	24.4	3.6	24.6	3.5
Total B Cells/mm^3	616	254	530	149	581	219
Rosette Inhibition Titer	517	173	1766	1090	1024	931
Phytohemagglutinin Response, CPM	99,921	9904	91,212	17,198	96,390	13,822
Concanavalin A Response, CPM	53,369	12,061	51,813	18,948	52,739	15,000
Pokeweed Response CPM	36,397	6659	36,161	11,784	36,304	8940

Immune Function According to Histologic Type of Lung Cancer

Table XIII depicts results of immunologic testing in patients with lung cancer classified according to histologic type. The predominant histologic type was squamous cell carcinoma accounting for 76% (38/50), with 14% being adenocarcinoma and 10% oat cell, or small-cell undifferentiated carcinoma. Statistical analysis was not performed because of the small numbers in the adenocarcinoma and oat cell groups.

For quantitative T and B cell parameters no difference was noted between the squamous- and adeno-carcinoma groups. Compared to these two groups, however, the oat cell group had decreased percent and total T cells yet increased percent and total early T cells. The small numbers involved do not permit any conclusions about the significance of this observation.

Although all functional parameters were markedly depressed for all histologic types compared to controls, the adenocarcinoma group had slightly better rosette inhibition and PHA responses than the squamous carcinoma group, while inhibition titer, PHA response and PWM response in the oat cell group were more abnormal than in the squamous group.

Table XIII. Immunologic Parameters in Lung Cancer Patients According to Histologic Type

Test	N =	Total	Squamous	Adeno	Oat
		50	38	7	5
% T Cells		45.7 ± 11.9	46.5 ± 11.9	46.3 ± 11.0	38.4 ± 13.6
Total T Cells/ mm^3		609 ± 424	604 ± 443	655 ± 362	576 ± 424
% Early T Cells		17.6 ± 4.8	17.3 ± 4.3	17.4 ± 5.4	20.2 ± 7.2
Total Early T Cells/mm^3		237 ± 160	222 ± 149	264 ± 165	310 ± 242
R.I. Titer (Reciprocal)		2808 ± 1741	2637 ± 1591	2272 ± 1381	2916 ± 881
Phytohemagglutinin Response CPM		43,302 ± 28,580	42,699 ± 27,905	57,085 ± 31,367	21,000 ± 15,108
Pokeweed Mitogen Response CPM		14,610 ± 11,517	15,106 ± 12,431	16,317 ± 8596	6891 ± 4395

Sensitivity of the Individual Immunologic Tests

To determine the relative sensitivity of the individual tests used in our immunoprofile, we determined the number of abnormal test responses in each group studied. An abnormal response was defined as any value differing from the control mean by more than two standard deviations of the control mean. These results are presented in Table XIV.

In the control and UGU groups all test results fell within two standard deviations of the control mean with the exception of one abnormal % T cell value in each group and one rosette inhibition titer in the UGU group.

In the moderate atypia group the rosette inhibition titer was abnormal in 16 of 37, while the % T cell level was abnormal in 10 of 37. All other tests were only infrequently abnormal with five or fewer responses greater than two standard deviations from the control mean.

In the moderate-marked atypia group the rosette inhibition titer was again most frequently abnormal (7/10) with all other tests being abnormal in five or fewer individuals. In this group both % T cells and PHA response were abnormal in five of 10 patients.

Table XIV. Sensitivity of Individual Immunologic Tests in Pulmonary Metaplasia/Neoplasia Patients

Group	N	% T	Total T	% Early T	Total T	Total B	RI Titer	PHA (CPM)	CON A (CPM)	PWM (CPM)
				Number of Patients with Values Greater Than Two Standard Deviations from the Control Mean						
Control	57	1	0	0	0	0	0	0	0	0
UGU	32	1	0	0	0	0	1	0	0	0
Moderate Atypia	37	10	5	3	1	0	16	4	1	1
Moderate-Marked Atypia	10	5	4	2	3	0	9	5	3	4
Marked Atypia	11	5	6	4	6	1	11	7	5	5
Carcinoma in situ	9	5	5	4	5	0	9	5	5	4
Invasive Carcinoma Carcinoma	50	19	25	14	24	12	48	38	32	26

In the marked atypia and carcinoma in situ groups the rosette inhibition titer was abnormal in all 20 individuals (11/11 marked atypia; 9/9 CIS). All other tests were considerably less sensitive. PHA response was abnormal in 60% of the individuals in these two groups (7/11 marked atypia; 5/9 CIS). Total T cells and total early T cells were abnormal in 11/20 each, while % T cells and Con A response were abnormal in half (10/20).

In the invasive carcinoma group the rosette inhibition test was abnormal in 96% of patients tested (48/50). No other test approached this sensitivity. The PHA response was abnormal in 76% (38/50), and Con A in 64% (32/50). Total T cells, total early T cells and PWM response were all abnormal in approximately 50% of the lung cancer patients. The least sensitive tests were % T cells with 38% abnormal; % early T cells with 28%; and total B cells at 24%.

If the marked atypia, carcinoma in situ and invasive carcinoma groups are considered together as the "neoplastic" groups, one notes that the rosette inhibition test was abnormal in 97% (68/70), compared to 71% for PHA response (50/70), the next most frequently abnormal parameter. Con A was abnormal in 60% (42/70), while total T cells, total early T cells and PWM response were all abnormal in 50% of cases. The remaining tests were relatively insensitive in detecting abnormalities in these individuals with neoplastic lesions, being abnormal in only 40% or fewer cases.

DISCUSSION

Many investigators have documented abnormal immune function in patients with carcinoma of the lung [7,19,15]. The results reported here, however, represent the first attempt to apply immunologic assessment to individuals with apparent preneoplastic lesions of the respiratory tract. We feel that the results obtained clearly indicate that such an approach can be of great value diagnostically and predictively in high-risk population groups.

In assessing the effect of smoking on immune function we found no significant reduction in immunocompetence between smoking and non-smoking controls. We did observe, however, increased total T cells, total early T cells and total B cells in the heavy smokers. These increased quantitative values associated with heavy smoking may result from the chronic irritation and inflammation induced in the bronchial tree by cigarette smoke. Although increased numbers of T and B cells were observed, the function of these \ subpopulations as measured by rosette inhibition titer, PHA and PWM response was if anything slightly depressed compared to nonsmokers. These qualitative changes were mild and not statistically significant, however. These data provide no evidence that smoking per se impairs immune competence.

To assess the effect of isolated uranium mining exposure on immune function, we studied nonsmoking uranium miners with known normal or mildly atypical sputum cytology. The carcinogenic promoter associated with uranium mining is not conclusively known, though extensive epidemiologic studies have demonstrated a strong correlation between lung cancer and duration and amount of exposure in the mines to alpha radiation from radon daughters [22]. We found, however, that there were no observable differences in immune function between nonsmoking miners and controls, regardless of the degree of exposure. This was true, of course, only for those individuals with normal or mildly atypical sputum cytologies. Minimal cellular changes, such as mildly atypical squamous metaplasia, are usually the result of inflammation and are reversible when the inflammatory agent is removed. The finding of normal immune function suggests that these mild changes are a local reaction to inflammation, while higher degrees of atypia represent carcinogenic changes associated with systemic as well as local effects. Uranium miners with normal cytologies who also smoked had immunologic profiles which did not differ significantly from controls or from nonsmoking miners. However, when these miners were evaluated according to their smoking habits, an interesting observation was made. Total T cells were moderately decreased and the rosette inhibition titer slightly elevated in the light and moderate smoking groups compared to controls and nonsmoking miners. In the heavy smoking group of miners, total T cells were elevated compared to nonsmoking miners, but this increase was considerably blunted compared to the increase observed in the control heavy smokers. Functionally, the rosette inhibition titer was elevated in all the smoking miner groups, with the greatest change observed in the heavy smokers. This difference almost reached statistical significance when compared to nonsmoking controls. The quantitative increase in T and B cells is blunted in the uranium miners, while functional competence is decreased to a slightly greater extent than in smokers alone. Clearly, more individuals in each category have to be studied before any conclusions can be reached. It is also clear that the immune changes observed in the groups of uranium miners with pulmonary cytopathology were specific to the pathologic changes with, at most, only minor contributions from the exposure to carcinogens per se.

Immunologic abnormalities were detected in significant proportions in the groups with dysplastic or neoplastic changes on sputum cytologic exam. In the moderate atypia group immunologic abnormalities were noted in 20–40% of those studied depending on the test, with the most striking changes seen with the rosette inhibition test. Indeed, on the basis of this test were detected what we believe are two distinct subpopulations within the moderate atypia group. Approximately 40% had abnormal rosette inhibition titers associated with abnormalities in the other immunologic parameters. On the other hand, the 60% with normal inhibition titers resembled the control populations closely with all other immunologic parameters being normal. Interestingly, the general impression of Saccomanno and his colleagues [3,4] from data accumulated over many years and the examination of approximately 150,000 sputum samples is that mild atypical squamous cell metaplasia is a common product of pulmonary inflammatory disease of any origin, although it may represent the initial response to carcinogens. In a specific individual case it is impossible to determine whether inflammatory or carcinogenic agents induce these changes. Further, the analysis of many cases showing moderate atypical squamous cell changes revealed that both inflammatory and carcinogenic effects are involved. An estimated 70-80% of the moderate atypical changes are due to inflammatory effect and are probably reversible with no further progression of abnormality or disappearance of the abnormal cells from sputum samples and reversion to normal histology. In the remaining 20–30% the moderate atypia is probably due to carcinogenic effect and as such is not reversible. If followed sequentially, the great majority of this subgroup will develop progressively more abnormal sputum cytology, with eventual development of lung cancer. With cytologic exam alone, moderate atypia is not recognizable as to whether it will develop into neoplasia. The results with the immunologic tests, in particular the rosette inhibition test, give the strong impression that they may be identifying individual cases in which the cellular changes are due to carcinogenic effect and which are committed to gradual progression to malignancy. If this finding is corroborated in further sequential study of these patients, this could represent a major argument for the inclusion of detailed immunologic assessment in any patient with moderate atypia on sputum exam. It also appears that the immunoprofile used remains normal when moderate atypia is due to inflammation alone regardless of cause. Further study is required to determine whether this conclusion is valid. It is tempting to suggest, however, that these immunologic tests become abnormal and thus predictive only when metaplastic changes have occurred which commit the abnormal cells to the path leading to neoplasia. In this regard, it is interesting that the mean rosette inhibition titer of the abnormal subgroup in the moderate atypias was equivalent to that observed for the marked atypia and carcinoma in situ groups.

Individuals with marked atypia all had markedly abnormal immunoprofiles. Of the tests used, only percent and total B cells were not significantly depressed in the group as a whole. In particular, the rosette inhibition test was markedly abnormal with no overlap in values with the control groups. Between 80 and 90% of those with marked atypias on sputum exam progress to develop lung carcinoma. Virtually all patients with cells characteristic of carcinoma in situ on sputum exam progress to invasive carcinoma. Immunologically all of these patients were markedly abnormal, especially in their rosette inhibition titers. For the rosette inhibition test we detected no difference between the marked atypia and carcinoma in situ groups. It has been the feeling of the cytopathologist involved in this study that marked atypia actually represents an irreversible step in the progression to carcinoma and should be considered a neoplastic rather than a late dysplastic or premalignant lesion. The immunologic data strongly support this view and suggest that the cytologic criteria for differentiating premalignant from malignant cells are incomplete.

The findings in the lung cancer group confirm previous studies reporting marked abnormalities. Even in the presence of established cancer, however, there is considerable variability in the results of individual tests. Results of the rosette inhibition test were the most strikingly abnormal in the lung cancer patients, with titers greater than two standard deviations from the control mean in 48 of 50 patients (96%). This high degree of sensitivity far exceeds any other individual parameter and confirmed previous findings in an earlier study of localized lung cancer. Gross et al. [7] demonstrated markedly abnormal rosette inhibition tests in 28 of 29

(97%) patients with undiagnosed coin lesions of the lung on chest X-ray. At thoracotomy these patients were found to have lung cancer. In patients with normal rosette inhibition tests and coin lesions on X-ray, benign tumors were found at surgery. This earlier study and the one reported here provide the impressive finding that 76 of 79 patients with early, localized lung cancer had abnormal rosette inhibition tests. With this high degree of predictability in early cancer, it is not surprising that the test detects changes in patients with preclinical or even preneoplastic lung lesions. Indeed, in all 20 patients with marked atypia or carcinoma in situ the rosette inhibition test was abnormal.

We feel that these results provide compelling evidence that immunologic defects are present very early in the development of lung cancer. Abnormalities in the moderate atypia group suggest that either detectable immunologic changes occur at the very earliest stage of committed progression to cancer as a result of carcinogenic effect on the bronchial epithelium, or that underlying immunologic defects act as permissive changes selecting or predisposing individuals exposed to carcinogens to irreversible progression to neoplasia. The answer to whether the immunologic changes are primary or secondary to the development of neoplastic cells awaits further prospective sequential studies of this uranium miner population with emphasis on the immunologic and cytologic study of those individuals currently with normal sputum cytology.

The conclusions regarding the presence of immunologic abnormalities in preneoplastic states and the usefulness of the rosette inhibition test were confirmed in another human cancer by La Via's group in Atlanta [23]. This group of investigators studied rosette formation and inhibition in patients with dysplasia and carcinoma in situ of the cervix. The rosette inhibition test was significantly depressed in the group with moderate dysplasia, a premalignant lesion. Similar to our findings, marked abnormalities were observed in those patients with severe dysplasia or carcinoma in situ, the two groups being indistinguishable from each other.

Clearly, the rosette inhibition test is capable of measuring changes associated with cells having undergone neoplastic transformation. It is not yet known what the rosette inhibition test measures, although it seems likely that either functional competence of T cells represented by high-affinity or high-density receptors for SRBC, or a subpopulation with some, as yet, undefined characteristic extremely sensitive to the presence of malignancy is being measured. With the potential clinical usefulness of this test, further investigation into the mechanisms of action involved is required. Until these mechanistic studies become available, the rosette inhibition test can be considered a very sensitive marker for malignancy whose exact significance is unknown.

With combined cytologic and immunologic evaluation we are capable of more precisely identifying those individuals at highest risk of progressing to lung cancer. With the known latency periods for progression from moderate atypia to invasive carcinoma (4.8 yr) [3], this early identification could conceivably result in ample time for the localization of lesions and institution of definitive therapy. If future results in this population group continue to be as encouraging and striking as at present, the role of early institution of immunotherapy should be evaluated. The idea that manipulation of the immune system during those early periods of neoplastic development might alter the progression of cytologic abnormalities and the ultimate expression of malignancy is exciting.

ACKNOWLEDGMENTS

We would like to gratefully acknowledge cytotechnologists, Terry Read and Shanna Adkins, for their expert and invaluable technical help.

By acceptance of this article, the publisher recognizes that the U.S. Government retains a nonexclusive, royalty-free license to publish or reproduce the published form of this contribution, or to allow others to do so, for U.S. Government purposes.

The Los Alamos Scientific Laboratory requests that the publisher identify this article as work performed under the auspices of the U.S. Department of Energy.

REFERENCES

1. Burnet, F. M. "The Concept of Immunosurveillance," *Prog. Exp. Tumor Res.* 13:1-27 (1970).
2. Schwartz, R. S. "Another Look at Immunosurveillance," *New Eng. J. Med.* 293:181-184 (1975).
3. Saccomanno, G., V. E. Archer, O. Auerbach, R. P. Saunders and L. M. Brennan. "Development of Carcinoma of the Lung as Reflected in Exfoliated Cells," *Cancer* 30:256-270 (1974).
4. Saccomanno, G., R. P. Sauners, V. E. Archer, O. Auerbach, M. Kuschner and P. A. Becker. "Cancer of the Lung: the Cytology of Sputum Prior to the Development of Carcinoma," *Acta Cytologica* 9:13-420 (1965).
5. Schreiber, H., G. Saccommano, D. H. Martin and L. Brennan. "Sequential Cytological Changes during Development of Respiratory Tract Tumors Induced by Hamsters by Benzo(a)pyrene-Ferric Oxides," *Cancer Research* 34:689-698 (1974).
6. Hayata, Y., H. Kato, M. C. Chow, M. Tachibana, M. Tawara, N. Hayashi, T. Kawauchi, Y. Seo and R. Anemiya. "Studies of the Carcinogenic Process in Experimental Squamous Cell Carcinoma in Canine Lungs," *Nippon Kyobu Shikkan Gakkai Zasshi* 15:759-768 (1977).

7. Gross, R. L., A. Latty, E. A. Williams and P. M. Newberne. "Abnormal Spontaneous Rosette Formation and Rosette Inhibition in Lung Carcinoma," *New Eng. J. Med.* 292:438-443 (1975).
8. Wybran, J., M. C. Carr and H. H. Fudenberg. "The Human Rosette-Forming Cell as a Marker of a Population of Thymus-Derived Cells," *J. Clin. Invest.* 51:2537-2543 (1972).
9. Brain, P., and J. Gordon. "Rosette Formation by Peripheral Lymphocytes. II. Inhibition of the Phenomenon," *Clin. Exp. Immunol.* 8:441-449 (1971).
10. Concannon, J. P., M. H. Dalbow, C. P. Eng and J. Conway. "Immunoprofile Studies for Patients with Bronchogenic Carcinoma. I. Correlation of Pre-Therapy Studies with State of Disease," *Int. J. Radiat. Oncol. Biol. Phys.* 2:447-454 (1977).
11. Dellon, A. L., C. Potvin and P. B. Chretien. "Thymus-Dependent Lymphocyte Levels in Bronchogenic Carcinoma: Correlations with Histology, Clinical Stage, and Clinical Course after Surgical Treatment," *Cancer* 35:687-694 (1975).
12. Han, T., and H. Takita. "Immunological Impairment in Bronchogenic Carcinoma: A Study of Lymphocyte Response to PHA," *Cancer* 30: 616-620 (1972).
13. Rees, J. C., J. L. Rossio, H. E. Wilson, J. P. Minton and M. C. Dodd. "Cellular Immunity in Neoplasia. Antigen and Mitogen Responses in Patients with Bronchogenic Carcinoma," *Cancer* 36: 2010-2015 (1975).
14. Wanebo, H. J., B. Rao, N. Miyazawa, N. Martini, M. P. Middleman, H. F. Oettgen and E. J. Beattie, Jr. "Immune Reactivity in Primary Carcinoma of the Lung and its Relation to Prognosis," *J. Thor. Cardiovasc. Surg.* 72:339-350 (1976).
15. Gross, R. L. "Current Status of Immunologic Studies in Human Lung Carcinoma," Los Alamos Scientific Laboratory Report LA-7371-SR (1978).
16. Saccomanno, G., R. P. Saunders, H. Ellis, V. E. Archer, B. G. Wood and P. Becker, "Concentration of Carcinoma or Atypical Cells in Sputum," *Acta Cytologica* 7:305-310 (1963).
17. Boyum, A. "Isolation of Mononuclear Cells and Granulocytes from Human Blood. Isolation of Mononuclear Cells by One Centrifugation, and of Granulocytes by Combining Centrifugation and Sedimentation at 1 g," *Scand. J. Clin. Lab. Invest.* 21(97):77-89 (1968).
18. Jondal, M., G. Holm and H. Wigzell. "Surface Markers on Human T and B Lymphocytes. I. A Large Population of Lymphocytes Forming Non-Immune Rosettes with Sheep Red Blood Cells," *J. Exp. Med.* 136:207-215 (1972).
19. Wybran, J. and H. H. Fudenberg. "Thymus-Derived Rosette-Forming Cells in Various Human Disease States: Cancer, Lymphoma, Bacterial and Viral Infections and Other Diseases," *J. Clin. Invest.* 52:1026-1032 (1973).

20. Stobo, D., and W. E. Paul. "Functional Heterogeneity of Murine Lymphoid Cells. III. Differential Responsiveness of T Cells to Phytohemagglutinin and Concanavalin A as a Probe for T Cell Subsets," *J. Immunol.* 110:362-375.

21. Keightley, R. G., M. D. Cooper and A. R. Lawton. "The T Cell Dependence of B Cell Differentiation Induced by PWM," *J. Immunol.* 117:1538-1544 (1976).

22. Wagoner, J. K., V. E. Archer, F. E. Lundin, Jr., D. A. Holaday and J. W. Lloyd. "Radiation as the Cause of Lung Cancer Among Uranium Miners," *New Eng. J. Med.* 273:181-187 (1964).

23. Sawanobori, S., R. B. Ashman, A. J. Nahmias, B. B. Benigno and M. F. La Via. "Rosette Formation and Inhibition in Cervical Dysplasia and Carcinoma in Situ," *Cancer Research* 37:4332-4335 (1977).

SECTION III

INFORMATIONAL NEEDS
AND
CHEMICAL CLASSIFICATION

CHAPTER 15

PREPARATION OF CARCINOGEN MONOGRAPHS

Alfred F. Meiners
    Midwest Research Institute
    Kansas City, Missouri

INTRODUCTION

Midwest Research Institute (MRI) is completing a 3-yr program sponsored by the National Cancer Institute (NCI) to prepare laboratory safety monographs for supervisors, safety professionals and laboratory workers concerned with carcinogens. Seventeen monographs, covering 63 carcinogenic compounds have been prepared. Table I lists the compounds and their classifications for the monographs on the basis of chemical structure. The compounds were selected by NCI based on a survey of carcinogens used in the laboratories of the Department of Health, Education and Welfare (HEW).

The program team is multidisciplinary, consisting of individuals with training and experience in organic and analytical chemistry, occupational and environmental health, industrial hygiene and occupational safety, pharmacology and toxicology, preventive medicine and cancer epidemiology.

The NCI intends to make these monographs available through the National Technical Information Service (NTIS). In addition, summaries of the information in the monographs will be widely distributed through NCI's own information services.

Information has been obtained through extensive computer-assisted and manual literature searches. In spite of the many thousands of publications concerning these compounds, published information on safety procedures applicable to the research laboratory is very limited. Also, safety information is difficult to locate through literature searches, because it may be

Table I. Listing of Monographs and Carcinogens

1. Polycyclic Aromatic Hydrocarbons
   Benz[a]anthracene
   Benzo[a]pyrene
   7-Bromomethylbenz[a]anthracene
   7,12-Dimethylbenz[a]anthracene
   3-Methylcholanthrene

2. Nitrosamines
   N-Nitrosodibutylamine
   N-Nitrosodiethylamine
   N-Nitrosodimethylamine
   N-Nitrosodipropylamine
   1,4-Dinitrosopiperazine
   N-Nitrosopiperidine

3. Nitrosamides
   N-Methyl-N'-nitro-N-
   nitrosoguanidine
   N-Nitroso-N-ethylurea
   N-Nitroso-N-methylurea
   N-Nitroso-N-ethylurethane
   N-Nitroso-N-methylurethane

4. Chloromethyl Ethers
   bis(Chloromethyl) ether
   Chloromethyl methyl ether

5. Aminofluorene Derivatives
   N-Acetoxy-2-fluorenylacetamide
   N-2-Fluorenylacetamide (2-AAF)

6. Aziridines
   Dimethylethylenimine
   Ethylenimine
   Propylenimine

7. Aromatic Amines and Related
   Compounds
   4-Aminobiphenyl
   4-Nitrobiphenyl
   Benzidine
   3,3'-Dichlorobenzidine
   3,3'-Dimethoxybenzidine
   3,3'-Dimethylbenzidine
   4,4'-Methylene bis-
   (2-chloroaniline) (MOCA)
   1-Naphthylamine
   2-Naphthylamine
   m-Toluenediamine

8. Polychlorinated Biphenyls (PCB)

9. Ethers, Oxides and Epoxides
   Diepoxybutane
   p-Dioxane
   4-Nitroquinoline-1-oxide

10. Hydrazines
    1,1-Dimethylhydrazine
    1,2-Dimethylhydrazine
    Hydrazine
    Methylhydrazine
    Procarbazine

11. Nitrogen Mustards
    Chlorambucil
    Uracil Mustard

12. Halogenated Hydrocarbons
    Carbon tetrachloride
    Chloroform
    1,2-Dibromo-3-chloropropane
    Ethylene dibromide
    Vinyl chloride

13. Nitrofuran Derivatives
    N-[4-(5-Nitro-2-furyl)-2-thiazolyl]-
    formamide

14. Sulfonic Acid Derivatives
    Bromoethyl methanesulfonate
    Ethyl methanesulfonate
    Methyl methanesulfonate
    1,3-Propane sultone

15. Carboxylic Acid Derivatives
    Ethionine
    β-Propiolactone
    Urethane

16. Azo and Azoxy Derivatives
    Diazomethane
    Cycasin
    o-Aminoazotoluene
    p-Dimethylaminoazobenzene
    3'-Methyl-4-aminoazobenzene

17. Aflatoxins

presented in the publication but is not indicated in the title or the abstract. This situation is changing rapidly, and excellent publications relating to laboratory safety are appearing, partly because of the impact and efforts of the ACS Division of Chemical Health and Safety. It is very important that this information be published and promulgated, because we feel that adequate precautions for carcinogen handling and disposal are not being taken in many laboratories.

Because of the limited amount of published safety information, the project team undertook a series of telephone and personal interviews with personnel at MRI and other laboratories noted for their capability in handling carcinogens. In general, we learned that there are a great many kinds of safety problems depending on the laboratory operation. However, in many cases, information and techniques developed by one laboratory can provide solutions to problems in another laboratory.

MRI has extensive experience in the synthesis of polycyclic aromatic hydrocarbon (PAH) metabolites and their radiolabeled analogs. A large program also exists for the analysis of a wide variety of carcinogens used in the NCI bioassay programs. In addition, there are extensive facilities for inhalation toxicity studies of volatile, halogenated hydrocarbons.

The project team visited the Illinois Institute of Technology Research Institute (IITRI), where a repository for the carcinogens used in the NCI bioassay program has been established. IITRI also conducts an NCI-sponsored training program entitled "The Safe Handling of Chemical Carcinogens in the Research Laboratory." A visit was also made to the National Center for Toxological Research (NCTR) at Pine Bluff, Arkansas, where animal feeding studies, involving tens of thousands of mice and rats, are being conducted using acetylaminofluorene (AAF), aromatic amines and other carcinogens. NCTR employs incineration extensively for the disposal of carcinogenic waste and has developed procedures for treating wastewater contaminated with carcinogens.

The project team also visited the Los Alamos Scientific Laboratories (LASL), where a variety of radiochemical safety practices have been adapted for working with carcinogens. LASL has also been developing analytical procedures for the detection of carcinogenic aromatic amines. LASL has an impressive capability with regard to respiratory protection.

The monographs contain the five major sections shown in Table II. The first major section deals with safety information, and the contents of this section will be discussed below. Four other sections of the monograph provide important background information:

> In Section III information is provided concerning the identification of the carcinogens, their chemical and physical properties and a review of their chemical reactions.

Section IV contains information concerning the chemical and biological formation of the carcinogens, their occurrence in nature, and their uses, especially in the laboratory.

Section V is a review of sampling and analysis methods. The methods are described, their limitations in terms of interferences and sensitivity are noted, and their applicability to laboratory problems is indicated. Special emphasis is placed on methods which would provide the ability to detect the carcinogen on surfaces, in air and in water.

Table II. Outline of Carcinogen Monograph

I. Introduction
II. Safety Information
    A. Summary of Hazards
        1. Health hazards
        2. Chemical hazards
        3. Physical hazards
    B. Containment
        1. Laboratory facilities
        2. Protective equipment
        3. Carcinogen handling
        4. Environmental control
    C. Emergency Procedures
        1. First-aid treatment
        2. Emergency access
        3. Ventilation failure
        4. Fires
        5. Accidental spills
    D. Medical Surveillance
        1. Preassignment physical
        2. Periodic examination
        3. Acute toxic exposure
        4. Health records
        5. Surveillance procedures
III. Chemical and Physical Properties
    A. Identification
    B. General, Physical and Chemical Data
    C. Chemical Reactivity
IV. Formation, Occurrence and Uses
V. Sampling and Analysis
VI. Biological Effects and Medical Data
    A. Health Hazards
    B. Pharmacologic Data
        1. Absorption
        2. Distribution
        3. Metabolism (metabolic products)
        4. Excretion (time required)
    C. Toxicologic Data
        1. Toxic effects
        2. Carcinogenic effect

The last major section of the monographs is a review of biological effects and medical data. Available information concerning their toxic, carcinogenic, mutagenic and teratogenic hazards to human health is reviewed and summarized. The review of animal toxicity data includes information concerning target organs and the dosage required to produce each toxic effect. The review of pharmacologic data includes available information concerning absorption, distribution, metabolism and excretion.

The first part of the safety information section (Section II) presents a concise summary of the hazards involved in handling each compound, including chemical and physical hazards as well as health hazards. The second part contains information pertinent to the containment of carcinogens, specifically the laboratory facilities required and the necessary protective equipment. The third part deals with procedures for carcinogen handling in various laboratory operations.

We are particularly concerned about current safety practices in animal operations. From the available biological data, it is apparent that the administration of many carcinogens results in the excretion of unchanged carcinogen or carcinogenic metabolites. We feel that as long as the animal is excreting these carcinogens, the area should be subject to the same safety precautions applicable to the handling of carcinogens in the chemical laboratory. Since the cages and litter are contaminated with carcinogens, precautions should be taken to protect laboratory workers within the animal rooms. However, we feel that the design of most animal laboratories precludes this possibility because of the ventilation required to protect the animals from disease—the air flow over the cages is generally toward the animal handler, not away from him. Attempts to protect the worker by means of a surgical mask are inadequate because such a mask provides poor protection against inhaled aerosols.

Other problem areas occur in necropsy and histology operations. In many carcinogen administration operations animal tissues are contaminated with carcinogens at necropsy, and there is experimental evidence that the carcinogens can be transferred into the solvents used in histology procedures. These tissues and solvents should be handled in the same manner as carcinogens in a chemical laboratory.

The safety information section also describes procedures for the protection of the environment; information is provided concerning methods for treating exhaust air, disposing of waste fluids and solids, incineration, burial and landfill. We feel that much additional information needs to be developed in these areas, because many currently used practices are unacceptable. There are objections and limitations to the two primary disposal methods—incineration and burial or landfill. Incineration has the advantages of being capable of destroying the carcinogen at the source and being applicable to most kinds of carcinogenic waste. However, incineration is not in general use by laboratories for a variety of reasons, e.g., lack of knowledge concerning incinerator design and conditions for complete destruction, emission control problems, energy and cost requirements.

Incinerator operating conditions which provide total destruction have been established for only two of the carcinogens covered by the monographs. However, we believe that at least half of these compounds could be destroyed by moderate incineration conditions, and that all of the compounds could be destroyed under the conditions of temperature and contact time that are known to destroy other refractory organic compounds. However, until the effectiveness of these conditions have been established, incineration could be hazardous because of the potential for discharge and dissemination as a result of incomplete combustion.

Alternate and less desirable methods for the disposal of laboratory carcinogens are presently being employed. Burial or landfill disposal is employed extensively. However, in our opinion, this is the least desirable method because of possibilities for future problems. Regulatory agencies, however, have approved some disposal sites where air and water contamination possibilities have been reduced to a minimum.

Decontamination techniques are also discussed in the monographs under the topic of environmental control. Decontamination includes the physical removal of a carcinogen or the destruction of the carcinogen *in situ*. A great deal of new information is required concerning destruction techniques; for example, there are no acceptable chemical destruction techniques for over half of the carcinogens covered by the monographs. (The status of decontamination techniques is discussed in another chapter included in this volume, "Carcinogen Spills, A Challenge to Laboratory Safety Capability.")

The third major topic in the safety information section deals with procedures to follow in case of emergency and with methods for preventing or minimizing the effects of accidents. Because of the potential for carcinogenic aerosols or vapors produced during a laboratory accident, emergency procedures must be developed to offer maximum containment plus personnel protection. It is impossible to describe emergency procedures that will encompass all laboratories because of wide variations in the nature of the experiments, physical layout of the laboratories, and number of employees. It is, however, important to recognize certain emergencies as potential routes for carcinogen exposure.

The most serious emergencies are fires, explosions and power failures; all three may occur at the same time. Personnel within the laboratory must be able to exit rapidly without contaminating surrounding areas. Procedures for safe removal of injured personnel must be developed, and provisions must be made for administering appropriate first-aid. Provisions also must be made for extinguishing fires and cleaning up contaminated areas.

Ventilation failure presents a hazardous problem because laboratories or glove boxes would no longer be safe for use. Therefore, an emergency power supply should be available.

Provisions for dealing with major emergencies should be inherent in the laboratory design. Laboratory personnel should be trained to deal with emergencies, but personnel in other areas should also be trained, and systems for summoning these personnel in emergencies should be installed.

Laboratory personnel and emergency personnel must also be trained to use appropriate respiratory equipment and fire-extinguishing devices. They also must be trained to administer first-aid and to perform cleanup operations.

The last part of the safety information section deals with medical surveillance. There is general agreement that laboratory workers exposed to carcinogens should have preassignment and periodic examinations, employee education programs should be provided, and accurate medical records should be kept for 20 years or more. However, there is considerable disagreement and even ignorance over what specific tests should be included in a medical examination.

In this section we have attempted to describe pertinent surveillance procedures and their usefulness in a language which can be understood by the intended audience. The procedures include a variety of diagnostic and screening techniques and, where possible, known methods for detecting occupational exposure. These procedures can provide important indications that the worker should be removed from laboratory exposure.

Many cancer screening programs currently in clinical use are not relevant to the problem of laboratory carcinogen exposure; in general, the tumors produced in animals by carcinogens are not the kinds of tumors that human clinical screening procedures will detect. Therefore, relevant animal exposure data are reviewed in this section, accenting the kinds of observations that may be pertinent in the development of methods for detecting human exposure.

CHAPTER 16

MUTAGENESIS, CARCINOGENESIS AND TERATOGENESIS INFORMATION SYSTEMS

J. S. Wassom

Environmental Mutagen Information Center
Environmental Teratology Information Center
Information Center Complex/Information Division
Oak Ridge National Laboratory
Oak Ridge, Tennessee

INTRODUCTION

One of the most frustrating problems facing scientists today in all areas of toxicology is the problem of information accessibility. This problem has resulted from the overwhelming amount of information produced annually. Several decades ago, access to information was not a major problem because it could be obtained through the "invisible college" of communicating with colleagues and the reading of key journals. As science has advanced, these methods of acquiring information are no longer adequate to keep pace with the volume of material now being written and published in literally thousands of journals and other publication forms.

Because of the emphasis now being placed on determining whether the many chemical substances or mixtures to which humans are exposed may cause adverse health effects, the production of toxicological information is increasingly significant. Due to this increase, information and computer scientists have made great progress in the techniques to acquire, store and retrieve information. In most areas of toxicology, however, many sources must still be searched in order to assure the adequate retrieval of pertinent information. Fortunately, this is not quite the case with respect to the three toxicological disciplines addressed here. Comprehensive information can be obtained from single sources for mutagenicity through the Environmental Mutagen Information Center (EMIC) and teratogenicity through the Environmental Teratology Information Center (ETIC). The complex field of carcinogenicity is not so fortunate, although there are several key sources that can be used to obtain information. These sources are the HEW/Public Health Service Publication No. 149 series entitled *Survey of Compounds Which Have Been Tested for Carcinogenic Activity,* the *International Agency for Research on Cancer Monographs* and *Bulletins, Carcinogenesis Abstracts,* and the computer files TOXLINE, CANCERLIT, CANCERPROJ and RTECS (Registry of Toxic Effects of Chemical Substances) available through the National Library of Medicine.

This chapter reviews the previously mentioned information resources which are available for use as access to the literature in the three specific toxicological research areas of mutagenicity, carcinogenicity and teratogenicity.

ENVIRONMENTAL MUTAGEN INFORMATION CENTER (EMIC)

EMIC is a computerized information facility which was organized in 1969 at the Oak Ridge National Laboratory (ORNL) located in Oak Ridge, Tennessee. The mission of the center is to collect, organize and disseminate information of relevance to the subject of environmental mutagenesis. The decision to begin such an activity was stimulated by the fact that many geneticists who were concerned about the genetic hazards of environmental chemicals were finding it difficult to keep up with the literature. Because of this concern, the involvement of the research community in EMIC's operation began during the early stages of its development.

Papers selected for entry into the EMIC file contain information that is primarily concerned with the testing of chemicals (or other environmental agents, excluding for the most part papers dealing solely with ultraviolet and ionizing radiation) for mutagenicity. Papers are also selected that contain information on peripheral subjects that may be useful in understanding the known or suspected mutagenic activity of environmental agents.

A variety of methods is used to locate publications of interest. The most productive is the manual searching of 40 key journals which regularly publish data on mutagenesis studies (Table I). These journals are scanned as soon as they are available and yield about 50% of the papers selected to become a part of the EMIC data base. The other 50% is obtained by searching large data bases such as those produced by the Chemical Abstracts Service (CAS), the BioSciences Information Service (*Biological Abstracts and BioResearch Index),* the Institute for Scientific Information, and the U.S. Department of Agriculture *(AGRICOLA).* These files are searched by computer using a specific set of terms relevant to genetics and mutagenicity.

Table I. Key Journal Sources Used by EMIC

Mutation Research	Radiation Research
Soviet Genetics (USSR)	Toxicology and Applied
Cancer Research	Pharmacology
Genetics	Journal of Molecular Biology
Journal of Bacteriology	Canadian Journal of Genetics and
Nature (London)	Cytology
Molecular and General Genetics	Doklady Biological Sciences (USSR)
Proceedings of the National	Biochemical Pharmacology
Academy of Sciences USA	Bulletin of Experimental Biology
Biochimica et Biophysica Acta	and Medicine (USSR)
Experimental Cell Research	Cytologia
Chemico-Biological Interactions	Lancet
Cytology and Genetics (USSR)	Virology
Japanese Journal of Genetics	Journal of Virology
Experientia	International Journal of Radiation
Hereditas	Biology and Related Studies in
Journal of Cell Biology	Physics, Chemistry, and Medicine
Biochemical and Biophysical Research	Journal of General Microbiology
Communications	Biochemistry
Human Genetics	Nucleus (Calcutta)
Science (Washington)	Chromosome
Tsitologiya	Gann
Journal of the National Cancer	Journal of Reproduction and
Institute	Fertility
Comptes Rendus Hebdomadaires des	
Seances de l'Academie des Sciences,	
Serie D: Sciences Naturelles	

Other secondary sources such as *Genetic Abstracts, Carcinogenesis Abstracts, Current Contents* and *Excerpta Medica* are manually screened as are books, symposia and other publications. Further, geneticists around the world assist by sending reprints of their work and copies of material from journals and books published in their respective countries. Such cooperation is frequently the only means of obtaining information from foreign sources.

It is only after a copy of a publication is obtained that information is prepared for computer input. Preparation of input consists basically of recording bibliographic details and keywords which describe the organisms and test systems used in the study and the chemicals or other agents evaluated. After this information has been recorded on work sheets and edited, it is then entered into the computer file. CAS registry numbers are assigned to all chemicals whenever these numbers are available. These unique numbers are used as the primary means of searching the EMIC file. They provide links to other data bases or reference documents such as the aforementioned series, RTECS, and the agent registry file of ETIC. The information extracted from the published literature and contained in the EMIC file may be retrieved by free-text searching of titles, abstracts or specific keyword categories. Controlled vocabulary searching can also be accomplished by querying some of the specific indexing fields such as compound(s) tested, CAS registry number(s), publication type, test object (specific and general classification), cell type(s), sex of test organism(s), experimental conditions under which the test object was treated, and biological endpoint of the study or assay system used. Additionally, the chemical agents studied are combined with agents from EMIC's sister center, ETIC, and retained in an agent registry file where other pertinent information parameters are associated with each entry (Table II). Terms may be searched singly or in combination with other terms using Boolean logic. Chemicals in the EMIC/ETIC agent registry can be searched on the basis of structural features or characteristics by using any of the methods found in the following categories:

1. synonyms and CAS registry numbers
2. name fragments
3. molecular formulas
4. molecular weights
5. structure or structural fragments by Wiswesser line formula notation codes
6. structure or structural fragments by diagram via the EPA/NIH substructure search system.

Table II. Components of the EMIC/ETIC Agent Registry

EMIC name	Storage
CAS registry number	Hydrolysis rate
Preferred name	Toxicity
Synonyms	Metabolism
Molecular formula	Safety
Molecular weight	Toxicological data (LD_{50}) locator
Wiswesser line formula notation	Carcinogenic data locator
Usage	Teratogenic data locator
Description	Procurement sources
Boiling point	EMIC availability
Specific gravity	Mutagenicity assay(s) or organism(s) in
Vapor density	which compound has been tested
Solubility	Animal(s) in which teratology testing
	has been done

Output from EMIC's computerized data base can take the form of publications, specialized indexed bibliographies, computer-readable tapes, or microfiche. The data base is available on-line to anyone with access to either the National Library of Medicine's TOXLINE system or the Department of Energy's RECON system.

The EMIC data base now contains 26,000 papers which contain testing data on approximately 8,000 different chemicals. This center has proved to be a successful effort in the establishment of a specialized information center closely allied with and supported by the scientific discipline it serves. For a detailed description of EMIC and its information collecting and processing techniques, see Wassom and Malling [1].

ENVIRONMENTAL TERATOLOGY INFORMATION CENTER (ETIC)

The literature of teratogenesis is found in a variety of journals, books, and symposia. Pertinent articles from this primary literature (Table III) may be referenced in one or more of the partial listing of secondary sources shown in Table IV. Even though there is considerable overlap in the literature covered by these secondary information sources, gaps exist which make it necessary to screen all of these sources to obtain comprehensive coverage.

The task of searching and acquiring literature in this field is presently beyond the means of most researchers or institutions. In order to overcome this situation, the National Institute of Environmental Health Sciences (NIEHS) made funds available to ORNL for the purpose of establishing an information center for teratology. ETIC was therefore organized in 1975. The center follows the same operational concepts and design which were outlined in the previous section for EMIC. Its purpose is to collect, organize and disseminate information on the evaluation of chemical, biological and physical agents for teratogenic activity. The information in the ETIC file is available to individual researchers and physicians, as well as institutions and government research and regulatory agencies. Easy access to this literature facilitates health assessment, research planning, and the prevention of duplication of effort in the field of environmental teratology. Information in the ETIC data base is obtained from reports in the open literature relating to teratogenicity testing and evaluation of dietary deficiencies and chemical, biological and physical agents in warm-blooded animals. The main focus is on the administration of an agent to a pregnant animal and examination of the offspring at or near birth for structural or functional anomalies. Particular attention is given to papers which implicate agents in the production of congenital defects in man. The selection of papers for the ETIC data base will soon be expanded to include information on subjects such as methodology, embryology, human syndrome identification, placental transfer, pharmacokinetics and metabolism.

Table III. Key Journal Sources Used by ETIC.

Teratology	Pediatrics
Toxicology and Applied Pharmacology	Experientia
Lancet	Obstetrics and Gynecology
American Journal of Obstetrics and Gynecology	New England Journal of Medicine
Anatomical Record	Journal of Reproduction and Fertility
Proceedings of the Society for Experimental Biology and Medicine	Food and Cosmetics Toxicology
	American Journal of Diseases of Children
Comptes Rendus des Seances de la Societe de Biologie et de ses Filiales	Journal of Experimental Zoology
British Medical Journal	Journal of Dental Research
Nature	Comptes Rendus Hebdomadaires des Seances de l'Academie des Sciences, Serie D: Sciences Naturelles
Pediatric Research	
Federation Proceedings, Federation of American Societies for Experimental Biology	Endocrinology
	Journal of Animal Science
	Environmental Health Perspectives
Journal of Pediatrics	Biology of the Neonate
Journal of Nutrition	Canadian Medical Association Journal
Arzneimittel-Forschung	Bulletin of Experimental Biology and Medicine (USSR)
Journal of Embryology and Experimental Morphology	Annals of the New York Academy of Sciences
Journal of the American Medical Association	Fertility and Sterility
Science	American Journal of Anatomy
Congenital Anomalies (Senten Ijo)	Journal of Pharmacology and Experimental Therapeutics
Oyo Yakuri (Pharmacokinetics)	Archives of Environmental Health

The ETIC file now contains information extracted from 16,000 references which have been published in over 1,800 primary literature sources. At the present time (March 1979), the agent registry of the center contains information on 4,000 unique chemical agents. The ETIC agent registry file has been combined with the EMIC agent registry to better facilitate data entry and file coordination. Information categories for the EMIC/ETIC agent registry are shown in Table II. A description of this file is found in the section describing EMIC.

ETIC will provide many of the same services as EMIC, but these services will be determined by the funding agency as user needs are assessed. The ETIC file, like that of EMIC, is available on-line via TOXLINE and RECON. This provides the scientific community with ready access to the literature of teratology and enhances the overall utility of these two valuable on-line information systems.

Information in the ETIC file may be retrieved by entering the desired free-text terms as they appear in titles and specific keyword fields. Some of the specific indexing fields used at ETIC are those for bibliographic

Table IV. Secondary Sources Used by ETIC to Obtain Teratology Information

---

Manually Searchable
   Biological Abstracts
   BioResearch Index
   Chemical Abstracts
   Carcinogenesis Abstracts
   Current Contents
   Excerpta Medica
   Genetics Abstracts
   Government Reports Announcements
   Index Medicus
   Nutrition Abstracts and Reviews
   Nuclear Science Abstracts
   Pollution Abstracts
   Teratology Lookout
   Handbooks, textbooks, review articles, monographs (e.g., T. H. Shepard's
     Catalog of Teratogenic Agents published by Johns Hopkins Press,
     Baltimore, MD, 1976)
Computer Searchable On-line Information Systems
   DIALOG/Lockheed Information Systems
   ORBIT/Systems Development Corporation
   MEDLINE, TOXLINE, CANCERLIT, CANCERPROJ, RTECS, EPILEPSY/
     National Library of Medicine
   RECON/Department of Energy

---

information, type of publication, agent(s) or condition(s) tested, CAS registry number(s), test organism (general and specific classification), classification of the observed anomaly, or endpoint of the study.

CARCINOGENESIS INFORMATION RESOURCES

Cancer research as a science under the toxicological research umbrella poses its own problems of definition. This is reflected in the information activities which try to contain the knowledge being generated in this complicated research area. As previously stated, there is no single information source for carcinogenicity. Users must therefore consult several secondary publication sources and/or computer files to cover the field adequately. The information resources that are **recommended** for accessing the carcinogenicity literature and discussed in this section are the following:

1. *Survey of Compounds Which Have Been Tested for Carcinogenic Activity,* HEW/Public Health Service Publication No. 149

2. *International Agency for Research on Cancer Monographs* and *Bulletins* (IARC publications)

3. *Carcinogenesis Abstracts*

4. TOXLINE
5. CANCERLIT
6. CANCERPROJ
7. RTECS

Survey of Compounds Which Have Been Tested for Carcinogenic Activity, HEW/Public Health Service Publication No. 149

This series of large volumes, which has become known as PHS-149, was first published by the Public Health Service in 1951. There are currently seven issues which cover selected literature through 1973. The first issue of PHS-149 was compiled by Dr. Jonathan Hartwell and covered the literature through 1947. This issue appeared as a second edition to a compendium published earlier by Dr. Hartwell. The second issue of PHS-149, published in 1957, covers the literature for the period 1948-1953 and was compiled by Dr. Hartwell with assistance from Dr. Philippe Shubik. These compendiums were published to meet the need for a comprehensive information source for chemical carcinogenicity. The National Cancer Institute (NCI) assumed direct responsibility for continuing the production of these volumes in 1969 when they published the third issue covering the 1954-1960 literature. In the succeeding years, issues have appeared covering the years 1961-1967, 1970-1971 and 1972-1973. Work is currently under way to cover the 1974-1978 literature. These publications have become one of the most often used information resources for determining whether a particular chemical has been tested for carcinogenicity. Entries in PHS-149 are presented in tabular form with the extracted experimental data keyed to the test chemical. Chemicals appearing in the later issues of PHS-149 are linked to their CAS registry number(s), and a cumulative agent index is available on computer tape for the later issues. Since only the chemical index has been computerized, the real value of these publications has not been fully exploited. There is an urgent need for the data in this entire collection to be made available in machine-readable form.

International Agency for Research on Cancer Monographs and Bulletins (IARC Publications)

In 1971, the International Agency for Research on Cancer (IARC) initiated a program to evaluate the carcinogenic risk of chemicals to humans with the objective of producing monographs on individual chemicals. Specifically, the program's commission is to publish critical reviews of data on carcinogenicity for groups of chemicals to which humans are exposed. The data selected to be included in these monographs are to be evaluated in terms of human risks and to indicate where additional research efforts are needed. The monographs summarize the evidence for the carcinogenicity of individual chemicals along with other relevant information such as that for mutagenicity and teratogenicity. The critical analyses of the data in the monographs are intended to assist national and international authorities in formulating decisions concerning preventive measures. The IARC monographs have become widely accepted and used as an authoritative source of information on the carcinogenicity of environmental chemicals. Since the program began in 1971, 18 volumes of the monographs have been published through October 1978. A total of 381 separate chemical substances have been evaluated in these 18 volumes.

In addition to the monographs, the IARC also publishes information bulletins entitled *Survey of Chemicals Being Tested for Carcinogenic Activity*. This project was started in 1973 for the purpose of publicizing on-going research on long-term carcinogenicity testing throughout the world. The major aims of the project are to avoid unnecessary duplication of research, to increase communication among scientists, and to make a census of available research facilities as well as chemicals being tested for carcinogenicity. These information bulletins list chemicals under investigation, animal species and strains, routes of exposure, stage of experiments, principal investigators, and references to published reports of completed studies.

Through these publications, monographs and information bulletins, the IARC is providing a valuable information service to the field of carcinogenicity. This is without question the most significant work now occurring in the area of carcinogenicity information.

Carcinogenesis Abstracts

Carcinogenesis Abstracts is a monthly publication service of NCI and is produced through a contract with the Franklin Institute of Philadelphia. The journal serves as a vehicle through which current documentation of carcinogenesis research highlights are compiled, condensed and disseminated on a regular basis. Issues of this publication normally contain 300 abstracts and 300 citations (unaccompanied by corresponding abstracts). Abstracts and citations refer to the current scientific literature that describes the most significant carcinogenesis research carried on at NCI, other governmental agencies, and private institutions. *Carcinogenesis Abstracts* is intended to be a highly useful current awareness tool for scientists engaged in carcinogenesis research or related areas. To increase their usefulness, subject, author, Wiswesser line formula notation, and CAS registry number indexes are provided. Cumulative indexes are also provided after the final regular issue each year. These abstracts are available on-line via the National Library of Medicine's computer system called CANCERLIT. This system is described in the next section.

TOXLINE

TOXLINE (TOXicology Information on-LINE) is the National Library of Medicine's extensive collection of computerized toxicology information containing over 380,000 references to published human and animal toxicity studies, effects of environmental chemicals and pollutants, adverse drug reactions, and analytical methodology. This rapidly expanding data base, assembled by the Toxicology Information Program, contains full bibliographic citations, almost all with abstracts and/or indexing terms, and CAS registry numbers, from primary journals dating from 1975. Older information is in the TOXLINE backfile, TOXBACK. TOXLINE information is derived from secondary sources and special collections of material. The component sub-files currently providing the most relevant material to TOXLINE are:

1. Chemical Abstracts Service: *Chemical-Biological Activities* (CBAC), from 1965;
2. BioSciences Information Service: *Abstracts on Health Effects of Environmental Pollutants,* from 1972;
3. American Society of Hospital Pharmacists: *International Pharmaceutical Abstracts,* from 1970;
4. National Library of Medicine: *Toxicity Bibliography,* from 1968;
5. Environmental Protection Agency: *Pesticides Abstracts,* from 1966;
6. Hayes File on Pesticides, 1940-1966 (citations only);
7. Environmental Mutagen Information Center, Oak Ridge National Laboratory, from 1968; and
8. Environmental Teratology Information Center, Oak Ridge National Laboratory, from 1950.

Citations on a subject such as carcinogenesis may be retrieved from TOXLINE by entering the desired free-text terms as they appear in titles, keywords and abstracts of articles. Chemical substances can be entered by their corresponding CAS registry number(s) after consulting the CHEMLINE file. There is no controlled vocabulary governing the inclusion or exclusion of terms in TOXLINE. Terms may be entered singly or combined by means of the Boolean operators AND, OR, and AND NOT. Searches may be limited to specific years of publication, secondary sources, or authors since these are all searchable elements. Citations and abstracts may be printed on-line at the user's terminal, or off-line and mailed to the user from the National Library of Medicine. Users may select a print format varying from a brief identification of author(s), title and source to a complete listing of the bibliographic record, including the abstract.

To retrieve earlier references from the TOXLINE system, the TOXBACK file must be searched. TOXBACK contains approximately 200,000 records and is searchable in the same manner as TOXLINE, with the exception that the search is not done on-line. The biggest shortcoming of TOXLINE is that when one searches the whole system, numerous duplicated references are obtained.

CANCERLIT

The CANCERLIT (formerly called CANCERLINE) data base, available on-line from the National Library of Medicine, is sponsored by the International Cancer Research Data Bank (ICRDB) program of NCI and contains over 100,000 abstracts of articles relating to all aspects of cancer. The original data base was created from abstracts which had appeared in *Cancer Therapy Abstracts* from 1967-1973 and in *Carcinogenesis Abstracts* from 1963-1973. The scope of these data bases has been enlarged to include not only the selected cancer topics appearing in these two secondary journals, but *all* other cancer-related articles. In addition, proceedings of meetings, government reports, symposia reports, selected monographs, books and theses are also abstracted for inclusion in the data base. The collection of materials on all aspects of cancer began in early 1976, and the processing of additional source material began in late 1976. CANCERLIT is updated monthly with approximately 3,000 citations.

CANCERPROJ

The CANCERPROJ data base is available on-line from the National Library of Medicine and is also sponsored by the ICRDB program of NCI. This data base contains summaries of on-going cancer research projects which have been provided by cancer scientists in many countries. The data for the project descriptions are processed by the Current Cancer Research Projects Analysis Center (CCRESPAC) of the ICRDB program which is located at the Smithsonian Science Information Exchange (SSIE) in Washington, D.C. CANCERPROJ, which is updated every three months, includes projects funded during the most recent three fiscal years and currently contains approximately 15,000 summaries. These summaries include federal as well as privately supported grants and contracts. All records in the data base contain English summaries and are **retrievable** by free-text searching, i.e., any significant word in the title, summary, or assigned index terms can be used in a search statement. Controlled vocabulary searching can also be done in CANCERPROJ using index terms from the SSIE thesaurus. It is intended that each project description will be updated once a year.

RTECS

RTECS is available on-line from the National Library of Medicine and is the computerized version of the National Institute for Occupational Safety and Health's *Registry of Toxic Effects of Chemical Substances,* 1977 edition. This file contains toxicity data (including carcinogenicity) for approximately 30,000 chemical substances. Also included are threshold limit values, recommended standards in air, aquatic toxicity data, use classification, molecular formula and molecular weight.

In searching RTECS records on a given chemical, route of administration, species and effect may be retrieved. Chemical substances can be entered by their CAS registry number(s) or name(s). Search terms may be entered singly or combined by means of the Boolean operators AND, OR, and AND NOT. To search this file for carcinogenicity information, one must search the toxicity data field. Using the truncated word Carcinogen, one finds 2,654 chemicals which have carcinogenic data available on them. This information may have been selected from the PHS-149 or IARC monographs discussed earlier. It may also reference work in the primary literature and whether or not the chemical has been tested in NCI's bioassay program.

Collectively the information resources just discussed offer the best coverage of the carcinogenicity literature. They are by no means the only ones available, but they are the best sources available at the present time. There is a great need for all of these resources to be pulled together into a central source and operated as a specialized toxicological information center similar to EMIC and ETIC.

CONCLUSIONS

Information systems and other resources which cover the literature from three specific areas of toxicology (mutagenesis, carcinogenesis and teratogenesis) are available for use by the scientific community. Being aware of and using these information tools is necessary if one is to keep up with the voluminous literature now being produced annually in each of these three research areas. The EMIC and the ETIC make the worldwide literature of mutagenesis and teratogenesis available from single sources. These files are continually being updated and improved to meet the changing needs of researchers, administrators and government officials. The field of carcinogenesis is not so fortunate, and one must seek help from several sources. A number of key sources were discussed which will provide users the best coverage of this complex subject.

With the recent, widespread realization that some chemicals may pose severe long-term threats to human health, access to the toxicological literature is paramount. The information activities outlined in this paper—for mutagenesis, carcinogenesis and teratogenesis—provide an essential service to those responsible for testing, evaluating and regulating substances to which humans are exposed.

ACKNOWLEDGMENTS

Rarely is a scientific endeavor accomplished without the work and aid of others. The information activities addressed in this paper are the end products of work of numerous individuals. It is with pleasure that special thanks and credit are given to these people, especially the dedicated staffs of the Environmental Mutagen and the Environmental Teratology Information Centers.

This work was sponsored by the National Institute of Environmental Health Sciences under Interagency Agreements 40-247-70 and 40-524-75 under Union Carbide Corporation contract W-7405-eng-26 with the U.S. Department of Energy.

By acceptance of this article, the publisher or recipient acknowledges the U.S. Government's right to retain a nonexclusive, royalty-free license in and to any copyright covering the article.

REFERENCES

1. Wassom, J. S., and H. V. Malling. "Specialized Information Centers In Toxicology. I. Environmental Mutagen Information Center (EMIC)," in *Advances in Modern Toxicology*, W. G. Flamm and M. A. Mehlman, Eds. (Washington, DC: Hemisphere Publishing Corporation, 1978). p. 351.

CHAPTER 17

SYNTHETIC FOSSIL FUEL TECHNOLOGIES: HEALTH PROBLEMS AND INTERSOCIETY COOPERATION

R. B. Gammage and J. E. Turner
Health and Safety Research Division
Oak Ridge National Laboratory
Oak Ridge, Tennessee

INTRODUCTION

The potential health impacts of synthetic fossil fuel products are considered mainly in terms of complex and potentially carcinogenic mixtures of polynuclear aromatic (PNA) compounds. These components of oils and tars present an especially perplexing range of problems to those concerned with health protection. The nature of these problems, such as multifactorial exposure, is discussed within a framework of current and future standards to regulate human exposure. Some activities of government agencies, national laboratories and professional societies are described. A case can be made for pooling the resources of these groups to achieve better solutions for assessing the acceptability of the various technologies and safeguarding human health.

Synthetic fossil fuel technologies embrace coal, tar sand and oil shale, and their extraction and conversion into more pliable forms of energy. Potential health problems arise from the production of a multitude of chemical agents in gaseous, liquid and solid forms. The workplace and the general environment are impacted. Government agencies such as the Occupational Safety and Health Administration (OSHA), the Environmental Protection Agency (EPA), and the Public Health Service (PHS) impose standards appropriate to their area of concern. For example, the occupational standard for phenol is set at 5 ppm when it occurs as skin contamination. The EPA 1977 standard for phenols in effluents is 2 ppb by weight averaged over a period of 30 days. The limit for phenol in drinking water as set by the PHS is only 1 ppb.

SIMPLE POLLUTANTS

The health hazards of some synfuel pollutants are quite well understood, and these agents are relatively easy to deal with, e.g., product gases carbon monoxide, hydrogen sulfide and ammonia. For each there is an OSHA-controlled, maximum allowable exposure expressed as an 8-hour, time-weighted average, or threshold-weighted average (TWA). A higher exposure level for a shorter duration is also permitted. If simultaneous exposure to more than one of these agents takes place, then the sum of the fractional TWA should not exceed unity. Multicomponent exposures of "simple" pollutants that produce biologically similar effects can, therefore, be handled satisfactorily.

COMPLEX TARS AND OILS

Within the oils and tars produced by synfuel operations are the complex and potentially carcinogenic mixtures of PNA compounds. In contrast to the simple pollutants, these compounds present an especially perplexing range of problems to those concerned with health protection. It will be worthwhile to enumerate these problems; their breadth and magnitude help to emphasize the interdisciplinary approach required for their resolution and reinforce the need for pooling the resources of various scientific societies.

Concentration Limit for Coal Tar Pitch Volatiles (CTPV)

With respect to high-boiling PNA compounds, there is but a single standard, and it relates to occupational control of coal tar pitch volatiles in particulate form. In 1967 the American Conference of Government Industrial Hygienists adopted a threshold limit value (TLV) of 0.2 mg of benzene-soluble CTPV per m^3 of air [1], PNA compounds being soluble in benzene (or cyclohexane). Recently, a NIOSH criteria document [2] recommended that a new standard of 0.1 mg of cyclohexane extractables per m^3 of air be introduced for coal tar products.

Listed components of CTPV [1] were anthracene, phenanthrene, chrysene, pyrene, benzo(a)pyrene (BaP), and acridine. Of these, BaP is usually used as a proxy for the group because it is strongly carcinogenic and because it occurs commonly where high-boiling PNA compounds are found. In 1975 an OSHA standards advisory committee recommended a BaP limit of 0.2 $\mu g/m^3$ of air [3], but to date this concentration limit is not a federally authorized standard.

Multifactorial Exposure and Synergism

In viewing the whole array of potential chemical hazards produced by fossil fuel technologies, the carcinogens are the most conspicuous. The carcinogens are hazardous at low levels of exposure, have delayed action with no immediate warning, and have grave consequences. What makes the issuance of standards for specific PNA compounds so difficult is the complex, multicomponent nature of oils, tars and CTPV, and the strongly concertive or synergistic actions they can have on each other. For example, the apparently innocuous single compounds of pyrene, fluoranthene and catechol are co-carcinogenic in combination with BaP [4,5] and enhance the carcinogenicity of the latter. Of the aliphatic hydrocarbons that could be produced in coal gasification, dodecane is a remarkable tumor potentiator, lowering the BaP threshold dose for skin tumorgenicity by a factor of 10^3 [6]. Phenol also has co-carcinogenic potential attributable to its irritant properties [7]. The gas products of fossil fuel combustion, sulfur dioxide and nitrogen dioxide, may likewise act as co-carcinogens [8]. These problems of multifactorial exposure, synergism, and the controversial issue of a safe concentration limit for a carcinogen reduce the expectation that exposure limits for individual, high-boiling PNA compounds can be defined in a manner similar to occupational standards for the 400 compounds currently under OSHA control.

Differences between Crude Oils

The cyclohexane-soluble fraction of total particulate matter is by itself an insufficient index of the mutagenic and carcinogenic potential of synthetic crudes. Measurement of just the BaP content as an indicator compound of the whole PNA group can also be inadequate or misleading. The subject of proxy PNA compounds and the pros and cons of gauging mutagenic and carcinogenic potential via BaP were discussed recently [9]. Evidence is accumulating to suggest that azaarenes and aromatic amines are increasingly suspect as important synfuel mutagens; 10 to 80% of the mutagenicity of a series of synthetic oils arises from basic constituents compared to about 2% for petroleum crudes [10]. As an extreme example, the mutagenic activity of a Synthoil-derived, ether-soluble base fraction was comparable to that of pure BaP [11]. Although it has been pointed out that comparative compositional studies are still on a preliminary level, it appears that coal-derived crudes are characterized by their greater aromatic content, and the shale oils by their greater content of nitrogen compounds [12]. A recommendation is made that occupational and environmental surveillance programs include azaarenes and amines among the constituents to be monitored [10]. Additionally, because of significant compositional differences that exist among crudes, the occupational monitoring requirements should differ for their respective industries [12].

It is possible, nevertheless, to make some comparison of the relative potencies of the products of petroleum, shale oil, and the oils and tars derived from coal. Mouse dermal bioassay is widely accepted as a measure of carcinogenicity [13]. Data published by Coomes [13] are shown in Table I. The implication of this study is that crude shale oil is no more carcinogenic than common industrial fuel oil from petroleum but that coke-oven tar is about five times more potent. Clearly, these data indicate that one is dealing with very complex situations that proffer taxing difficulties for those who may be charged with responsibilities for formulating additional standards.

Table I. Mouse Dermal Carcinogenicity of Shale Oils and Related Materials[a]

Material	P_{MC}[b]
Whole Shale Oil	0.10
Upgraded Shale	0.03
Industrial Fuel Oil	0.17
Coke-Oven Coal Tar	0.54
Cracked Sidestream	0.26
Naphthenic Distillate	0.06

[a] From Coomes [13].
[b] "Carcinogenicity" relative to 3-methylcholanthrene.

Volatile PNA Vapors and Contaminated Surfaces

There are two types of exposure situations involving PNA compounds where progress in the near future may be possible in establishing guidelines and setting standards. The di- and tricyclic aromatic hydrocarbons, such as naphthalene and quinoline and their alkyl derivatives, have appreciable vapor pressures at ambient temperatures. Portable instruments are being developed that have multicomponent analytical capability for measuring these compounds in the vapor phase in the workplace [14]. Some naphthalene derivatives can accelerate the action of BaP, whereas others have an inhibiting effect [15]. Quinoline is a recognized carcinogen and mutagen [16] and is potentially dangerous as a respiratory carcinogen because of its high volatility. Only naphthalene has an OSHA concentration limit that is 10 ppm. A case can be made for establishing concentration limits for some of the other volatile PNA compounds that have been mentioned.

The other situation where quantification is currently lacking involves contaminated surfaces. Instrumentation is in advanced stages of development for measuring the intensity of gross fluorescence from workplace surfaces [17]. Polycyclic aromatic compounds, as a group, generally fluoresce strongly. A standard might be appropriate and practical for indicating whether or not remedial action is necessary or whether cleanup has been effected to a satisfactory degree.

ADDITIONAL HEALTH FACTORS

There are, of course, other important aspects of the overall health problem that are not directly involved with monitoring. The EPA has a program to establish multimedia environmental goals that are levels of contaminants or degradants that do not produce negative effects in surrounding populations or ecosystems [18]. Criteria to meet such goals include lists of effluents with minimum acute toxicity for undiluted streams of pollutants and ambient level goals for the dispersed pollutants.

Another approach to risk assessment involves establishment of composite hazard indices [19] that will be based on estimates of the carcinogenic potential of certain chemicals from their cytotoxic effects in vitro. Analysis of a number of experimental systems has indicated a direct relationship between in vitro cell survival and cancer incidence [20]. Additional aspects of the overall health picture involve modeling at the cellular level, biological endpoints [20], bacterial and animal testing [21], protective measures involving barrier creams [21], or application of antioxidants [22], medical testing and surveillance [22,23], procedures for decontaminating [21] and waste disposal schemes.

A fertile basis exists for intersociety cooperation, cooperation that would provide the presently absent body of impartial experts to make objective judgments about the acceptability of specific technologies from the standpoint of human and environmental health.

ACTIVITIES OF SOCIETIES AND FEDERAL AGENCIES

Faced with the health problems posed by synthetic fuel technologies, a number of organizations with professional interests and legal responsibilities are taking action. It is generally recognized that the cooperation of various local and federal agencies with mutual–and sometimes conflicting– requriements is essential. The scientific and technical problems are enormous. The resources available for their solution must be used in the optimum manner with a minimum of duplication to obtain the most benefit for human health.

We have tried to learn of the activities of various organizations, both within the federal government and outside, in areas of health protection for synthetic fuel technologies. In some instances, we have made personal contacts with knowledgeable individuals, such as committee chairmen, to learn about their activities and plans as well as the work of others. While we have undoubtedly not covered every important effort, the information we have obtained, and its pertinence to intersociety cooperation, should be of interest to members of the American Chemical Society (ACS) Division of Chemical Health and Safety.

Table II summarizes some activities of federal agencies, national laboratories, and professional societies. We shall briefly describe each.

Federal Agencies

The National Institute of Occupational Safety and Health (NIOSH), in accordance with the Occupational Safety and Health Act of 1970, has research efforts in four areas for occupational health hazards associated with coal gasification. These activities include [24]:

1. industrial hygiene characterization of gasification plants;
2. a comprehensive series of recommendations for gasification plant development based on existing knowledge;
3. development of a health maintenance and health surveillance protocol for gasification plant employees; and
4. a program to evaluate and recommend engineering and process design alterations, workplace monitoring systems, safe work practices, and protective equipment to prevent disease in workers employed in gasification plants.

The environmental Protection Agency (EPA) has recognized the need to control exposures to acceptable levels. They have established a list of toxic substances associated with related aqueous effluents [25]. These have been put into a number of chemical categories, one of which contains 16 PNA hydrocarbons that are to be monitored in effluents. The EPA's Industrial Environmental Research Laboratory (IERL) at Research Triangle Park, NC, has sponsored a series of symposia on environmental aspects of fuel conversion technology [18]. These activities are directed toward furthering sampling and assessment work. The evaluation of the Kosovo Lurgi gasification plant in Yugoslavia is the largest and most comprehensive of IERL's commercial activities dealing with data aquisition.

Table II. Selected Examples of Interorganizational, Interdisciplinary
and Intersociety Liaison on Health Problems Related to
Synthetic Fossil Fuel Technologies

Organization	Example of Activity	Reference
NIOSH	Conducts research in four areas concerned with coal gasification; develops criteria documents	2, 24
EPA	Classifies hazardous substances; sponsors symposia on environmental aspects of synfuel technologies	18, 25
DOE	Balanced program plan; develops information overviews; develops coal gasification facility plans	21, 22, 26
IRLG	Four agencies pool and share information	27, 28
BNL	Maintains a working group on monitoring needs for coal conversion and oil shale	29
ORNL	Life sciences synthetic fuels program; EMIC; EMIC; sponsors symposia and workshops	21, 22, 26 23, 30
ACS	Division of Chemical Health and Safety; international cosponsorship of meetings	
ICPEMC	Develops statements as bases for guides and regulations concerning mutagenic and carcinogenic chemicals	
AIHA	Maintains several standing technical committees	
HPS	Holds sessions on hazards of nonradioactive pollutants included in some meetings; compares chemical and radiation cell survival data	20, 31 32, 33
EMS	Polls members on formation of current data file on chemical hazards by EMIC; reports on environmental mutagenic hazards	34
SOEH	Sponsors symposia and workshops on key problems	
ASTM	Task forces currently developing standards for occupational exposure to a variety of chemicals	

The Department of Energy (DOE) instigated the development of a balanced program plan [26], identifying specific needs for biomedical and environmental research and development. Comprehensive information overview documents have also been assembled on the environmental, health and control aspects of coal conversion [22]. In the area of low-Btu gasifiers in industry, environmental and health plans have been written for the first two units (Duluth, MN, and Pike County, KY). Health problems are addressed with respect to issues, requirements and tasks. For example, one of the issues for the University of Minnesota gasification facility is whether the occupational work force is being adequately protected. One of the requirements is to establish the level and nature of exposure in a worker's environment at each stage of gasification. Four specific tasks are to:

1. select, install and operate in-plant area monitors for selected pollutants (e.g., PNA compounds, CO and H_2S),
2. identify and monitor potential sources of fugitive emissions or leaks,
3. review and select personal monitors for selected pollutants (especially for coal oil or coal tar separation operations), and
4. correlate information for consistency, uncertainties and definition of industrial hygiene needs.

DOE works extensively through its national laboratories and energy research centers. From among these broad programs, two examples—one at Brookhaven National Laboratory and one at Oak Ridge National Laboratory—will be described.

The Interagency Regulatory Liaison Group (IRLG) was formed in August 1977 by the heads of four agencies: the Consumer Product Safety Commission, EPA, the Food and Drug Administration, and OSHA. The information uncovered by this group clearly illustrates the potential for duplication of effort and the need for interorganizational liaison. An early survey revealed that these four agencies alone had some 300 ongoing projects at a cost of $39 million concerned with control of toxic substances [27]. The agencies agreed to pool and to share information and to develop cooperative efforts to optimize health protection programs. One of their working groups has recently drawn up development plans [28] for 24 toxic entities (e.g., asbestos, cadmium, coke oven emissions, nitrosamines, polychlorinated biphenyls, radiation, and polyvinylchloride). For each, the report summarizes the agencies' authority to regulate the adverse biological effects, opportunities to avoid conflicts and duplication, economic ramifications of regulations, and recommendations for future action. The agencies will also establish a joint computerized information system on toxic substances that will contain all regulations and pertinent legal decisions.

Regulation of coke oven emission sources concerns both OSHA and EPA and presents a potential area of conflict. On October 22, 1976, OSHA promulgated a new standard for coke oven emissions of 150 μg of benzene-soluble particulates per cubic meter of air, averaged over 8 hours. The standard was to be phased in over a period of three years. The EPA is concerned about emission sources, such as wet-coal charging operations, battery stacks and quench towers, that could impact public health. A background information document is being assembled that includes health risk assessment and selection of a surrogate, such as BaP, that can be related to visible emissions, the general physical appearance of some of the coke oven emissions. OSHA is concerned that if EPA proceeds with separate rule-making, its own standard may be preempted because of the way in which Section 4(b)(1) of the Occupational Safety and Health Act of 1970 is drafted [28].

National Laboratories

Brookhaven National Laboratory (BNL) has established a working group on assessing industrial hygiene monitoring needs for the coal conversion and oil shale industries. It is an active organization with a clearly defined function—evaluating instrumentation and monitoring needs. The group, which is chaired by Otto White, Jr., of BNL, "was formed as an initial effort to avoid a traditional problem associated with new industries, i.e., not recognizing health hazards concurrent with the development of the technology" [29]. In its preliminary report, the group identifies research and development requirements for assessing potentially hazardous exposures. They classify these as being:

1. immediately hazardous to life and health (e.g., O_2 deficiency, explosive coal dust);
2. high risk, but not immediately hazardous (e.g., some organics, metals, fibers and dust); and
3. moderate risk and not immediately hazardous.

The working group met again in November 1978. A more comprehensive report is being prepared.

The Oak Ridge National Laboratory (ORNL) life sciences synthetic fuels programs provide examples of other interdisciplinary work in which the national laboratories are participating. These programs represent a very broad approach, addressing the whole gamut of problems: chemical characterization, health and safety, biological effects, environmental transport and ecological effects, control technology, and assessment and siting. Eight laboratory divisions participate in this program. A life sciences committee on synthetic fossil fuels has succeeded in formulating human and environmental health assessment documents specific to the low-Btu coal gasifier at the University of Minnesota at Duluth [21] and is in the process of doing the same for the low-Btu gasifier in Pike County, KY, and the H-coal liquefaction plant at Catlettsburg, KY. Symposia and workshops are also organized [23,30]. Numerous computerized data bases, such as that of the Environmental Mutagen Information Center, exist at ORNL.

Professional Societies

The American Chemical Society's (ACS) April 1979 meeting represents an important acitivity of the society's Division of Chemical Health and Safety.

The subject of the meeting, "Safe Handling of Chemical Carcinogens, Mutagens and Teratogens: The Chemists' Viewpoint," attests to the recognition of the importance of the problems we have been describing. The meeting's international scope is emphasized by the co-sponsorship of the Chemical Society of Japan and the participation of the Royal Australian Chemical Institute, the New Zealand Institute of Chemistry, and the Chemical Institute of Canada. Meetings of this kind afford important opportunities for intersociety cooperation, liaison, and exchange of ideas and information.

The International Commission for Protection Against Environmental Mutagens and Carcinogens (ICPEMC) was founded in January 1977, sponsored by the Institut de la Vie and affiliated with the International Association of Environmental Mutagen Societies. It has recruited some 20 members from universities, research laboratories and industry. The primary objective of ICPEMC is "to identify and promote scientific principles in the fields of environmental mutagenesis, carcinogenesis, and toxicity." The commission will develop statements to serve as a basis for guides and regulations to prevent or minimize deleterious effects of chemicals in man. ICPEMC has formed five committees to review specific areas. These areas are:

1. short-term screening systems,
2. relationships between carcinogens and mutagens,
3. preparation of a registry of national regulatory principles,
4. risk estimate procedures, and
5. epidemiological approaches.

ICPEMC has also formed task groups to generate its priorities and statements. The commission secretary is P. H. M. Lohman, Medical Biological Laboratory TNO, Rijswijk, Netherlands. The formation of ICPEMC is reminiscent of the International Commission on Radiological Protection, the foremost international organization in the field of radiation protection standards. Such commissions can play a vital role as scientific reviewing bodies, free of governmental and political objectives.

The American Industrial Hygiene Association (AIHA) has several standing technical committees in areas related to problems that arise in synthetic fossil fuel technology. H. E. Runion, Chairman of the Hygienic Guides Committee, Albuquerque, NM, informed us of a session on occupational health aspects of solvent refined coal processes and products included at the Chicago meeting of the AIHA in May 1979. AIHA also has a technical committee on workplace environmental exposure levels.

The Health Physics Society (HPS) was founded as a professional organization dedicated to the protection of man from the potential harmful effects of ionizing radiation while realizing its benefits for mankind. While its principal theme has been radiation, the society has provided a forum for discussion of the potential hazards from nonradiation pollutants. Its 1974 midyear symposium on population exposures included a session on exposure to nonradioactive pollutants [31]. The journal *Health Physics* has also published discussions of the role of this society. It has been pointed out that the membership of the HPS constitutes a significant national resource for addressing problems from human exposure to chemical insults [32]. The lack of input from the health physics profession in the formulation of programs to attack problems of chemical exposures is regrettable [33]. In another effort, the authors have been active as members of a committee on chemical pollutants formed recently in the HPS East Tennessee Chapter. This committee requested that the board of directors of the parent HPS bring to the attention of the membership the question of HPS activity in the field of chemical health hazards. While the HPS did not overtly assume an expanded role as a matter of stated policy, it has not discouraged members from presenting their views at its meetings and in its journals. In this regard, one avenue of approach to chemical hazards is the application of data we have acquired on radiation. For example, cell survival data are being used as a basis for comparing damage from chemical insults with damage from radiation [20].

The Environmental Mutagen Society (EMS) has polled its members on the proposal of the Environmental Mutagen Information Center at Oak Ridge National Laboratory to build a current computerized information file. Often, data on chemicals, such as mutagenesis assays, require considerable time to reach publication in the open literature. EMS is considering forming a new data file to accept such information from investigators as soon as it is released. Restrictions on the use of any data in the file would be determined by the submitter. The existence and use of this file would in no way alter normal publication procedures.

Committee 17 of the EMS has published an article [34] describing methods (principally screening systems) for detecting environmental mutagens, ways of assessing the potential health impact of environmental mutagens, and regulatory principles for preventing environmental mutagenesis. In this report it is pointed out that a direct comparison can be made between mutagenic effects produced by chemicals and by radiation, for which a large body of data exists. In analogy with the radiation unit, rem (roentgen-equivalent-man), one defines the rec (rem-equivalent-chemical) as the dose (average concentration multiplied by exposure time) that produces an amount of genetic damage equivalent to that produced by 1 rem of radiation. This committee recommends "specific limits for the environmental distribution of mutagenic agents, including both ionizing radiations and chemical compounds, such that the resulting genetic damage does not exceed a 12.5% increase over the spontaneous mutational background" [34].

The Society for Occupational and Environmental Health (SOEH) was founded in 1972 to identify physical, chemical and other hazards in the occupational and general environments and to propose actions to reduce their danger. SOEH urges a multidisciplinary approach to the key problems in all their facets. It has sponsored a number of conferences and workshops on specific issues, such as beryllium, vinyl and polyvinylchlorides, and lead and arsenic.

The American Society of Testing and Materials (ASTM) E-34 Committee is working actively. Thirteen task forces are currently developing draft standards for occupational exposure to a wide variety of hazardous chemicals, potentially dangerous procedures, and safety equipment. Polynuclear aromatic hydrocarbons are not included. Consideration, however, is being given to formation of a task force on PNA hydrocarbons that could limit itself initially to a few of the more seemingly solvable problems such as those mentioned in the section "Volatile PNA Vapors and Contaminated Surfaces." Such a task force would provide the focus for discussion and definition of the various problems and deciding where practical solutions are desirable or possible.

SUMMARY OF ORGANIZATIONAL ACTIVITIES

While by no means exhaustive, this survey of synthetic fuel health problems and the examples of the activities of various organizations are revealing. The efforts of government agencies sometimes involve conflicting requirements of the promotor and the protector in the same institution, as do cooperative efforts between government and industry. In contrast to the role of the International Commission on Radiation Protection or the National Council on Radiation Protection and Measurement in radiation protection, there is no neutral international or national scientific body to which conflicts and disputes can be taken. Perhaps the newly organized ICPEMC might succeed in filling this gap.

Scientific societies are active to various degrees themselves and through intersociety liaisons. However, no society has taken a clear lead. Perhaps an ASTM task group comes closest to providing a vehicle for a concerted program. The authors believe that all must work together to define the problems in their broadest context and to begin developing standards. Some of the easier tasks would appear to be agreeing on guidelines for the volatile PNA hydrocarbons and surface contamination.

ACKNOWLEDGMENT

This research was sponsored by the Office of Health and Environmental Research, U.S. Department of Energy, under contract W-7405-eng-26 with the Union Carbide Corporation. By acceptance of this article, the publisher or recipient acknowledges the U.S. Government's right to retain a nonexclusive, royalty-free license in and to any copyright covering the article.

REFERENCES

1. "American Conference of Government Industrial Hygienists: Threshold Limit Values for 1967—Recommended and Intended Values," ACGIH, Cincinnati (1967), p. 7.
2. "Criteria for a Recommended Standard—Occupational Exposure to Coal Tar Products," DHEW (NIOSH), Publication No. 78-107 (1977).
3. *Occup. Safety Health Reporter* 4:1639 (1975).
4. Hoffmann, D., and E. L. Wynder. "Studies on Gasoline Engine Exhaust," *J. Air Poll. Control Assoc.* 13:322-327 (1963).
5. Van Duuren, B. L., C. Katz and B. M. Goldschmidt. "Cocarcinogenic Agents in Tobacco Carcinogenesis," *J. Nat. Cancer Inst.* 51:703-705 (1973).
6. Bingham, E., and H. E. Falk. "Environmental Carcinogens: The Magnifying Effect of Cocarcinogens on the Threshold Response," *Arch. Environ. Health* 19:779-783 (1969).
7. Tye, R., and K. L. Stemmer. "Experimental Carcinogenesis of the Lung: Influence of Phenols," *J. Nat. Cancer Inst.* 39:175-186 (1967).
8. Von Nieding, G. "Possible Mutagenic Properties and Carcinogenic Action of the Irritant Gaseous Pollutants NO_2, O_3, and SO_2," *Environ. Health Persp.* 22:91-92 (1978).
9. Gammage, R. B. "Preliminary Thoughts on Proxy PNA Compounds in the Vapor and Solid Phase," *Proc. of the Symp. on Assessing Industrial Hygiene Monitoring Needs for the Coal Conversion and Oil Shale Industries*, Brookhaven Natl. Lab., Upton, NY, BNL 51002, pp. 173-188 (1979).
10. Ho, C.-H., M. R. Guerin, B. R. Clark, T. K. Rao and J. L. Epler. "Azaarenes and Aromatic Amines Identified as Important Mutagens in Synthetic Crude Oils," *Science* (submitted).
11. Guerin, M. R., C.-H. Ho., B. R. Clark, J. L. Epler and T. K. Rao. "Separation of Mutagenic Components in Synthetic Crudes," presented at the 175th Natl. Meeting of the Am. Chem. Soc., Anaheim California, March 12-17, 1978.
12. Griest, W. H., M. R. Guerin, B. R. Clark, C.-H. Ho, I. B. Rubin and A. R. Jones. "Relative Chemical Composition of Selected Synthetic Crudes," *Proc. of the Symp. on Assessing the Industrial Hygiene Needs for the Coal Conversion and Oil Shale Industries*, Brookhaven Natl. Lab., Upton, NY, November 6-7, 1978.

13. Coomes, R. M. "Health Effects of Oil Shale Processing," *Quart. Colorado Sch. Mines* 71(4):101 (1976).

14. Gammage, R. B., T. Vo-Dinh, A. R. Hawthorn, J. H. Thorngate and W. W. Parkinson. "New Techniques for Measuring PNA in the Workplace," *Advances in Chemistry Series, Analytical Chemistry of Liquid Fuel Sources: Tar Sands, Oil Shale, Coal, and Petroleum,* (170) pp. 78-98 (1978).

15. Schmeltz, I., J. Tosk, J. Hilfrich, N. Hirota, D. Hoffman and E. L. Wynder. "Bioassays of Naphthalene and Alkylnaphthalenes for Cocarcinogenic Activity: Relation to Tobacco Carcinogenesis," *Carcinogenesis, Polynuclear Aromatic Hydrocarbons* 3:47-60 (1978).

16. Dong, M., I. Schmeltz, E. LaVoie and D. Hoffmann. "Azaarenes in the Respiratory Environment: Analysis and Assays for Mutagenicity," *Carcinogenesis, Polynuclear Aromatic Hydrocarbons* 3:97-108 (1978).

17. Schuresko, D. D. "A Portable Monitor to Detect PNA Contamination of Work Area Surfaces," *Proc. of the Symp. on Assessing the Industrial Hygiene Needs for the Coal Conversion and Oil Shale Industries,* Brookhaven Natl. Lab., Upton, NY, BNL 51002, pp. 211-222 (1979).

18. Kingsbury, G. L. "Development of Multimedia Environmental Goals for Pollutants from Fuel Conversion Processes," *Symp. Proc: Environmental Aspects of Fuel Conversion Technol., III,* EPA-600/7-78-063, pp. 53-75 (1978).

19. Walsh, P. J., G. G. Killough, and P. S. Rohwer. "Composite Hazard Index for Assessing Limiting Exposures to Environmental Pollutants: Formulation and Derivation," *Environ. Sci. Technol.* 12:799-802 (1978).

20. Griffin, D., T. D. Jones and P. J. Walsh. "Chemical Cytotoxicity: A Cancer Promoter," in *Polynuclear Aromatic Hydrocarbons,* P. W. Jones and P. Leber, Eds. (Ann Arbor, MI: Ann Arbor Science Publishers, Inc., 1979), pp. 723-732.

21. "Proposed Environmental and Health Program for University of Minnesota Gasification Facility," K. E. Cowser, Ed., Oak Ridge National Laboratory, Oak Ridge, TN, January 23, 1978.

22. Braunstein, H. M., E. D. Copenhaver and H. A. Pfuderer. "Environ-. mental, Health, and Control Aspects of Coal Conversion: An Information Overview," ORNL/EIS-94 (Vol. 1) and ORNL/EIS-94 (Vol. 2), (1977).

23. Gammage, R. B. "Proc. of the Second ORNL Workshop on Exposure to Polynuclear Aromatic Hydrocarbons in Coal Conversion Processes," March 9-11, 1977, CONF-770361 (1977).

24. Young, R. J., W. J. McKay and J. M. Evans. "Coal Gasification and Occupational Health," *Am. Ind. Hyg. J.* 39:985-997 (1978).

25. Wilkinson, J. E., P. E. Strup and P. W. Jones. "Quantitative Analysis of Selected PAH in Aqueous Effluent by High-Performance Liquid Chromatography," in *Polynuclear Aromatic Hydrocarbons,* P. W. Jones and P. Leber, Eds. (Ann Arbor, MI: Ann Arbor Science Publishers, Inc., 1979), pp. 217-230.

26. "Balanced Program Plan, Vol. IV, Coal Conversion," ORNL-5123 (1976).
27. "Regulating Hazardous Substances," *Environ. Sci. Technol.* 13(2): 146-148 (1979).
28. Interagency Regulatory Liaison Group (CPSC, EPA, FDA, OSHA), "Hazardous Substances," Dec. 1, 1978.
29. White, O. "Working Group on Assessing Industrial Hygiene Needs for the Coal Conversion and Oil Shale Industries," Report BNL-24925, Brookhaven National Laboratory, Upton, NY, 11973, August 1978.
30. "Symposium on Potential Health and Environmental Effects of Synthetic Fossil Fuel Technologies," September 25-28, 1978, CONF-780903 (1979).
31. "Symposium on Population Exposures, Eighth Midyear Topical Symposium of the Health Physics Society," Knoxville, TN, October 21-24, 1977, CONF-741018, available from the National Technical Information Service, U.S. Department of Commerce, Springfield, VA 22161.
32. Turner, J. E., K. E. Shank, A. S. Loebl and C. E. Easterly. "The Role of the Health Physicist in the Development of Safe Energy Sources," *Health Phys.* 34:189-190 (1978).
33. Gammage, R. B., J. H. Thorngate, W. W. Parkinson, A. R. Hawthorne and T. Vo-Dinh. "On the Desirability of the Health Physics Society Assuming Responsibilities in Nonnuclear and Nonradiation Fields," *Health Phys.* 35:711-714 (1978).
34. "Environmental Mutagenic Hazards," *Science* 187:503-514 (1975).

CHAPTER 18

POTENTIAL INDUSTRIAL CARCINOGENIC AND MUTAGENIC ALKYLATING AGENTS

Lawrence Fishbein

U.S. Department of Health, Education
and Welfare
Food and Drug Administration
National Center for Toxicological Research
Jefferson, Arkansas

INTRODUCTION

The universe of potentially hazardous chemicals is quite broad and includes classes of agents drawn from use categories such as industrial chemicals, pesticides, food additives and drugs per se, as well as their trace synthetic impurities and/or degradation products. Additionally, a broad spectrum of hazardous *naturally* occurring toxicants is known to exist.

It is generally acknowledged that the past few decades have witnessed an unparalleled expansion of the chemical industry, with the concomitant development of many new organic chemical products as well as enhanced product application. Hence, the number and amounts of chemicals and end products to which man is potentially exposed are staggering.

There are approximately 3.5 million known chemicals with about 25,000-30,000 chemicals in significant production in the United States alone. It is estimated that about 700 to 3000 new industrial chemicals are introduced per year. In the past decade the production of synthetic organic chemicals has expanded by 255%.

Some 2500 individual chemicals or mixtures are reported to be in current use by the plastics industry alone as antioxidants, antistatics,

329

plasticizers, stabilizers and ultraviolet absorbers. The number of possible combinations of these agents can be equally staggering if not bewildering.

It should also be noted that while the numbers of individuals directly involved in the preparation of these chemicals and their by-products (e.g., plastics and polymers) are relatively small compared to many industrial segments and processes, the degree of exposure to potentially hazardous (carcinogenic and mutagenic) substances can be very substantial indeed. Substantially greater numbers of individuals may be indirectly exposed to these potential carcinogens and mutagens via:

1. use applications which may contain entrained materials, and
2. inhalation, ingestion or absorption of these agents via air, water and food sources resulting from escape into the atmosphere, leaching into water and food.

Exposure to chemical agents is known to cause a range of occupational cancers, mainly of the skin, bladder, lungs and nasal sinuses.

Concomitant with the potential cancer risk of environmental agents is the growing concern over the possibility that future generations may suffer from genetic damage by mutation-inducing chemical substances to which large segments of the population may unwittingly be exposed.

Chemical carcinogens and mutagens represent a spectrum of agents varying in activity by a factor of at least 10^7 with strikingly different biological activities, ranging from highly reactive molecules that can alkylate macromolecules and cause mutations in many organisms to compounds that are hormonally active and have neither of these actions. It must be admitted that all of the chemicals on the market, a relatively small proportion— approximately 7000–have been tested to determine their cancer-causing potential; approximately 1000 compounds have thus far been found to be tumorigenic in test animals.

We do not know with precision what percentage of *existing* chemicals as well as those which enter the environment annually may be hazardous, primarily in terms of their potential carcinogenicity and mutagenicity. Although the etiology of human neoplasia, with rare exceptions, is unknown, it is held by some that a large number of cancers can be directly or indirectly attributed to environmental factors. At present, the most influential single carcinogenic exposure appears to be cigarette smoking. Modes of exposure to chemicals include diets, personal habits such as smoking, and external environmental air and water pollution.

The major objectives of the review are to: (1) consider and collate a number of industrially significant alkylating compounds encompassing a spectrum of structural categories that have been reported to be carcinogenic and/or mutagenic in order to better assess the nature of the present potential risk; and (2) to determine whether there are structural and biological similarities among these agents which would better permit a measure of predictability and prioritization in both the screening of new or untested compounds, and to determine which of the existing potential chemical carcinogens should be investigated in long-term bioassays.

It is useful to briefly summarize several key considerations of reactivity of chemical carcinogens that are particularly germane for the predictive value of mutagenicity tests in chemical carcinogenesis. Many chemical carcinogens are reactive electrophiles per se, e.g., alkylating agents, acylating agents, and other electrophiles [1-7].

The majority of carcinogens (procarcinogens) and many mutagens require metabolic activation in the host for transformation to their so-called "ultimate" reactive forms. Some procarcinogens are often chemically or spontaneously converted to ultimate carcinogens by hydrolytic reactions and exhibit a broad spectrum of activity in many species and target organs. Other procarcinogens which require host-controlled biochemical activation (dependent on specific enzyme systems) may exhibit more specific and/or restricted carcinogenic activity. It should also be noted that the procarcinogen and its derivatives are subject to deactivation reactions which can lead to compounds possessing either no carcinogenic activity or less carcinogenic potential than the parent compound.

The common denominator of these ultimate reactive metabolites of carcinogens is their electrophilicity. They are compounds which react with electron-rich sites in cellular nucleic acids and proteins causing mutagenic effects frequently paralleled by the onset of DNA repair processes.

Figures 1 through 4 illustrate typical activation reactions (procarcinogens to proximate carcinogen to ultimate carcinogen) for a variety of familiar agents. These figures summarize the classic work of the Millers and Weisburgers and their co-workers, as well as Clayson, Magee, Brooks, Lawley, Preussman and many others [1-7].

As summarized by Brusick, "if chemical carcinogens or their electrophilic metabolites induce genetic changes which directly or in association with other cellular dysfunctions result in the malignant transformation of normal cells to potential tumor cells, then by the detection of mutagenic activity, potential carcinogens can be identified" [7]. According to the scheme of Brusick, only carcinogens that have a reactive electrophilic state are expected to be detected by mutagenic assays (Figure 5). Figure 6 illustrates sites of interaction of chemical carcinogens with DNA in vivo and in vitro.

The category of direct-acting alkylating agents can be divided into 13 major subdivisions: epoxides, lactones, alkylsulfates, cyclic aliphatic sulfuric acid esters, sultones, aryldialkyltriazenes, diazoalkanes, phosphoric acid esters, alkane halides, alkyl halides, halogenated alkanols, halogenated

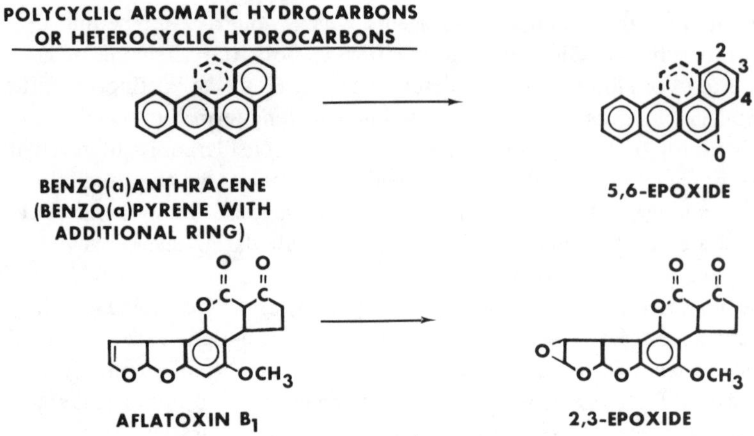

POLYCYCLIC AROMATIC HYDROCARBONS OR HETEROCYCLIC HYDROCARBONS

BENZO(a)ANTHRACENE (BENZO(a)PYRENE WITH ADDITIONAL RING)

5,6-EPOXIDE

AFLATOXIN B$_1$

2,3-EPOXIDE

Figure 1. Typical activation reactions (procarcinogen to proximate carcinogen to ultimate carcinogen) for PAH or heterocyclic hydrocarbons and aflatoxin B$_1$.

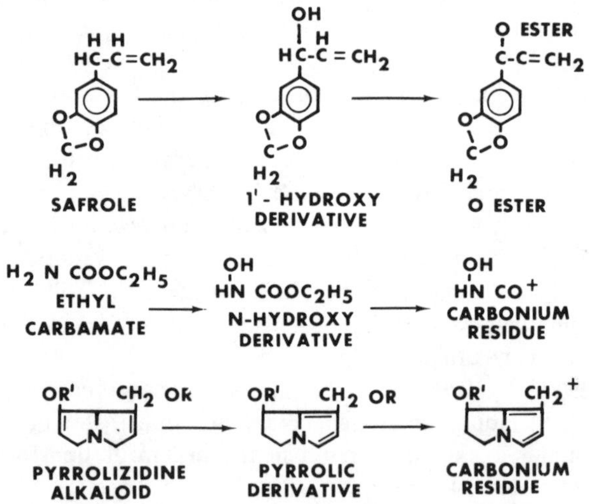

SAFROLE

1'-HYDROXY DERIVATIVE

O ESTER

ETHYL CARBAMATE

N-HYDROXY DERIVATIVE

CARBONIUM RESIDUE

PYRROLIZIDINE ALKALOID

PYRROLIC DERIVATIVE

CARBONIUM RESIDUE

Figure 2. Typical activation reactions (procarcinogen to proximate carcinogen to ultimate carcinogen) for safrole, ethyl carbamate and pyrrolizidine alkaloid.

ethers and aldehydes. The industrial alkylating agents and acylating agents considered in this overview are limited to organic compounds and selected on factors including: their reported carcinogenicity and/or mutagenicity, their chemical structures and relationship to known chemical carcinogens and mutagens, their volume or use characteristics and suggested or estimated potential populations at risk.

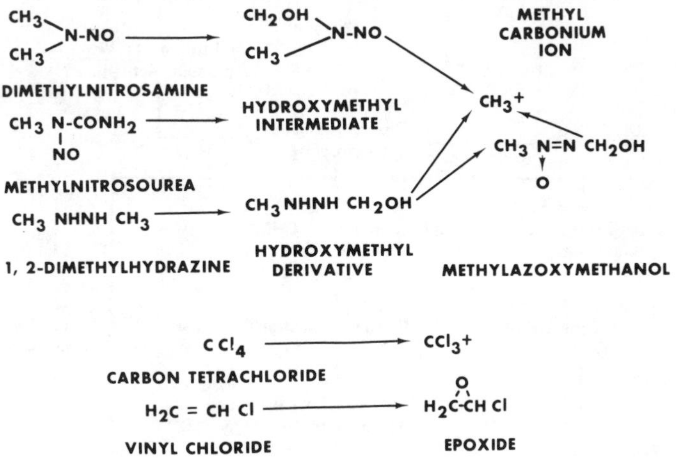

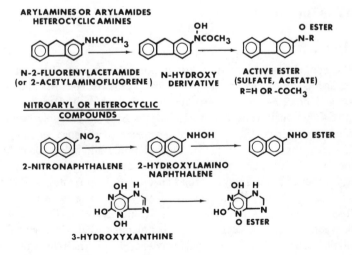

Figure 3. Typical activation reactions (procarcinogen to proximate carcinogen to ultimate carcinogen) for dimethylnitrosamine, methylnitrosourea, 1,2-dimethylhydrazine, carbon tetrachloride and vinyl chloride.

Figure 4. Typical activation reactions (procarcinogen to proximate carcinogen to ultimate carcinogen) for N-2-fluorenylacetamide or 2-acetylaminofluorene, 2-nitronaphthalene and 3-hydroxyxanthine.

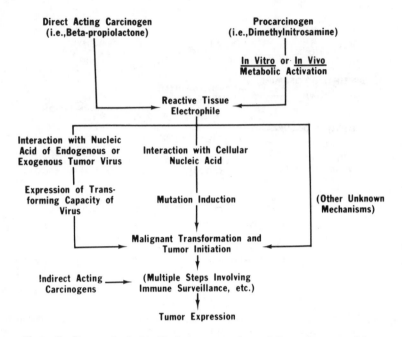

Figure 5. Proposed relationship between carcinogenicity and mutagenicity.

ALKYLATING AGENTS

Epoxides

The epoxides represent the most important category of industrial alkylating agents. Epoxides are electrophilically reactive and can bind to DNA,
RNA and proteins both in vivo and in vitro [8-10]. The presence of a
reactive functional group (as in epichlorohydrin) or a double bond (as in
glycidaldehyde) near the epoxide also appears to enhance carcinogenicity
by allowing the reagent to act as a difunctional alkylating agent for macromolecules. The epoxides such as those depicted in Figures 7 and 8 are
widely produced and enjoy a broad spectrum of applications. For example,
approximately 4200 million pounds of ethylene oxide were produced in
1976 and used in the production of ethylene glycol, acylic monoionic
surface-active agents, glycol ethers, ethanolamine, diethylene glycol, cyclic
nonionic surface-active agents, polyethylene glycol, triethyleneglycol,
polyether phenols, as an intermediate for polyethylene terephthalate
polyester fiber and film production [11]. It is also widely used in fumigation and cold sterilization of medical devices including cannulas, plastic

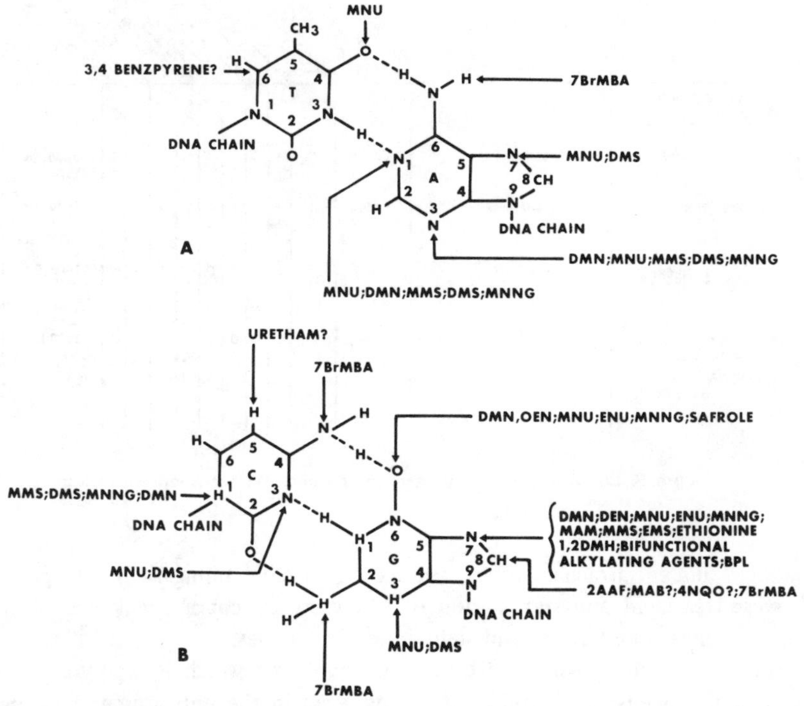

Figure 6. Sites of interaction of chemical carcinogens with DNA in vivo and in vitro.

				Mutagenicity								
Class	Chemical Name & Synonym	CAS#	Carcin- ogenicity	Bacteria	Yeast	Neurospora	Drosophila	Mammalian Cells	Human Cells	Dominant Lethal	Host Mediated	Production a/ Quantites
I. Alkylating Agents												
A. Epoxides												
$H_2C\text{-}CH_2$ ⟍O⟋	Ethylene Oxide b	75-21-8	−	+	0	+	+	+	0	+	0	4,870 x 10⁶ lbs (1975)
$H_2C\text{-}CHCH_3$ ⟍O⟋	Propylene Oxide b	75-26-9	+	+	0	+	+	0	0	0	0	2,315 x 10⁶ lbs (1975)
$H_2C\text{-}CHCH_2CH_3$ ⟍O⟋	Butylene Oxide (1,2-Epoxybutane; Propyl Oxirane)	106-88-7	−	−	0	0	0	0	0	0	0	10 x 10⁶ lbs (1974)
$H_2C\text{-}HCH_2Cl$ ⟍O⟋	Epichlorohydrin b	106-89-8	+	−	0	+	+	+	+	−	+	450 x 10⁶ lbs (1976)

Figure 7. Potential industrial carcinogens and mutagens–epoxides.

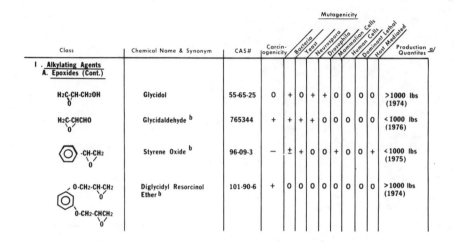

Figure 8. Potential industrial carcinogens and mutagens—epoxides.

syringes and intratracheal tubes, and as a fungicidal fumigant in the post-harvest treatment and sterilization of whole spices, copra, black walnut, meats, cocoa, dried fruits and dehydrated vegetables.

Ethylene oxide possesses a three-membered ring which is highly strained and readily opens under mild conditions; even in the unprotonated form, it reacts with nucleophiles to undergo S_N2 reactions. Ethylene oxide reacts with DNA, primarily at the N-7 position of guanosine, forming N-7-hydroxyethylguanine [12]. It reacts with active hydrogen compounds and with inorganic chloride to form ethylene chlorohydrin and ethylene glycol which can exist as trace residues (along with unreacted ethylene oxide per se) on sterilized products. Approximately 98.8 million pounds of ethylene oxide are estimated to be released during its rise applications [13]. Approximately 200,000 individuals are estimated to be exposed to ethylene oxide. The two major populations at risk to the potential adverse effects of ethylene oxide are (1) individuals who use this agent in the operation of sterilization equipment on a routine basis and/or who spend most of their time in the immediate area of the operation of this equipment, and (2) individuals who use ethylene oxide as a fumigant on a routine basis and/or often enter storage chambers shortly after fumigation [14].

Ethylene oxide is mutagenic in *S. typhimurium* TA 1535, *Neurospora crassa, A. nidulans* and *Drosophila melanogaster,* producing dominant lethal mutations in rats and chromosome aberrations in rats and mammalian somatic cells [15].

It should be stressed that ethylene oxide readily converts to the glycol in an aqueous medium and to ethylene chlorohydrin if chloride ions are present [16]. Ethylene chlorohydrin is mutagenic in the Ames test with *S. typhimurium* [17].

1,2-Butylene oxide (1,2-epoxybutane) is used as a corrosion inhibitor, as a fuel additive to prevent carburetor icing and improve antiknock properties, and as a scavenger in chlorinated solvents such as trichloroethylene and methyl chloroform at levels of 3 to 8% [11]. 1,2-Epoxybutane can be polymerized or copolymerized with other alkylene oxides to yield polyethers and polyurethanes [18]. The use of 1,2-epoxybutane as a corrosion inhibitor in water pipes suggests the possibility of trace levels of the agent leaching into water supplies. It has been shown to be strongly mutagenic in *E. coli* WP2 and uvrA⁻ and *S. typhimurium* TA 100 and weakly positive in WP2 and TA 1535 [19].

Epichlorohydrin (1-chloro-2,3-epoxypropane; chloropropylene oxide) is used extensively as an intermediate for the manufacture of synthetic glycerins, epoxy resins (e.g., via the reaction of Bisphenol-A) and elastomers, in the preparation of glycidyl ethers, paper sizing agents, ion exchange resins, surface-active agents, corrosion inhibitors, inks and dyes, as a solvent for resins, gums, cellulose and paints, and as an intermediate in the preparation of pharmaceuticals, textile coatings and cleaning agents [20].

Approximately 550 million pounds of epichlorohydrin were produced in the U.S. in 1975. NIOSH estimated that approximately 50,000 U.S. workers are occupationally exposed to epichlorohydrin [21].

Epichlorohydrin has recently been reported to produce squamous cell carcinomas of the nasal epithelium in rats following inhalation at levels of 100 ppm for 6 hr/day [22]. Epichlorohydrin is mutagenic (without metabolic activation) at concentrations of 1-50 nM/hr in *S. typhimurium* GY6 and TA 100 tester strains [23], as well as in TA 1535, *E. coli* WP2 and WP2 uvrA[1]; it is mutagenic with metabolic activation in G46, TA 1538 and TA 98, and induces recessive lethal mutations in *Drosophila melanogaster* [24].

Glycidol (2,3-epoxy-1-propanol) is widely employed in textile finishings as a water-repellent finish and as an intermediate in the production of glycidyl ethers, esters and amines of industrial utility. It is mutagenic in *Drosophila* [24], *Neurospora* and *S. typhimurium* TA 98 (for frame-shift mutagens) and TA 100 (for base-pair mutagens) both with and without metabolic activation [25].

Styrene oxide (1,2-epoxy ethyl benzene; phenyl oxirane) is used primarily as a reactive diluent in epoxy resins and as an intermediate in the preparation of agricultural chemicals, cosmetics, surface coatings, and in the treatment of textiles and fibers. It has been detected as a by-product in commercial samples of styrene chlorohydrin as well as in effluent water from latex manufacturing plants in Louisville, KY, and from chemical manufacturing plants in Louisville and Memphis [26].

It should be stressed that styrene oxide is a metabolite in the proposed transformation of styrene to hippuric acid in man and animals [27,28]. Styrene is produced in enormous quantities (e.g., 2864 million kg in the U.S. and 7000 million kg worldwide in 1976) [29]. The principal areas of application of an estimated 87% of the styrene consumed in the U.S. in 1976 were in the production of plastics and resins (polystyrene resins) (61%); acrylonitrile-butadiene-styrene terpolymer (ABS) and styrene-acrylonitrile copolymer (SAN) resins (11%); styrene-butadiene copolymer resins (8%); unsaturated polyesters (7%); and styrene-butadiene rubber (SBR) (11%). Styrene oxide has been found mutagenic in *S. typhimurium* TA 1535 [30-32] and TA 100 [31,32] without metabolic activation and in *S. pombe* and *S. cerevisiae*; it induces a dose-dependent increase of forward mutations in somatic cells in culture [33]. However, the aspects of the mutagenicity of styrene per se are somewhat conflicting. For example, styrene in the presence of a 9000-g supernatant from livers of rats pretreated with the PCB Clophen C or Aroclor 1254 induced reverse mutations in *S. typhimurium* TA 1535 and TA 100, was not mutagenic to TA 1537, TA 1538 and TA 98 [32,34] and was nonmutagenic with metabolic activation in spot tests and plate incorporation assays in TA 1535, 1537, 1538, 98 and 100 tester strains at concentrations up to 1 mg/plate [35].

While styrene oxide appeared to be a potent inducer of sister chromatid exchanges (SCE) in CHO cells, styrene itself did not increase the number of SCE per metaphase, even in the presence of a metabolic activation system. The metabolic activation system decreased the SCE induction caused by styrene oxide. Induction of SCE by styrene in the presence of metabolic activation occurred when cyclohexane oxide was used as an inhibitor of the enzyme epoxide hydrase [36].

Although the eight epoxides depicted in Figures 7 and 8 are of principal concern based on their potential carcinogenicity and/or mutagenicity, production quantities and use patterns, it is important to note that there are a number of additional industrial epoxides of potential toxicological significance. However, very much less is known of their toxic properties. For example, 21-25 million pounds of alkyl (predominantly C_{12} and C_{14}) glycidyl ethers were used in the U.S. in 1975 for the captive production of alkyl glyceryl ether sulfonates which are used primarily as shampoos, light-dirty detergents, combination soaps, stabilizers for PVC resins and chlorinated paraffins, and as reactive diluents for epoxy resins. It has been been estimated that the annual growth rate for use of these alkyl glycidyl ethers in the manufacture of either sulfonates will be 8-9% by 1982 [11].

Figure 9 illustrates the structures of four glycidyl ethers (phenyl-, butyl-, allyl- and isopropyl glycidyl ethers) which have industrial utility primarily as reactive diluents in epoxy resin systems and stabilizing halogenated compounds. NIOSH estimates that about 118,000 workers are potentially exposed to glycidyl ethers [37]. Phenylglycidyl ether (PGE) is mutagenic in *S. typhimurium* TA 1535 and TA 100 with and without metabolic activation, but inactive in TA 1537, 1538 or TA 98 [38]. The PGE transformed secondary hamster embryo cells, but was weakly mutagenic in the host-mediated assay in mice and was inactive in the dominant lethal test [37].

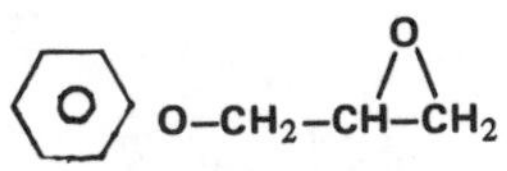

Phenylglycidyl Ether (PGE)

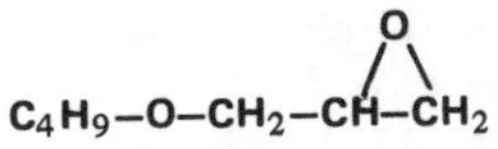

Butylglycidal Ether (BGE)

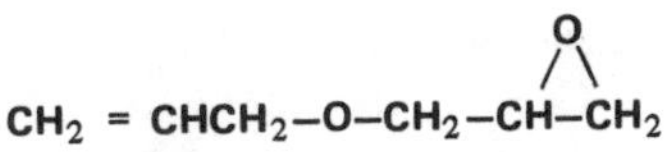

Allylglycidyl Ether (AGE)

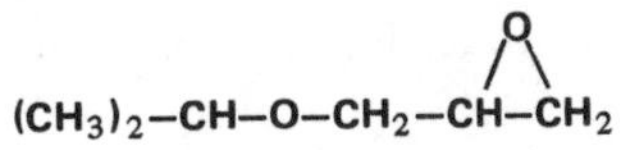

Isopropylglycidyl Ether (IGE)

Figure 9. Glycidyl ethers.

Butyl glycidyl ether (BGE) is positive in the dominant lethal test and is suspected of inducing testicular atrophy in rats [36]. This finding coupled with the induction of dominant lethals suggests that an active form of BGE may reach the testes. Testicular degeneration has been shown in several animal species following exposure to other glycidyl ethers [37].

A variety of epoxidized esters are used in substantial quantities as plasticizers, primarily for PVC resins, where they also function as heat and light stabilizers (synergistically with barium-cadmium-zinc stabilizers). The major epoxy esters used in the U.S. in 1974 (in millions of pounds) were: epoxidized soya oils, 127; epoxidized linseed oil, 5.5; octyl (*n*-octyl and 2-ethylhexyl) epoxy tallates, 14.9; and epoxidized toll oils, octyl epoxy stearates and other epoxidized esters, 6.5 [11].

Epoxy resins are used extensively for protective coatings and in paints and adhesives. About 90% of the epoxy resins used are manufactured by condensation of two molecules of epichlorohydrin with one or more molecules of bisphenol-A (2,2-*bis*(4-hydroxyphenyl)-propane). More than

260 million pounds of epoxy resins were manufactured in the U.S. in 1977 [39]. Epoxy resins are diepoxides, and bifunctional alkylating agents are known to be mutagenic [23,30].

A number of epoxy resins prepared from epichlorohydrin and bisphenol-A are illustrated in Figure 10. They were recently found

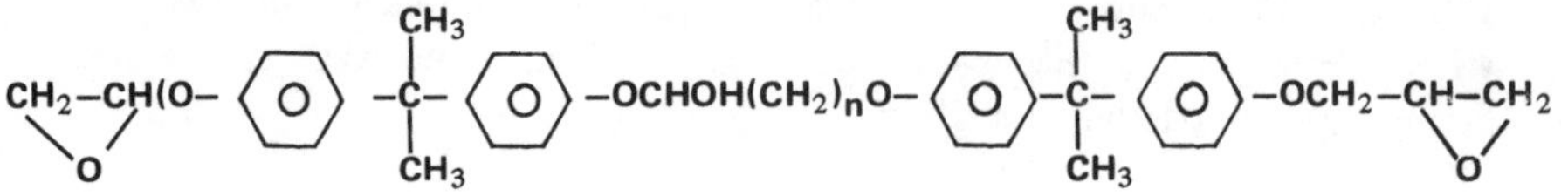

Epikote 828 n = 0
Epikote 1001 n = 1
Epikote 1004 n = 3

Figure 10. Epoxy resins prepared from epichlorohydrin and bisphenol-A.

mutagenic (without metabolic activation) in *S. typhimurium* TA 100 [40]. Epikote 828 (which is basically the diglycidyl ether of bisphenol-A) was the most active compound of the resins tested, and both Epikote 828 and Epikote 1001 were more mutagenic than the positive control epichlorohydrin. The mutagenic activity of the epoxyresins and epichlorohydrin was reduced almost tenfold in assays with TA 100 and metabolic activation. Epikote 828 with metabolic activation in the presence of NADP was mutagenic in TA 1535. The activation of the aromatic epoxy resins as found in TA 1535 was not caused by decomposition of the compounds and liberation of bisphenol-A since the latter was not active in TA 1535 or TA 100 both with and without metabolic activation.

Exposure to the resins during their manufacture is possible either by skin contact with the compound or by inhalation of air contaminated with droplets or powder particles of epoxy resin [40].

Nishioka and Ohtans [41] recently reported the mutagenicity of a number of bisphenol-A type epoxide resins (n=0, n=5 and n=14) in TA 100 with and without metabolic activation, and nonmutagenicity in TA 98, indicating that they are base-change type mutagens. In addition, these epoxide adhesives were positive in DNA repair tests. It was suggested that the higher-molecular-weight epoxide compounds generally exhibited lower mutagenic activity due to their decreased permeability and/or solubility [40].

There are additional aspects of epoxides that should be noted. Many epoxides derived from olefinic or aromatic compounds are mutagenic for microorganisms [6,30,42-45] or mammalian cells in cultures. Additionally, a number of epoxides also transform cells in culture to malignancy [45-47]. It is generally acknowledged that aliphatic epoxides (alkene oxides) are active intermediates in the metabolism of alkene compounds, and that arene oxides through their binding to biopolymers such as DNA, RNA and protein are responsible for the toxic, carcinogenic and mutagenic effects of aromatic compounds [48,49].

We are cautioned, however, in extrapolating the adverse properties of some arene oxides to epoxides in general [50-52]. For example, Glatt and co-workers [52] recently reported that epoxidation may actually prevent some compounds from being biotransformed to mutagenically reactive metabolites; the carcinogen *trans*-4-acetylaminostilbene (I) ions metabolized into an epoxide (II) which was nonmutagenic in the Ames test with strains TA 1535, TA 1537, TA 1538, TA 98 and TA 100 (in contrast to the parent compound). The threo-α·β-dihydrodiol, formed metabolically from *trans*-4-acetylaminostilbene and from its α,β-epoxide, was also nonmutagenic in the above tester strains.

It should also be noted that the drug epoxy metabolites carbamazepine-10,11-oxide, cyclobenzaprine-10,11-oxide and cyporheptadiene-10,11-oxide are not mutagenic [53]. Wade et al. [51] recently studied the mutagenicity of 17 aliphatic epoxides using *S. typhimurium* TA 100 and TA 1535 tester strains. Mutagenicity depended on the degree of substitution around the oxirane ring. While monosubstituted oxiranes were the most potent mutagens in both strains, 1,1-disubstitution resulted in the complete loss or reduction of mutagenicity. *trans*-1,2-Disubstituted and tetrasubstituted oxiranes all lacked mutagenicity while the *cis*-1,2-disubstituted oxiranes tested were weakly mutagenic in TA 100 only. For the monosubstituted compounds, mutagenicity appears to be related to the elctrophilicity of the epoxide. Electron-withdrawing groups on the epoxide (e.g., halogens) would create a stronger electrophile with increased reactivity to bionucleophiles such as DNA, and hence the epoxide would exhibit enhanced mutagenicity [51].

Lactones

Lactones constitute a class of highly reactive compounds that possess a broad spectrum of current and suggested industrial uses including: wood processing, protective coatings and impregnation of textiles, modification of flax cellulose, urethane foam manufacture, intermediates in the preparation of insecticides, plasticizers and medicinals (Figure 11).

The chemical β-propiolactone (hydracrydic acid, BPL) is by far the most important lactone produced commercially. It is prepared by the condensation of ketone with formaldehyde. It should be noted that both these reactants have been found mutagenic [54]. The most extensive use of BPL has been in plastic polymerization processes, in the production of acrylic acid and esters. Lesser amounts are used in the synthesis of propionic derivatives, in the sterilization of blood plasma, tissue grafts and surgical instruments, and as a vapor disinfectant in enclosed spaces. (The latter uses are believed to have been discontinued in several countries.) The very high chemical reactivity of BPL is due to the presence of a strained four-membered lactone ring. It reacts very rapidly with nucleophilic centers such as proteins, particularly sulfur-containing amine acids and nucleic acids. The predominant alkylated base in DNA and RNA exposed to BPL is 7-(2-carboxyethyl) guanine [56]. Adenine is alkylated to a lesser extent at the 3-position. The BPL acts as an alkylating agent by undergoing ring-opening at the O-CO bonds with un-ionized molecules and at the CH_2-O bonds with ionized molecules. The BPL is carcinogenic, producing mostly sarcomas at the site of location. It is mutagenic in *Neurospora, S. cerevisiae,* and in bacteriophages and viruses; it induces chromosome aberrations and SCE in mammalian cells and malignant transformation in hamster embryo cells. Because the biological half-life of BPL in vivo is probably too short for substantial quantities of the alkylated form to reach target sites, it is difficult to assess the impact of BPL on humans.

γ-Butyrolactone (1,4-butanolide) is used primarily as a solvent in the extraction of butadiene and polymers and for the production of 2-pyrrolidone and N-methyl-2-pyrrolidone, which are intermediates for the production of homo- and copolymers (employed as film formers in hair sprays, as clarifying agents in beer and wine, and as blood expanders). There is a paucity of data on the mutagenicity of γ-butyrolactone.

Aziridines

Aziridines are extremely reactive alkylating agents which can undergo two major types of reactions: (1) ring-preserving reactions in which an aziridine (e.g., ethyleneimine) acts as a secondary amine reacting with

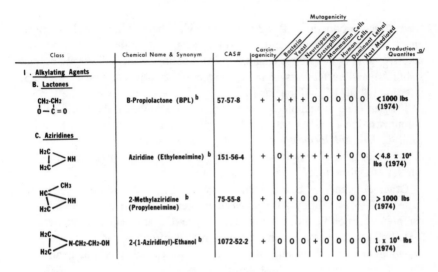

Figure 11. Potential industrial carcinogens and mutagens—lactones.

many organic functional groups containing an active hydrogen, undergoing replacement reactions of the hydrogen atom by nucleophilic attack at one of the methylene groups; and (2) ring-opening reactions similar to those undergone by ethylene oxide. Aziridines, because of their dual functionality and high degree of reactivity, exhibit actual or potential utility in a broad range of applications including: textiles (crease-proofing, dyeing and printing, flame-proofing, water-proofing, shrink-proofing, form stabilization and stiffening), adhesives and binders, petroleum products and synthetic fuels coatings, agricultural chemicals, ion exchange resins, curing and vilcanizing polymers, surfactants, paper and printing, antimicrobials, flocculants and chemotherapeutics [57,58].

The most important aziridine is ethyleneimine (aziridine) which is used principally as a chemical intermediate to provide one or more aziridinyl-($CH_2 CH_2$-N-) or ethyleneimino-(-CH_2-CH_2NH-) substituents (Figure 11).

Approximately 50% of the ethylenimine produced in the U.S. is polymerized to polyethylenimine which contains less than 1 ppm residual monomer. Polyethylenimine is used principally as a flocculant in water treatment, in the paper industry where it is used as a wet-strength additive as an adhesion promoter in various coating applications, and in the textile industry (to improve dyeing and printing for water-proofing and to impart antistatic properties).

Of the remaining 50% of the ethylenimine produced, most is used as a chemical intermediate in drug, cosmetic and dye manufacture. It is also used in the production of N-2-hydroxyethylenimine (2-aziridinyl ethanol) and triethylenemelamine, and as a intermediate and monomer for oil additive compounds, ion exchange resins, coating resins, adhesives, polymer stabilizers and surfactants. Annual production of ethylenimine in the U.S. is estimated at 1.3 million kg [59].

Ethylenimine is included in the U.S. Occupational Safety and Health Administration (OSHA) list of 14 "occupational" carcinogens, It is mutagenic in *Drosophila melanogaster* [60], *Neurospora crassa* [61], *S. cerevisiae* and *S. typhimurium* [30], and it induces chromosome aberrations in cultured human cells [62].

Other aziridines of commercial utility are 2-methyl aziridine (propylenimine) and 2-(1-aziridinyl)ethanol. The former is used as an intermediate for polymer modification in the adhesive, textile and paper industries. 2-Methyl aziridine is a potent carcinogen that affects a wide range of organs in the rat when administered orally [63], and it is mutagenic in the *Salmonella*/microsome test system [30].

The compound 2-aziridinylethanol (β-hydroxy-1-ethyl aziridine) is prepared from the addition of aziridine to ethylene oxide (both reactive intermediates which are carcinogenic and mutagenic as previously discussed). It is reported to be used commercially in the modification of latex polymers for coatings, textile resins and starches, as well as in the preparation of modified cellulose products such as paper, wood fibers and fabrics [58]. 2-(1-Aziridinyl)-ethanol is carcinogenic in mice, producing malignant tumors at the site of its injection [64]. It has been reported to induce sex-linked recessive lethals in *Drosophila melanogaster* [65].

Aliphatic Sulfuric Acid Esters

Alkyl sulfates such as dimethyl and diethyl sulfates are very reactive alkylating agents that have been employed extensively both in industry and the laboratory for converting active-hydrogen compounds such as phenols, amines and thiols to the corresponding methyl and ethyl derivatives [66] (Figure 12).

Dimethyl sulfate (DMS) has been used extensively as a methylating agent both in industry and the laboratory. Its utility includes the methylation of cellulose, preparation of alkyl lead compounds and preparation of alkyl ethers of starch. It is also used as a solvent for the extraction of aromatic hydrocarbons and as a curing agent for furyl alcohol resins and the polymerization of olefins. DMS has been employed commercially for the preparation of quaternary ammonium methosulfate salts (via its reaction with the respective tertiary amine) which are used as cationic surfactants [66] and as an intermediate in drug synthesis.

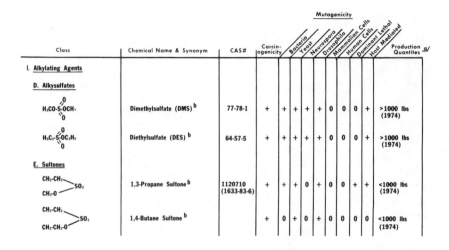

Class	Chemical Name & Synonym	CAS#	Carcinogenicity	Bacteria	Yeast	Neurospora	Drosophila	Mammalian Cells	Human Cells	Dominant Lethal	Host Mediated	Production Quantities [a]
I. Alkylating Agents												
D. Alkysulfates												
$H_3CO\text{-}S\text{-}OCH_3$ (O,O)	Dimethylsulfate (DMS) [b]	77-78-1	+	+	+	+	+	0	0	0	+	>1000 lbs (1974)
$H_5C_2\text{-}S\text{-}OC_2H_5$ (O,O)	Diethylsulfate (DES) [b]	64-57-5	+	+	+	+	+	0	0	0	+	>1000 lbs (1974)
E. Sultones												
$CH_2\text{-}CH_2$ / $CH_2\text{-}O$ SO₂	1,3-Propane Sultone [b]	1120710 (1633-83-6)	+	+	+	0	+	0	0	+	+	<1000 lbs (1974)
$CH_2\text{-}CH_2$ / $CH_2\text{-}CH_2\text{-}O$ SO₂	1,4-Butane Sultone [b]		+	0	+	0	+	0	0	0	0	<1000 lbs (1974)

Figure 12. Potential industrial carcinogens and mutagens—alkysulfates and sultones.

Dimethyl sulfate has been listed among the industrial substances suspect of carcinogenic potential for man. The current TLV in the U.S. is 1 ppm [67].

Diethyl sulfate (DES) has been used in a variety of ethylation processes and organic syntheses including finishing of cellulosic yarns, etherification of starch and preparation of cationic surfactants [66]. Both DMS and DES have been shown to be carcinogenic in the rat [66] and mutagenic in *S. typhimurium, E. coli, Neurospora, S. pombe* and *Drosophila* [66].

Cyclic Aliphatic Sulfuric Acid Esters

Similar to dialkyl sulfates, alkyl alkanesulfonates and alkane sultones, cyclic aliphatic acid esters are monofunctional alkylating agents which react with neutral or ionic nucleophiles, Y or Y⁻, along the general pathway (1) or (2) (Figure 13).

Members of this class–1,2-ethylene sulfate (ESF, I), 1,3-butylene sulfate (BSF, II), and 1,3-propylene sulfate (PSF, III)–are used to introduce sulfoxylalkyl groups into nitrogen heterocycles [68], especially into cyanine dyes [69,70] (Figure 13).

The cyclic sulfates ESF, PSF and BSF revert the tester strain TA 1535 of *S. typhimurium* in vitro indicating their ability to induce base substitutions [4]. Compared with alkyl sulfates and sulfonates, the mutagenic activity in the plate test was 1,3-propane sultone > 1,3-propylene sulfate > 1,3-butylene sulfate > 1,4-butane sultone > 1,2-ethylene sulfate > diethyl sulfate > dimethyl sulfate.

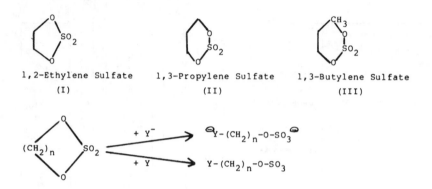

1,2-Ethylene Sulfate	1,3-Propylene Sulfate	1,3-Butylene Sulfate
(I)	(II)	(III)

Figure 13. Cyclic aliphatic sulfuric acid esters.

Sultones

Sultones such as the 1,3-propane and 1,4-butane derivatives are being increasingly employed in industry to introduce the sulfopropyl and sulfobutyl groups ($-CH_2 CH_2 CH_2 SO_3^-$ and $-CH_2 CH_2 CH_2 CH_2 SO_3^-$, respectively) into polymer chains containing nucleophilic centers in order to enhance water solubility and convert an anionic character [58] (Figure 12).

The compound 1,3-propane sultone is a monofunctional alkylating agent which reacts with nucleophiles, Y-, along the general pathway (1) or (2) as follows [71]:

$$Y^- + \begin{array}{c} CH_2\text{-}CH_2 \\ | \quad\quad SO_2 \\ CH_2\text{-}O \end{array} \longrightarrow Y\text{-}CH_2 CH_2 CH_2 SO_2 O^- \qquad (1)$$

$$Y + \begin{array}{c} CH_2\text{-}CH_2 \\ | \quad\quad SO_2 \\ CH_2\text{-}O \end{array} \longrightarrow Y^+\text{-}CH_2 CH_2 CH_2 SO_2 O^- \qquad (2)$$

A large number of sulfopropylated products and their potential uses [58,72] include:

1. derivatives of amines, alcohols, phenols, mercaptans, sulfides and amides useful as detergents, wetting agents, lathering agents and bacteriostats;

2. soluble starches used in the textile industry;
3. solubilized cellulose which is reported to have soil-suspending properties;
4. dyes;
5. an antistatic additive for polyamide fibers;
6. cation exchange resins (prepared by condensing the sulfonic acid product derived from phenol and propane sultone formaldehyde);
7. phosphorus-containing sulfonic acids (produced from organic phosphines, neutral esters of trivalent phosphorus acids, and phosphorus and phosphoric triamides), useful as insecticides, fungicides, surfactants and vulcanization accelerators [58].

1,3-Propane sultone is carcinogenic in the rat when administered orally, intravenously or by prenatal exposure [58,63,64]. It is mutagenic in *S. pombe*, *S. cerevisiae* [73] and *S. typhimurium* TA 1535 [74] and is active in the transformation of Golden Syrian hamster embryo cells in vitro [75].

As a typical alkylating agent, the biological activity of 1,3-propane sultone may be attributed to its reaction with genetic material [73,76]. As a bifunctional agent, it is likely to introduce cross-links between DNA strands, thus interfering with normal replication of DNA and inhibiting its synthesis.

Diazoalkanes

Diazoalkanes represent an extremely reactive class of alkylating agents. Diazoalkanes are sufficiently basic to abstract protons from many compounds containing acidic hydrogens, the rate of protonation increasing as the acidity of the proton donor increases. The protonated diazoalkane (an alkyldiazonium ion) is exceedingly unstable, losing molecular nitrogen and yielding a carbonium ion which becomes affixed to whatever nucleophile is available. Hence, the overall reaction is a replacement of the nitrogen of the diazoalkane by the hydrogen and accompanying nucleophilic portion of the protic compound (Figure 14).

Because of its toxicity and its explosive nature, diazomethane is not manufactured for distribution and sale. When used as a methylating agent in the laboratory, it is produced and used in situ. Most laboratory preparations of diazomethane during the late 1940s and the 1950s were probably made from N-methyl-N'-nitro-N-nitrosoguanidine. However, in most countries in recent years, it is believed to be made from N-nitroso-methyl-*p*-toluenesulfonamide [77].

Diazomethane is a powerful methylating agent for acidic compounds such as carboxylic acids, phenols and enols and, as a consequence, is both an important laboratory reagent and has industrial utility (with acids,

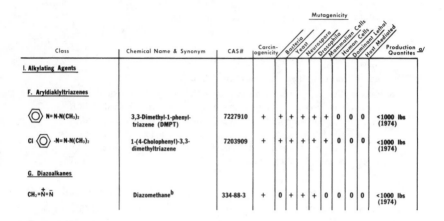

Figure 14. Potential industrial carcinogens and mutagens—aryldiakyltriazenes and diazoalkanes.

diazomethane yields esters; with enols, it gives O-alkylation) [77]. When heated, irradiated with light of the appropriate wavelength, or exposed to certain copper-containing catalysts, diazomethane loses molecular nitrogen and forms carbene, via $CH_2 N_2 \longrightarrow CH_2 : + N_2$. Carbenes are exceedingly reactive species which, for example, can add to alkenes to form cyclopropanes. Carbenes can react with the electrons of a carbon-hydrogen bond to "insert" the carbon of the carbene between carbon and hydrogen, e.g., transforming -CH to -C-CH$_3$ [78].

Diazomethane can react with many biological molecules, especially nucleic acids and their constituents. For example, its action on DNA includes methylation at several positions on the bases and the deoxyribose moiety, as well as structural alterations that result in lower resistance to alkaline hydrolysis and altered hyperchromicity [79]. Acid hydrolysis of diazomethane-treated DNA yields 7-methylguanine and 3-methylguanine, while acid hydrolysis of diazomethane-treated RNA yields 7-methylguanine, 1-methyladenine and 1-methylcytosine [79].

Diazomethane has been found to be carcinogenic in limited studies in mice and rats, the only species tested [77,80]. The mutagenicity of diazomethane in *Neurospora, S. cerevisiae* and *Drosophila* as well as the implication of diazomethane in the mutagenesis of nitroso compounds has been described [54,77,81].

The carcinogenicity of diazoacetic ester (ethyl diazoacetic ester, ethyl diazoacetate) (DAAE) $N^- = N^+ = CHCOOC_2 H_5$ in Wistar rats, Syrian hamsters and Swiss mice has recently been reported [82].

Aryldialkyltriazenes

Triazenes of the general formula $X - \emptyset - N = N - N(CH_3)_2$ (x = substituent; $\emptyset$ = phenyl or a heterocyclic residue) are industrial intermediates as well as antineoplastic agents that have been patented as rodent repellents and herbicides. The target organs of the carcinogenicity activity of the majority of triazenes are the kidney, the central nervous system and the brain, and, less frequently, the heart [83,84] (Figure 14).

The mutagenicity of a number of these agents has been reported in *S. typhimurium* (metabolically activated) [85], *Drosophila melanogaster* [86], *Neurospora crassa* [87], *S. cerevisiae* [86,88] and in human lymphocyte chromosomes in vitro [88].

The observed carcinogenicity, mutagenicity and toxicity are suggested to be dependent on at least two molecular mechanisms [86]. One mechanism involves nonenzymic cleavage of the diazoamino side chain liberating arenediazonium cations. In the other mechanism, the major metabolic pathway is an enzymic oxidative monodealkylation yielding the corresponding monoalkyltriazenes, with subsequent hydrolysis yielding alkylating reactants (e.g., methylating species similar to those formed from alkylnitrosoureas).

Phosphoric Acid Esters

Phosphoric acid, as a tribasic acid, can form mono-, di- and triesters with a broad spectrum of alcohols, thiols and phenols. A number of the resultant organophosphates have utility as alkylating agents, intermediates in chemical synthesis and as organophosphorus insecticides (e.g., dichlorvos, parathion, malathion and diazinon).

The common structural element of all organophosphates is = $\overset{|}{P} - \overset{|}{O} - \overset{|}{C} -$ with both phosphorus and carbon being electrophilic sites. Alkylating can occur as a result of nucleophilic attack on the carbon atom with subsequent cleavage of the C - O bond. Alternatively, a nucleophile can preferentially attack the phosphorus atom and undergo phosphorylation (Figure 15).

Trimethyl phosphate (TMP) has been employed mainly as a methylating agent in the preparation of dichlorvos via reaction with chloral. It is also used as a low-cost gasoline additive [89] and as a catalyst for polyester manufacture.

TMP is mutagenic in *S. typhimurium* tester strains with R factor plasmids [90], *Neurospora* and *Drosophila* [91] and induces chromosome breaks in cultured human lymphocytes [92].

tris-(2,3-Dibromopropyl)-phosphate (*tris*-BP) has been used principally as a flame retardant for synthetic fibers and fabrics such as polyester, acetate, triacetate and acrylics widely used in sleepwear garments. *tris*-BP

Class	Chemical Name & Synonym	CAS#	Carcin-ogenicity	Bacteria	Yeast	Neurospora	Drosophila	Mammalian Cells	Human Cells	Dominant Lethal	Host Mediated	Production Quantites a/
I. Alkylating Agents												
H. Posphoric Acid Esters												
$(CH_3O)_3P=O$	Trimethyl Phosphate (TMP)	512-56-1	0	+	0	+	+	+	+	0	0	7 x 10⁶ (1974)
$(C_2O)_3P=O$	Triethyl Phosphate (TEP)	78-40-0	0	0	0	0	+	0	0	0	0	1000 lbs (1974)
$BrCH_2CH(Br)CH_2O)_3P=O$	Tris(2,3-dibromopropyl)-phosphate (Tris-BP)	126-72-7	+	+	0	0	+	0	+	0	0	10 x10⁶ lbs (1975)
I. Alkane Halides												
$ClCH_2CH_2Cl$	1,2-Ethylene Dichloride	107-06-2	0	+	0	0	+	0	0	0	0	9165 x 10⁶ lbs (1974)
$BrCH_2CH_2Br$	1,2-Ethylene Dibromide[b]	106-93-4	+	+	+	+	+	+	−	−	−	332 x 10⁶ lbs (1974)
BrCH₂CHCH₂Cl BR	1,2-Dibromo-3-choropropane	96-12-8	+	+	0	0	0	0	0	0	0	

Figure 15. Potential industrial carcinogens and mutagens—phosphoric acid esters and alkane halides.

is added to fabrics used for children's garments to the extent of 5-10% by weight. About 65% of the 10 million pounds of *tris*-BP produced annually was formerly used for production of flame-retardant children's fabrics [93]. As a result of concern about its mutagenic [94,95] and carcinogenic [95,96] properties, sleepwear manufacturers ceased using *tris*-BP-treated fabrics in January 1977. The Consumer Product Safety Commission banned the sale of *tris*-BP-treated sleepwear in April 1977.

Significant quantities of *tris*-BP have also been used as flame retardants for a broad spectrum of other synthetic polymers including rigid and flexible polyurethane foams, cellulose nitrate surface coatings, polystyrene, paper coatings and rubber.

Commercial preparations of *tris*-BP are generally in two grades: HV (high in volatiles) and LV (low in volatiles). A typical LV sample has been reported to contain the following impurities (%): 1,2-dibromo-3-chloropropane (DBCP) (0.05); 1,2,3-tribromopropane (0.05); and 2,3-dibromopropanol (0.20) [97]. The carcinogenicity of the impurity DBCP in *tris*-BP should be noted. It caused a high incidence of squamous carcinoma of the stomach in both rats and mice as early as 10 weeks after oral intubation [98]. It is also mutagenic and is known to cause testicular atrophy in animals [99]; it has also been throught to cause sterility in workers engaged in its production.

Aldehydes

Formaldehyde is used extensively as a reactant in many commercial processes because of its high chemical reactivity and good thermal stability. These reactions can be arranged in three major categories: (1) self-polymerization reactions, (2) oxidation-reduction reactions, and (3) addition or condensation reactions with a large number of organic and inorganic compounds. The major uses of formaldehyde and its polymers are in the synthetic resin industry (e.g., in the production of urea-, formaldehyde-, phenolic-, polyacetol-, and melamine formaldehyde resins) and in the production of pentaerythritol and hexamethylenetetramine. It is also employed widely in agriculture, paper, textile and dyestuffs manufacture, medicine and analysis. In general, the major chemical reactions of formaldehyde with other compounds involve the formation of methylol ($-CH_2OH$) or methylene derivatives. Methylol ureas and methylol carbamates are used in the treatment of textiles for crease-resistant, crush-proof, flame-resistant and shrink-proof fabrics. Reaction of formaldehyde with hydrochloric acid can yield the carcinogenic *bis*-chloromethyl ether (BCME) [100,101] (Figure 16).

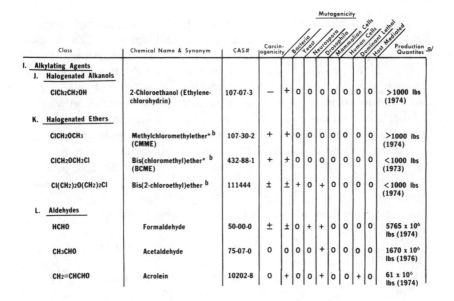

					Mutagenicity								
Class	Chemical Name & Synonym	CAS#	Carcin-ogenicity	Bacteria	Yeast	Neurospora	Drosophila	Mammalian Cells	Human Cells	Dominant Lethal	Host Mediated	Production Quantites a/	
I. Alkylating Agents													
J. Halogenated Alkanols													
ClCH2CH2OH	2-Chloroethanol (Ethylene-chlorohydrin)	107-07-3	—	+	0	0	0	0	0	0	0	>1000 lbs (1974)	
K. Halogenated Ethers													
ClCH2OCH3	Methylchloromethylether* b (CMME)	107-30-2	+	+	0	0	0	0	0	0	0	>1000 lbs (1974)	
ClCH2OCH2Cl	Bis(chloromethyl)ether* b (BCME)	432-88-1	+	+	0	0	0	0	0	0	0	<1000 lbs (1973)	
Cl(CH2)2O(CH2)2Cl	Bis(2-chloroethyl)ether b	111444	±	±	+	0	+	0	0	0	0	<1000 lbs (1974)	
L. Aldehydes													
HCHO	Formaldehyde	50-00-0	±	±	0	+	+	0	0	0	0	5765 x 10^6 lbs (1974)	
CH3CHO	Acetaldehyde	75-07-0	0	0	0	0	+	0	0	0	0	1670 x 10^6 lbs (1976)	
CH2=CHCHO	Acrolein	10202-8	0	+	0	0	+	0	0	+	0	61 x 10^6 lbs (1974)	

Figure 16. Potential industrial carcinogens and mutagens—halogenated alkanols, halogenated ethers and aldehydes.

Feldman [102] recently reviewed the reactions of formaldehyde with various components of biological importance (e.g., nucleic acids and nucleoproteins). The genetic and cytogenetic effects of formaldehyde and related compounds were surveyed recently by Auerbach et al. [103]. The mutagenicity of formaldehyde has been described extensively for *Drosophila* [103], *Neurospora* [103] and *E. coli* [55,103,104].

Acrolein (arylaldehyde; allyl aldehyde) is widely used in the production of acrylic acid, glycidaldehyde, glycerin, methionine, gluteraldehyde, hexane triol, and cycloaliphatic epoxy resins. Other important reactions of acrolein involve its ability to undergo a variety of polymerization reactions (homo-, co-, and graft) as well as reactions with ammonia and formaldehyde to yield the industrially important derivatives acrylonitrile and pentaerythritol.

Acrolein is mutagenic in *Drosophila melanogaster* [105] and *S. typhimurium* TA 1538 and TA 98 [106]. It has been postulated that acrolein might act in certain circumstances as a pre-carcinogen and/or pre-mutagen producing glycidal (CH_2 - CH - CHO) via epoxidation in vivo [107].

Alkane Halides

Ethylene dichloride (1,2-dichloroethane, EDC) is the principal alkane halide of industrial utility. The current U.S. consumption of EDC is about 10 billion pounds. The estimated U.S. domestic consumption pattern of EDC in 1976 was 86% as an intermediate for vinyl chloride; approximately 3% each as an intermediate for 1,1,1-trichloroethane (methyl chloroform and ethylene amines); 2% each as an intermediate for perchloroethylene, 1,1-dichloroethane and trichloroethylene, and as a lead scavenger for motor fuels [59]. EDC is also used in various solvent applications, and as a component with fumigants (with ethylene dibromide) for grain, upholstery and carpets. A total of 2 million workers in the U.S. receive some exposure to EDC with perhaps 200,000 receiving a substantial exposure primarily during its use as a solvent in textile cleaning and metal degreasing, in certain adhesives and as a component in fumigants [108] (Figure 15).

Ethylene dichloride is carcinogenic in male and female rats and mice [109]. It is a weak mutagen in *S. typhimurium* TA 1530, TA 1535 and TA 100 when tested without metabolic activation [90,110,111].

Ethylene dibromide (1,2-dibromoethane, EDB) is used in substantial quantities as a lead scavenger in tetra alkyl lead gasoline and antiknock preparations, as a soil and grain fumigant, as an intermediate in the synthesis of dyes and pharmaceuticals, and as a solvent for resins, gums and waxes. Approximately 245 million pounds of EDB were produced in the U.S. in 1977. NIOSH estimates that about 9000 employees are potentially exposed to EDB, although this figure would increase to about 600,000 if gasoline station attendants were included [112].

Ethylene dibromide induces squamous cell carcinomas in the stomachs of both rats and mice when administered via chronic oral intubation in corn oil at maximum tolerated dose (MTD) and at half-MTD [98]. Without metabolic activation EDB is mutagenic in S. typhimurium G46, TA 1530, TA 1535, TA 100 [90,110,111], E. coli [113,144] and Drosophila melanogaster [115].

The mutagenicity of the vicinal dibromides was suggested to be a consequence of their ability to react to form highly unstable bromonium ions in solution—as "biological alkylating agents" which can alkylate cellular nucleophiles including DNA (Figure 17). The initial product of alkylation of a hetero-atom such as O,N or S would be the 2-bromoethyl derivatives—a "half-mustard" type reagent capable of another alkylation reaction. Hence, 1,2-dibromoethane and 1,2-dichloroethane could be considered bifuncitonal alkylating agents, capable of introducing cross-links into biological materials [115].

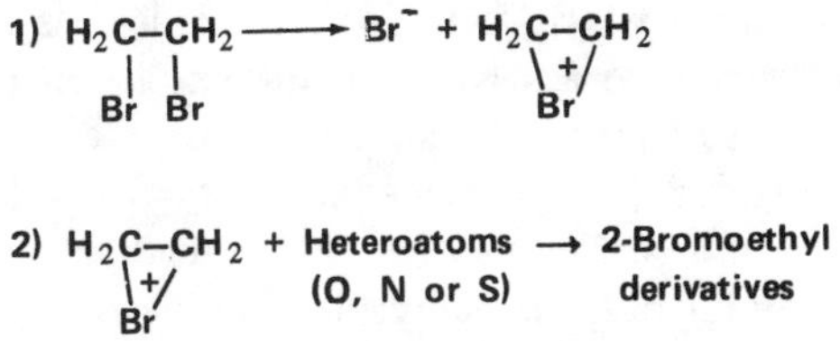

$$1) \quad H_2C-CH_2 \longrightarrow Br^- + H_2C-CH_2$$
$$\qquad\quad \underset{Br\ \ Br}{|\ \ |} \qquad\qquad\qquad \underset{Br}{\diagdown\!\overset{+}{}\!\diagup}$$

$$2) \quad H_2C-CH_2 + \text{Heteroatoms} \longrightarrow \text{2-Bromoethyl}$$
$$\qquad\quad \underset{Br}{\diagdown\!\overset{+}{}\!\diagup} \qquad\quad \text{(O, N or S)} \qquad\quad \text{derivatives}$$

Figure 17. Biological alkylating agents.

Nauman et al. [116] and Ehrenberg et al. [117] also designated ethylene dibromide as an alkylating agent, suggesting that it reacts via an S_N1 mechanism.

Antifertility effects of EDB have been attributed to a direct alkylating effect of its primary metabolite, the glutathione conjugate of bromoethane, which is a more reactive alkylating agent than EDB [118].

Alkyl Halides

Methyl chloride is widely used in the production of tetramethyl lead, silicones, butyl rubber, methyl cellulose, quaternary amines, as an inter-mediate in the manufacture of jet fuel additives and fungicides, as a refrigerant and a propellant in high-pressure aerosols [119]. It is also employed as a starting material in the manufacture of methylene chloride, chloroform, carbon tetrachloride and various bromochloro- and chloro-fluoromethanes. Approximately 377.6 million pounds of methylchloride were produced in the U.S. in 1976 [119]. NIOSH estimates that approximately 31,000 individuals are exposed to methyl chloride. Methyl chloride without metabolic activation is highly mutagenic in *S. typhimurium* TA 1535 [111,120] and TA 100 [111].

Methyl iodide, which is used primarily as a methylating agent in the preparation of pharmaceuticals and in organic synthesis, is mutagenic in *S. typhimurium* TA 100 without metabolic activation [111] and in *S. cerevisiae* [111]. It has produced lung tumors in mice after interperitoneal administration [121]. The alkyl halides have long been regarded as model compounds for investigations of the mode of action of alkylating agents. The production of lung adenomas in strain A mice is suggested to be a sensitive indicator of the carcinogenic potential of alkylating agents [121].

Methylene chloride is widely used for solvent degreasing, as a paint remover, in aerosol sprays, as a solvent for the extraction of naturally occurring heat-sensitive substances, and as a substitute for trichloroethylene for decaffeinating coffee [111]. Increasing utility of methylene chloride as a substitute for fluorocarbons in aerosol products is also forecast. The estimated annual production of methylene chloride is about 500 million kg [111]. It has recently been whosn to be mutagenic in *S. typhimurium* TA 98 and TA 100 [111,122].

Haloethers

Haloethers, primarily α-chloromethyl ethers, represent a category of alkylating agents of increasing concern due to the establishment of a causal relationship between occupational exposure to *bis*-chloromethyl ether (BCME) and chloromethyl methyl ether (CMME) and lung cancer in the U.S., Germany and Japan [123] (Figure 16).

BCME and CMME have been widely used in industry as chloromethylation agents for the preparation of anion exchange resins, formation of water repellents and other textile-treating agents, manufacture of polymers, and as solvents for polymerization reactions.

Potential sources of human exposure to BCME appear to exist primarily in areas including: (1) its use in chloromethylating (cross-linking) reaction mixtures in anion exchange production; (2) segments of the textile industry using formaldehyde-containing reactants and resins in the finishing of fabric and as adhesives in the laminating and flocking of fabrics; and (3) in the nonwovens industry which uses binders, thermosetting acrylic emulsion polymers comprising methyol acrylamide (a finite amount of formaldehyde is liberated on the drying and curing of these bonding agents). The potential for BCME formation increases with available formaldehyde and chloride (in both gaseous and liquid phases) [100,101]:

$$2Cl + 2HCHO + 2H^+ \longrightarrow ClCH_2 - OCH_2Cl + H_2O.$$

Van Duuren et al. [126-128] suggested that the α-halo ethers be classified with the biologically active alkylating agents (e.g., nitrogen mustards, epoxides, β-lactones). The high chemical reactivity of α-haloethers is attributed to the reactivity of the halogen atom in displacement reactions.

BCME and CMME are mutagenic in *E. coli* and *S. typhimurium* microbial systems without metabolic activation [128].

ACKNOWLEDGMENT

By acceptance of this article, the publisher or recipient acknowledges the U.S. Government's right to retain a nonexclusive, royalty-free license in and to any copyright covering the article.

REFERENCES

1. Miller, J. A., and E. C. Miller. "Metabolic and Reactivity of Chemical Carcinogens," *Mutation Res.* 33:25-26 (1975).
2. Miller, J. A. "Carcinogenesis by Chemicals: An Overview," G. H. A. Cowes Memorial Lecture, *Cancer Res.* 30:559-576 (1970).
3. Lawley, P. D. "Carcinogenesis by Alkylating Agents," in *Chemical Carcinogenesis*, C. E. Searle, Ed, ACS Monograph No. 173, (Washington, DC: American Chemical Society, 1976), pp. 83-244.
4. Weisburger, J. H., and G. M. Williams. "Metabolism of Chemical Carcinogens," *Cancer* (New York: Becker, 1975), pp. 185-234.
5. Weisburger, J. H. "Bioassays and Tests for Chemical Carcinogens," in *Chemical Carcinogens*, C. E. Searle, Ed., ACS Monograph No. 173 (Washington, DC: American Chemical Society, 1976), pp. 1-23.
6. Bartsch, H. "Predictive Value for Mutagenicity Tests for Chemical Carcinogenesis," *Mutation Res.* 38:177-190 (1976).
7. Brusick, D. J. "In Vitro Mutagenesis Assays as Predictors of Chemical Carcinogenesis in Mammals," *Clin. Toxicol.* 10:79-109 (1977).
8. Grover, P. L., and P. Sims. "Interaction of K-Region Epoxides of Phenanthrene and Dibenz(a,h)anthracene with Nucleic Acids and Histone," *Biochem. Pharmacol.* 19:2251-2259 (1970).

9. Lawley, P. D., and N. Jarman. "Alkylation by Propylene Oxide of Deoxyribonucleic Acid, Adenine, Guanosine and Deoxyguanylic Acid," *Biochem. J.* 126:893-900 (1972).

10. Wang, I. Y., R. E. Rasmussen and T. T. Crooker. "Isolation and Characterization of an Active DNA Binding Metabolite of Benz(a)-pyrene from Hamster Liver Microsomal Incubation Systems," *Biochem. Biophys. Res. Commun.* 49:1142-1149 (1972).

11. U.S. Environmental Protection Agency. "A Study of Industrial Data on Candidate Chemicals for Testing," Contract No. 68-01,41 09, Washington, DC, (February 1979).

12. Brookes, P., and P. D. Lawley. "The Alkylation of Guanosine and Guanylic Acid," *J. Chem. Soc.* 3923-3928 (1961).

13. Clement Associates, Inc. "Information Dossiers on Substances Designated by TSCA Interagency Testing Committee," October, 1977, Contract No. NSF-C-ENV-77-15417, Washington, DC, (1977).

14. U.S. Environemtnal Protection Agency. "Position Document for the Rebuttable Presumption Against Registration of Pesticide Products Containing Ethylene Oxice," *Chem. Reg. Report.* 1:1650-1657 (1978).

15. Fishbein, L. *Potential Industrial Carcinogens and Mutagens* (Amsterdam: Elsevier, 1979), pp. 93-117.

16. Willson, J. E. "Ethylene Oxide Sterilant Residues," *Bull. Parent. Drug Assoc.* 24:226-234 (1970).

17. Rosenkranz, H. S., and T. J. Wlodkowski. "Mutagenicity of Ethylene Chlorohydrin, A Degradation Product Present in Food Stuffs Exposed to Ethylene Oxide," *J. Agric. Food Chem.* 22:407-409 (1974).

18. Beitchman, B. D. "Cross-linked Isocyanurate-Polyurethane Elastomers and Plastics Prepared with Triethylenediamine-Cocatalyst Cominbations," *Rubber Age* 98:65-72 (1966).

19. Cline, J. C., C. Z. Thompson and R. E. McMahon. "A Convenient Technique for the Detection of Volatile Liquid Mutagens in Ten Tester Strains," 9th Annual Meeting of Environmental Mutagen Society, San Francisco, March 9-13, pp. 68-69 (1978).

20. Lowenheim, F. A. and M. K. Moran. "Epichlorohydrin," in *Faith, Keyes and Clark's Industrial Chemicals,* 4th Ed., (New York: John Wiley & Sons, Inc., 1975), pp. 335-338.

21. "NIOSH Recommends new epichlorohydrin standard, Revision on allyl chloride," *Toxic Materials News* 3:154 (1976).

22. "Epichlorohydrin Causes Nose Cancers in Rats, NYU's Nelson Reports," *Pesticide Toxic News* 5:27-28 (1977).

23. Sram, R., M. Cerna and M. Kucerova. "The Genetic Risk of Epichlorohydrin as Related to the Occupational Exposure," *Biol. Zbl.* 95:451-462 (1976).

24. Rapoport, I. A. "Action of Ethylene Oxice, Glycides and Glycols on Genetic Mutations," *Dokl. Acad. Nauk. SSR* 60:469-472 (1948).

25. Voogd, C. E. "Mutagenic Action of Epoxy Compounds and Several Alcohols," *Mut. Res.* 21:52-53 (1973).
26. Shackelford, W. M., and L. H. Keith. "Frequency of Organic Compounds Identified in Water," EPA No. 600/4-76-062; U.S. Environmental Protection Agency, Athens, GA, (1976), p.214.
27. Ikeda, M., and L. Imamura. "Evaluation of Hippuric, Phenyl Glyoxylic and Mandelic Acids on Urine as Indicators of Styrene Exposure," *Int. Arch. Arbeitsmed* 32:93-101 (1974).
28. Leibman, K. C. "Metabolism and Toxicity of Styrene," *Env. Health Persp.* 11:115-119 (1975).
29. *Monographs on the evaluation of Carcinogenic Risk of Chemicals to Man, Vol. 17* (Lyon: International Agency for Research on Cancer, 1978).
30. McCann, J., E. Choi, J. Yamasaki and B. N. Ames. "Detection of Carcinogens as Mutagens in the Salmonella/Microsome test: Assay of 300 Chemicals," *Proc. Nat. Acad. Sci.* 12:5135-5139 (1975).
31. Milvy, P., and A. J. Gardo. "Mutagenic Activity of Styrene Oxide (1,2-epoxyethylbenzene) as Presumed Styrene Metabolite," *Mut. Res.* 40:15-18 (1976).
32. Vainio, H., R. Paakkonen, K. Ronnholm, V. Raunio and O. Pelkonen. "A Study on the Mutagenic Activity of Styrene and Styrene Oxide," *Scand. J. Work, Env. Health* 3:147-151 (1976).
33. Loprieno, N. et al. "Mutagenicity of Industrial Compounds: Styrene and its Possible Metabolite Styrene Oxide," *Mut. Res.* 40:317-324 (1976).
34. deMeester, C., F. Poncelet, M. Roberfroid, J. Rondelet and M. Mercier. "Mutagenicity of Styrene and Styrene Oxide," *Mut. Res.* 56:147-152 (1977).
35. Stoltz, D. R., and R. J. Withey. "Mutagenicity Testing of Styrene and Epoxide in *Salmonella typhimurium,*" *Bull. Env. Contam. Toxicol.* 17:739-742 (1977).
36. deRaat, W. K. "Induction of Sister Chromatid Exchanges by Styrene and its Presumed Metabolite Styrene Oxide in the Presence of Rat Liver Homogenate," *Chem.-Biol. Interact.* 20:163-170 (1978).
37. "Criteria for a Recommended Standard: Occupational Exposure to Glycidyl Ethers," DHEW (NIOSH) Publication No. 78-166, U.S. Dept. of Health, Education and Welfare, Rockville, MD (1978).
38. Friedman, M. A., E. J. Greene, J. A. Sherrod and A. J. Salerno. "Activity of Phenylglycidyl Ether (PGE) in Genetic in vitro Screening Tests," *Pharmacologist* 20:154-159 (1978).
39. "Ames Test is Positive for Epoxy Resins," *Chem. Eng. News* p. 17 (December 1978).
40. Andersen, M., P. Kiel, H. Larsen and J. Maxild. "Mutagenic Action of Aromatic Epoxy Resins," *Nature* 276:391-392 (1978).
41. Nishioka, H., and H. Ohtani. "Mutagenicity of Epoxide Resins, Constituents and Commercial Adhesives, in Bacterial Test Systems," *Mutation Res.* 54:247-248 (1978).

42. Bartsch, H., C. Malaveille, A. Barbin, L. Tomatis and R. Montesano. "Mutagenicity and Metabolism of Vinyl Chloride and Related Compounds," *Environ. Health Persp.* 17:193-207 (1976).

43. Fishbein, L. "Industrial Mutagens and Potential Mutagens, I. Halogenated Derivatives," *Mutation Res.* 32:267-308 (1976).

44. Malaveille, C., H. Bartsch, A. Barbin, A. M. Camus and R. Montesano. "Mutagenicity of Vinyl Chloride, Chloroethylene Oxide, Chloroacetaldehyde and Chloroethanol," *Biochem. Biophys. Res. Commun.* 63: 363-370 (1975).

45. Wood, A. S. et al. "Mutagenic and Cytotoxic Activity of Benzo(a)-pyrene 4,5-7,8-9,10 Oxides and Six Corresponding Phenols," *Proc. Nat. Acad. Sci.* 72:3176-3180 (1975).

46. Huberman, E., T. Kuroki, H. Marquardt, J. K. Selkirk, C. Heidelberger, P. L. Grover and P. Sims. "Transformation of Hamster Embryo Cells by Epoxides and Other Derivatives of Polycyclic Hydrocarbons," *Cancer Res.* 32:1391-1396 (1972).

47. Huberman, E., H. Bartsch and L. Sachs. "Mutation Induction in Chinese Hamster V-79 Cells by Vinyl Chloride Metabolites, Chloroethylene Oxide and 2-chloroacetaldehyde," *Int. J. Cancer* 16:639-644 (1975).

48. Daly, J. W., D. M. Jerina and B. Witkop. "Arene Oxides and the NIH Shift: The Metabolism, Toxicity and Carcinogenicity of Aromatic Compounds," *Experientia* 28:1129-1149 (1972).

49. Testa, B., and P. Jenner. *Drug Metabolism: Chemical and Biochemical Aspects* (New York, Mercel Decker, Inc. 1976), pp. 56-61.

50. Oesch, F. "Metabolic Transformation of Clinically Used Drugs to Epoxides: New Perspectives in Drug-Drug Interactions," *Biochem. Pharmacol.* 25:1935-1937 (1976).

51. Wade, D. R., S. C. Airy and J. E. Sinsheimer. "Mutagenicity of Aliphatic Epoxides," *Mut. Res.* 58:217-223 (1978).

52. Glatt, H. R., H. G. Metler, H. G. Newman and Foiesch. "Metabolic Activation of *trans*-4-acetyl Aminostilbene: A Protective Mechanism Against Its Activation to a Mutagen," *Biochem. Biophys. Res. Commun.* 73:1025-1032 (1971).

53. Glatt, H. R., F. Oesch, A. Frigerio and S. Garattini. "Epoxides Metabolically Produced from Some Carcinogens and from Some Chronically Used Drugs," *Int. J. Cancer* 16:787-797)1975);

54. Rapoport, I. A. "Alkylation of the gene molecule," *Dokl. Akad. Nauk. SSSR* 59:1183-1186 (1948).

55. Nishioka, H. "Lethal and Mutagenic Action of Formaldehyde, Hcr$^+$ and Hcr$^-$ strains, *E. coli,*" *Mutation Res.* 17:261-265 (1973).

56. Brusick, D. J. "The Genetic Properties of Beta-propiolactone," *Mutation Res.* 39:241-256 (1977).

57. Fishbein, L. *Potential Industrial Carcinogens and Mutagens* (Amsterdam: Elsevier, 1979), pp. 118-120.

58. *Monographs on the Evaluation of Carcinogenic Risk of Chemicals to Man, Vol. 9* (Lyon: International Agency for Research on Cancer, 1975), pp. 37-46, 47-49, 61-65.

59. Stanford Research Institute. "A Study of Industrial Data on Candidate Chemicals for Testing," EPA-560/5-77-066, Menlo Park, CA: (1977), pp. 4-29 and 4-31.

60. Alexander, M. L., and E. Glanges, "Genetic Damage Induced by Ethylenimine," *Proc. Nat. Acad. Sci.* 53:282-285 (1965).

61. Ong. T. M., and F. J. deSerres. "Mutagenic Activity of Ethylenimine in *Neurospora crassa*," *Mutation Res.* 18:251-255, (1973).

62. Chang, T. H., and F. T. Elequin. "Induction of Chromosome Aberrations in Cultured Human Cells by Ethylenimine and Its Relation to the Cell Cycle, *Mutation Res.* 4:83-87 (1967).

63. Ulland, B., M. Finkelstein, E. K. Weisburger, J. M. Rice and J. H. Weisburger. "Carcinogenicity of Industrial Chemical Propylenimine and Propane Sultone," *Nature,* 230:460-461 (1971).

64. Van Duuren, B. L., S. Melchionne, R. Blair, B. M. Goldschmidt and C. Katz. "Carcinogenicity of Isoesters and Epoxides and Lactones: Aziridine Ethanol, Propane Sultone and Related Compounds," *J Nat. Cancer Inst.* 46:143-150 (1971).

65. Filippova, L. M., O. A. Pan'Shin and R. G. Kostyankovskii. "Chemical Mutagens, IV. Mutagenic Activity of Germinal Systems," *Genetika* 3:134-136 (1967).

66. *Monographs on the Evaluation of Carcinogenic Risk of Chemicals to Man, Vol. 4* (Lyon: International Agency for Research on Cancer, 1974), pp. 276-281.

67. "Threshold Limit Values for Chemical Substances in Workroom Air Adopted by ACHIG for 1976," American Conference of Governmental Industrial Hygienists, Cincinnati, OH (1976).

68. Lichtenberger, J., and R. Lichtenberger. "Sur les Sulfates de Diols," *Bull. Soc. Chim.* 1002–1005 (1948).

69. Brunken, J., G. Glöcilner and E. J. Poppe. "Über cyclische Sulfate und ihre Verwendung zur Herstellung von Sulfate Betainen," *Veroeff. Wiss. Photo-Lab. AGFA* 9:61 (1961).

70. Poppe, E. J. "Sensibilizierungsfarbstoffe mit sauren Substituenten," *Z. Wiss. Photogr., Photophys. Photochem.* 63:149-152 (1969).

71. Goldschmidt, B. M., K. Frenkel and B. L. Van Duuren. "The Reaction of Propane Sultone with Guanosine, Adenosine and Related Compounds," *J. Heterocyclic Chem.* 11:719-726 (1974).

72. Fischer, F. F. "Propane Sultone," *Int. Eng. Chem.* 56:41-42 (1964).

73. Osterman-Golkar, S., and C. A. Wachtmeister. "On the Reaction Kinetics in Water of 1,3-Propane Sultone and 1,4-Butane Sultone: A Comparison of Reaction Rates and Mutagenic Activity of Some Alkylating Agents," *Chem.-Biol. Interact.* 14:195-198 (1976).

74. Simmon, V. F. "In vitro Mutagenicity Assays With *Saccharomyces cerevisiae* D3," *J. Nat. Cancer Inst.* (1979).

75. Dunkel, V. C., J. S. Wolff and R. J. Pienta. "In vitro Transformation as a Presumptive Test for Detecting Chemical Carcinogens," *Cancer Bull.* 29:167-174 (1977).

76. Loveless, A. *Genetic and Allied Effects of Alkylating Agents* (London: Butterworths, 1966).

77. *Monographs on the Evaluation of Carcinogenic Risk of Chemicals to Man, Vol. 7,* (Lyon: International Agency for Research on Cancer, 1974), pp. 223-230.

78. Butsche, C. D., and D. J. Pasto. *Fundamentals of Organic Chemistry* (Englewood Cliffs, NJ: Prentice-Hall, Inc., 1975), p. 693.

79. Kriek, E., and P. Emmelot. "Methylation of Deoxyribonucleic Acid by Diazomethane," *Biochim. Biophys. Acta.* 91:59-66 (1964).

80. Schoental, R., and P. N. Magee. "Induction of Squamous Carcinoma of the Lung and of the Stomach and Esophagus by Diazomethane and N-methyl-N-nitroso Urethan Respectively," *Brit. J. Cancer* 188: 420-422 (1960).

81. Marquardt, H., F. K. Zimmermann and R. Schwaier. "The Action of Carcinogenic Nitrosamines and Nitrosamides on the Adenine-G-45 Reverse Mutation System of .*S. cerevisiae,*" *Z. Verebungslehre* 95:82-96 (1964).

82. Love, L. A., A. F. Pelfrene and H. G. Garcia. "Carcinogenicity of Diazoacetic Acids (DAAE)," *Anat. Rec.* 189:547-548 (1977).

83. Preussmann, R., S. Ivankovic, C. Landschutz, J. Gimmy, E. Flohr and U. Griesbach. "Carcinogene Wirkung von 13 aryldialkyl Traizenen an BD-Ratten," *Z. Krebsforsch* 81:285-310 (1974).

84. Preussmann, R., H. Druckrey, S. Ivankovic and A. von Hodenberg. "Chemical Structure and Carcinogenicity of Aliphatic Hydiazo, Azo and Azoxy Compounds and of Triazenes, Potential *in vivo* Alkylating Agents," *Ann. N.Y. Acad. Sci.* 163:697-716 (1969).

85. Malaveille, C., G. F. Kolar and H. Bartsch. "Rat and Mouse Tissue-Mediated Mutagenicity of Ring-Substituted 3,3-Dimethyl-1-phenyl Triazenes in *Salmonella typhimurium,*" *Mutation Res.* 36:1-6 (1976);

86. Kolar, G. F., R. Fahrig and E. Vogel. "Structure Activity Dependence in Some Novel Ring-Substituted 3,3'-dimethyl-l-phenyl Triazenes, Genetic Effect in *Drosophila* and *S. cerevisiae,*" *Chem. Biol. Interact.* 9:365-371 (1974).

87. Ong, T. M., and F. J. deSerres. "The Mutagenicity of 1-phenyl-3,3-dimethyl Triazene and 1-Phenyl-3-monomethyltriazene in *Neurospora crassa,*" *Mutation Res.* 13:276-300 (1971).

88. Vogel, E., R. Fahrig and G. Obe. "Triazenes, a New Group of Indirect Mutagens, Comparative Investigations of the Genetic Effects of Different Aryl Dialkyl Triazenes Using *S. cerevisiae,* the Host-Mediated Assay, *Drosophila melanogaster* and Human Chromosomes in vitro," *Mutation Res.* 21:123-136 (1973).

89. Ehrenberg, L., S. Osterman-Golkar, D. Singh and U. Lundquist. "On the Reaction Kinetics and Mutagenic Activity of Methylating and

Beta-Halogenoethylating Gasoline Additives," *Radiation Botany* 15: 185-187 (1974).

90. McCann, J., N. E. Spingarn, J. Kobori and B. N. Amers. "Detection of Carcinogens as Mutagens: Bacterial Tester Strains with R-factor Plasmids," *Proc. Nat. Acad. Sci.* 72:979-983. (1975).

91. Dyer, K. F., and P. J. Hanna. "Mutagenic and Antifertility Activity of Trimethyl Phosphate in *D. melanogaster*," *Mutation Res.* 16:327-330 (1972).

92. Sodermann, G. "Chromosome Breaking Effect of Gasoline Additive in Cultured Human Lymphocytes," *Hereditas* 71:335-339 (1972).

93. U.S. Environmental Protection Agency. "Status Assessment of Toxic Chemicals, No. 14, Tris(2,3-dibromopropylphosphate)," Industrial Environmental Research Laboratory, Cincinnati, OH (1977).

94. Prival, M. J., E. C. McCoy, B. Gutter and H. S. Rosenkranz. "Tris(2,3-dibromopropyl)-phosphate: Mutagenicity of a Widely Used Flame-retardant," *Science* 195:76-78 (1977).

95. Blum, A., and B. N. Ames. "Flame-retardant Additives as Possible Cancer Hazards," *Science* 195:17-23 (1977).

96. National Cancer Institute. "Results of Bioassay with Tris," National Institute of Health, Bethesda, MD (1977).

97. Kerst, A. F. "Toxicology of Tris(2,3-dibromopropyl)phosphate," *J. Fire Flamm. Fire Retardant Chem.* 1:205-215 (1974).

98. Powers, M. B., W. Voelker, N. P. Page, E. K. Weisburger and H. F. Kraybill. "Carcinogenicity of Ethylenedibromide (EDB) and 1,2-dibromo-3-chloropropane (DBCP)," *Toxicol. Appl. Pharmacol.* 33: 171-172 (1975).

99. Torkelson, T. R., S. E. Sadek, V. K. Rowe, J. K. Kodama, H. H. Anderson, G. S. Loquvam and C. H. Hine. "Toxicological Investigations of 1,2-dibromo-3-chloropropane," *Toxicol. Appl. Pharmacol.* 3:545-559 (1961).

100. Rohm & Hass Co. "News Release: Reactions of Formaldehyde and HCl forms Bis-CME," Philadelphia, PA, Dec. 27 (1972).

101. Kallos, G. J., and R. A. Solomon. "Investigation of the Formation of Bis(chloromethyl)ether in Simulated Hydrogen Chloride-Formaldehyde Atmospheric Environments," *Am. Ind. Hyg. Assoc. J.* 34:469-473 (1973).

102. Feldman, N. Y. "Reaction of Nucleic Acids and Nucleo-proteins with Formaldehyde," *Prog. Nucleic Acids Res. Mol. Biol.* 13:1-49. (1975).

103. Auerbach, C., M. Moutschendahmen and J. Moutschen. "Genetic and Cytogenetical Effects of Formaldehyde and Related Compounds," *Mutation Res.* 39:317-362 (1977).

104. Rosenkranz, H. S. "Formaldehyde as a Possible Carcinogen," *Bull. Env. Contam. Toxicol.* 8:242-248 (1972).

105. Rapoport, I. A. "Mutations Under the Influence of Unsaturated Aldehydes," *Dokl. Akad. Nauk. SSR* 61:713-715 (1948).

106. Bignami, M., G. Cardamone, P. Comba, V. A. Ortali, G. Morpurgo and A. Carere. "Relationship Between Chemical Structure and Mutagenic Activity in Some Pesticides: The Use of *Salmonella typhimurium* and *Aspergillus nidulans*," *Mutation Res.* 46:243-244. (1974).

107. Izard, C. "Recherches sur les effets mutagenes de l'acrolein et de des deux epoxydes: Le glycidol et le glycidal, sur S. cerevisiae," *CR Acad. Sci. Ser. D.* 276:3037-3040 (1973).

108. Baier, E. J. "Statement on Ethylene Dichloride Before the Sub-committee on Oversight and Investigations House Committee on Interstate and Foreign Commerce," Washington, DC, January 23, (1978).

109. National Cancer Institute. "Bioassay of 1,2-dichloroethane for Possible Carcinogenicity," Carcinogenesis Testing Program, DHEW Publ. No. (NIH) 78-1305, National Institutes of Health, Bethesda, MD: (January 1978).

110. McCann, J., V. Simmon, D. Streitweiser and B. N. Ames. "Mutagenicity of Chloroacetaldehyde, a Possible Metabolic Product of 1,2-dichloroethane (Ethylene Dichloride), Chloroethanol (Ethylene Chlorohydrin), Vinyl Chloride and Cyclophosphamide," *Proc. Nat. Acad. Sci.* 72:3190-3193 (1975).

111. Simmon, V. F., K. Kauhanen and R. G. Tardiff. "Mutagenic Activity of Chemicals Identified in Drinking Water," in: *Progress in Genetic Toxicology*, D. Scott, B. A. Bridges and F. H. Sobels, Eds. (Amsterdam: Elsevier/North-Holland Biomedical Press, 1977), pp. 249-256.

112. "Ethylene Dibromide: Institute Recommends Ceiling Limit One Milligram, Engineering Controls," *Cancer Res.* 34:2576-2579. (1974).

113. Brem, H., A. B. Stein and H. S. Rosenkranz. "The Mutagenicity and DNA Modifying Effects of Haloalkanes," *Cancer Res.* 34:2576-2579. (1974).

114. Rosenkranz, H. S. "Mutagenicity of Halogenated Olefins and Their Derivatives," *Env. Health Persp.* 21:79-84 (1977).

115. Vogel, E., and J. L. R. Chandler. "Mutagenicity Testing of Cyclamate and Some Pesticides in *Drosophila melanogaster*," *Experientia* 30:621-623 (1974).

116. Naumann, C. H., A. H. Sparrow and L. A. Schairer. "Comparative Effects of Ionizing Radiation and Two Gaseous Chemical Mutagens on Somatic Mutation Induction in One Mutable and Two Non-mutable Clones of *Tradescantia*," *Mutation Res.* 38:53-70 (1976).

117. Ehrenberg, L., S. Osterman-Holkar, D. Singh and U. Lundquist. "On the Reaction Kinetics and Mutagenic Activity of Methylating and Beta-halogenoethylating Gasoline Derivatives," *Radiat. Biol.* 15:185-194 (1974).

118. Edwards, K., H. Jackson and A. R. Jones. "Studies with Alkylating Esters, II. A Chemical Interpretation Through Metabolic Studies of

the Infertility Effects of Ethylene Dimethanesulfonate and Ethylene Dibromide," *Biochem. Pharmacol.* 19:1783-1789 (1970).

119. Clements Associates. "Information Dossiers on Substances Designated by TSCA Interagency Testing Commission," Washington, DC, (December 1977).

120. Andrews, A. W., E. S. Zawistowski and C. R. Valentine. "A Comparison of the Mutagenic Properties of Vinyl Chloride and Methyl Chloride," *Mutation Res.* 40:273-276 (1976).

121. Poirier, L. A., G. D. Stoner and M. B. Shimkin. "Bioassay of Alkyl Halides and Nucleotide Base Analogs by Pulmonary Tumor Response in Strain A Mice," *Cancer Res.* 35:1411-1415 (1975).

122. Jongen, W. M. F., G. M. Alink and J. H. Koeman. "Mutagenic Effect of Dichloromethane on *Salmonella typhimurium*," *Mutation Res.* 56:245-248 (1978).

123. OSHA. "Occupational Safety & Health Standards: Carcinogens," *Federal Register* 39(20):3768-3773, 3773-3776 (1974).

124. Nelson, N. "The Chloroethers—Occupational Carcinogens: A Summary of Laboratory and Epidemiology Studies," *Ann. N.Y. Acad. Sci.* 271:81-90 (1976).

125. Albert, R. E., B. S. Pasternack, R. E. Shore, M. Lippman, N. Nelson and B. Ferris. "Mortality Patterns Among Workers Exposed to Chloromethyl Ethers," *Env. Health Persp.* 11:209-214 (1975).

126. Van Duuren, B. L. "Carcinogenic Epoxides, Lactones and Halo-ethers and Their Mode of Action," *Ann. N.Y. Acad. Sci.* 163:633-651 (1969).

127. Van Duuren, B. L., B. M. Goldschmidt, C. Katz, L. Langseth, C. Mercado and A. Sivak. "Alpha-haloethers: A New Type of Alkylating Carcinogen," *Arch. Env. Health* 16:472-476 (1968).

128. Van Duuren, B. L, C. Katz, B. M. Goldschmidt, K. Frenkel and A. Sivak. "Carcinogenicity of Haloethers, II. Structure-Activity Relationships of Analogs of Bis(chloromethyl)ether," *J. Nat. Cancer Inst.* 48:1431-1439 (1972).

CHAPTER 19

CHEMICAL CAUSES OF PRENATAL
MALDEVELOPMENT

Herbert S. Posner

National Institute of Environmental
    Health Sciences
Research Triangle Park, North Carolina

INTRODUCTION

The painfully provocative title of a recent report was "Litigation-Produced Pain, Disease and Suffering: An Experience with Congenital Malformation Lawsuits" [1]. It involved more than 100 cases. Almost 20 years ago nearly 6000 cases of thalidomide-associated malformation were documented. Similar incidents have been reported, but they affected, prenatally, fewer individuals.

In order to understand how some chemical interactions with different biological systems are hazardous and some appear to be nonhazardous, we should know something about the biological substrate, the major variables of the system, and structure-activity relationships for the chemicals. This understanding is important for the following reasons: (1) the persons at risk are not ourselves, but the next generation; (2) the developing fetus is usually not observed directly during the nine-month pregnancy period, and chemical exposure is difficult to ascertain; (3) an individual's entire lifetime may be affected; and (4) ethical problems can arise, for example, whether a pregnancy should continue and how to deal with the occurrence of serious maldevelopment.

THE BIOLOGICAL SUBSTRATE

Although the conceptus at different stages of its development is generally the biological substrate, the substrate may also be the sperm, ova, placenta, or some of the other auxiliary biological components.

After fertilization in the human, there is a 14-day period of cell division followed by organization into the blastocyst. If there is interference during this period, death and rejection of the conceptus generally occur.

The next stage lasts until about the 50th day and is the major period of differentiation into organs and other tissues. The first organs to start formation are the nervous system, the heart and the eyes. These continue to develop as other organs—such as the alimentary tract, kidneys, liver, endocrine organs, placenta and skeletal system—begin their own development. From fertilization to about the 50th day is the embryonic period; the remaining prenatal time is the fetal period. These terms are sometimes used interchangeably.

From the 50th day on, the organism continues its differentiation, but growth and a reproportioning of the fetus is now dominant. Some types of maldevelopment can occur during this time.

After the 20th week or 5th month, the fetus may be able to survive outside the uterus in a supportive environment.

After birth, following the normal gestation period of 9 months, differentiation is still not complete. Development in the kidneys, growth of some smaller nerves in the brain, and myelinization of the axons of some nerves continue. The process of myelinization continues for several years. Further differentiation of the gonads is quiescent until puberty, when the male and female primary sexual systems then complete development and the secondary sexual characteristics appear.

There are several types of damage that can occur before birth. These include: birth defects, also called congenital malformations; cancer; mutation; defects expressed as an altered function rather than as a more easily identifiable structural change; and in utero growth retardation (small-for-date babies). After a normal 9-month gestation period, but when the birth weight is below about 1500 g, birth defects are often observed. Effects may be as subtle as learning or behavioral deficits or as visible as the shortening or absence of the long bones of the arms or legs. Combinations of effects sometimes occur in known syndromes or in unrelated manners. Sensitivity to these effects varies during the course of development. In some cases there is a short period of high vulnerability. Some effects may not become manifest until later in life, just as there are some genetic conditions that are not seen until middle age. However, exposures to disruptive influences do not necessarily lead to damage, because compensatory mechanisms are available to the system. In some instances the initial effects represent a simple maturational delay.

CHEMICAL TRANSPORT BETWEEN THE MOTHER AND CONCEPTUS

In experimental studies with rabbits, Fabro [2] and Sieber and Fabro [3] showed that before implantation of the blastocyst into the uterus, long before the placenta is formed, radioactively tagged chemicals are transported from the maternal circulation into both the uterine fluid and the blastocyst. They found that transport is generally greater in the cases of compounds that are more lipid-soluble, less ionized at the pH of body fluids, and that have lower molecular weights. However, nicotine accumulated in the blastocyst to a concentration four times that of the maternal plasma. Salicyclic acid also moved into the blastocyst much faster than expected from its more than 99% ionization at the pH of blood, 7.4.

In addition to the initial compounds tested, metabolites of many of these substances were also present in the blastocyst. For example, after maternal administration of caffeine, 1,3- and 1,7-dimethylxanthine and 1,3-dimethyluric acid were found; after nicotine, cotinene and demethyl-cotinene were present; and after isoniazid, acetylisoniazid and isonicotinuric acid accumulated.

The rate of transfer of substances across the placenta changes as the placenta develops [4,5]. The principles governing passage through the placenta are generally similar to those of passage into the blastocyst. Salicylate, however, crosses the placenta more rapidly than expected. Triameterene, a compound used as a diuretic in humans, crosses sheep placenta much more rapidly from the fetus to the mother than from the mother to the fetus shortly before birth [6,7]. Some high-molecular-weight compounds and some viruses can cross the placenta. At this time we do not have a highly precise understanding of those features of the placenta and molecular characteristics of the chemicals in question that influence the rate of transfer of substances across the placenta.

THE POPULATIONS AT RISK AND
MODES OF EXPOSURE

The direct population at risk for an agent that causes prenatal maldevelopment is, of course, the in utero differentiating conceptus. In this sense, the induction of prenatal maldevelopment is different from the carcinogenic and mutagenic transformations that occur in all exposed populations.

The exposure may be due to natural substances, drugs, foods and food additives, solvents, fuels, agricultural and garden products, air or water pollutants, chemicals on textiles, or components of household and other products [8]. Increasing numbers of women work in industries where they can be exposed to a greater number of chemicals; this situation cannot always be resolved by a refusal to employ "women of child-bearing age."

Toxicities can also result from contaminanted clothing, thereby exposing a worker's family by several modes of transfer. Disruptive influences may also be initiated by a primary effect in the male, perhaps mediated by sperm, as suggested by animal experiments.

CAUSES OF PRENATAL MALDEVELOPMENT:
STRUCTURE–ACTIVITY RELATIONSHIPS

Physical and Infectious Causes [9,10]

Artificial incubation of bird eggs was carried out in ancient Egypt. Hippocrates and Aristotle noted variabilities in the chicks after hatching. Some biological and environmental theories were suggested. Aristotle knew of many minor and much more serious abnormalities in humans, and he knew that some were compatible with life while others were not.

Pathologists of the 18th and 19th centuries classified the known types of human prenatal malformations. The obstretrician, Ballantyne, reviewed the morphology and physiology of malformations and was one of the first to discuss them in terms of embryology and abnormal development. Malformations can be caused by physical factors [11] such as constriction of a fetal part by the umbilical cord and fluid imbalances [12] that distort or apply pressure to structures. Some viral and other infectious conditions are known to cause prenatal maldevelopment [13].

Ionizing Radiation [14-18]

Ionizing radiation is known to act through chemical mechanisms. In the early part of the century, it was determined that X-rays produce malformations in experimental animals. Sufficient ionizing radiation is now known to cause a variety of birth defects and leukemia in children exposed in utero. Mutations have also been detected in experimental systems designed to examine genetic content.

Radiation from the atom bombs in Japan produced microcephaly and mental retardation in those exposed during the first trimester and a small reduction in growth rate in those exposed in the first postnatal years. An increased incidence of leukemia and thyroid tumors resulted from exposure during both periods.

Thalidomide

Before 1961, prenatal maldevelopment in animals and, in some cases, in humans was known to be related to nutritional and hormonal imbalances, antibiotic and chemotherapeutic treatments and to rubella (German measles) [19,20]. However, it was the thalidomide disaster that spurred research in the area and drew many scientific disciplines into the effort, e.g., organic chemists, biochemists, pharmacologists and toxicologists, as well as the zoologists, physiologists, pediatricians and pathologists.

Thalidomide was sold without prescription in Germany between 1957 and 1961 [21]. It was also tested widely elsewhere and was advertised as a safe sedative, especially during pregnancy. Reports then began to appear of effects on the peripheral nervous system. On this basis, a new-drug application was withheld in the U.S. pending further information. During this time, a variety of malformations were observed, the most prominent being the shortening or absence of the long bones of the arms and/or legs. These cases were rare, but by the time about 50 cases had been seen, Lenz [22] in West Germany and McBride [23] in Australia independently suggested that thalidomide might be the responsible agent. It was later found that malformation could occur after ingestion of a single dose as well as with multiple doses. However, defects were not observed in all exposed individuals. As indicated earlier, there were about 6000 children affected in utero.

Four groups of malformations are now known to be associated with thalidomide, depending on the stage during pregnancy at which exposure occurred. These are: effects on the upper limbs, the lower limbs, the ears and eyes, and the heart, kidneys and alimentary tract [24].

Thalidomide has been studied in a large number of species [25,26], but the rabbit and mouse, and occasionally the rat, are now being used most extensively for tests for structurally similar chemicals. Nonhuman primates, the chicken, the rabbit, and some other species have also been used to investigate embryological factors.

The rabbit was the first species to yield some of the malformations seen in humans [27] after exposure to thalidomide during pregnancy. Schumacher [28] mentioned the use of other species but limited his review of structurally similar chemicals to the rabbit. Jönsson [29] reviewed some of the tests in the rat and chicken as well as in the rabbit.

Scott et al. [30] found only a low incidence of malformation in mice and rats, and they reported only "nonspecific-type malformations." They discussed some possible causes for the differences in their results from those of Koch and of Köhler. Schumacher [28] published an excellent analysis of structure and activity findings. Jackson and Schumacher [31] recently found that the combination of borderline zinc deficiency and administration of a more stable thalidomide homolog yields human-type malformations in the rat. According to Schumacher, whose persistence may have been crucial to our present understanding of the causes of species differences [28]:

> Even if the embryotoxic effects could be traced back to a certain structural feature of the thalidomide molecule, this would be only partially satisfactory in explaining the mechanism of action. We must know why there are species differences, why there is a possible correlation

with metals, and we must know with what cellular constituent or constituents interactions take place, as well as the mechanistic aspects of
the interaction.

Structure-activity studies, as performed until now, will not, we feel,
provide the needed information and are therefore of no predictive value
with regard to teratogenicity in animals, much less in humans.

We suggest that only by rigorous standardization of such teratogen
testing protocols, using common methodology, can order replace
existing confusion in comparing the results of teratogenic research
between laboratories and in different species of animals.

Structure-activity studies with chemicals that are closely related in
molecular structure to thalidomide are very important and have been
widely used: (1) to seek related compounds that might be safer; (2) to
determine which species is most suitable for teratogenicity tests; (3) to
explain some of the aspects of the mechanism by which thalidomide is
teratogenic; (4) to partially exonerate thalidomide by determining if one
of its metabolites or perhaps some other aspect of its structure could
be involved more directly; and (5) to determine if the same structure-
activity relationships hold for other uses of thalidomide, for example, in
the treatment of leprosy and in cancer chemotherapy trials.

The compounds shown in Table I are teratogenic in the rabbit. Some
other compounds were determined by Schumacher [28] to be marginally
teratogenic. However, these were tested only in small numbers of animals.

Phthalimidinoglutarimide (EM_{12}) was found to be teratogenic in the
rabbit and monkey; in some cases it produced malformations similar to
those caused by thalidomide [37]. This compound produced about three
times as many teratogenic events as the same dose of thalidomide in the
rabbit, which may be related to its slower rate of hydrolysis. When administered intravenously, it was first found to be only minimally teratogenic
in the rat [37]. However, a concomitant minimal zinc deficiency has
resulted in some human-type malformations and a higher incidence of the
malformations in the rat [31].

N-Methylthalidomide was weakly teratogenic.

The hydrolysis products and several of the metabolites of thalidomide
are not teratogenic in vivo [25,38,39]. Most of these, however, are very hydro-
philic and do not cross membranes well. They are also excreted rapidly
in the urine. However, phthalimidoisoglutarimide methyl ester (the methyl
ester of one of the hydrolytic products of thalidomide) is teratogenic [36].
A small amount of the thalidomide is hydroxylated on the benzenoid
ring [40,41]; this also raises the possibility of the presence of small
amounts of hydroxylated hydrolytic products. Whether or not these con-
tribute to thalidomide teratogenesis is speculative [42]. It is possible that
thalidomide is transported to the target site and there converted to a more
proximate teratogen.

Table I. Compounds that are Teratogenic in the Rabbit

Structure	Name	Reference
	Thalidomide (+, – and ±)	32
	N-Methylthalidomide	33
	Phthalimidophthalimide	34,35
	Phthalimidoisoglutarimide Methyl Ester	36
	Phthalimidinoglutarimide	28,31, 37

Phthalimidophthalimide has been shown to be teratogenic. It had been postulated that the glutarimide ring of this compound is a requisite for teratogenicity. The compound is about as teratogenic as thalidomide in the rabbit [34]. It binds irreversibly to nuclear RNA, DNA, histones and lipoproteins of rat liver [35] and also hydrolyzes and acylates amines as does thalidomide [34,35,43]. In the case of thalidomide, Schumacher [28] and Jönsson [29] discuss chemical theories proposed for the teratogenic activity of thalidomide that provide useful starting points for understanding the mechanisms for teratogenicity of chemicals that have similar molecular configurations.

Table II shows compounds reported to be teratogenic in the mouse. It is seen that three of these, N-phthalyl-DL-glutamine, N-phthalyl-DL-

Table II. Compounds that are Teratogenic in the Mouse

Structure	Name	Reference
	Thalidomide	44
	N-Phthalyl-DL-glutamine	45
	N-Phthalyl-DL-isoglutamine	45
	N-Phthalyl-DL-glutamic acid	45
	Phthalimide	46
	1,3-Indandione	47
$-CH_3$	2-Methyl-1,3-indandione	47
	Bindon [Anhydrobis (Indanedione)]	47
	Bindon ethyl ether	47
	3-Azaphthalimide	46
	4-Azaphthalimide	46
	3,6-Diazaphthalimide	46
	3,5-Diazaphthalimide	46

Structure	Name	Reference
	3,4,5,6-Tetrahydro-phthalimide	48
−CH₃	N-Methyl-3,4,5,6-tetrahydrophthalimide	48
	1,2,3,6-Tetrahydro-phthalimide	48
−CH₃	N-Methyl-1,2,3,6-tetrahydrophthalimide	48
	3,6-Dithia-3,4,5,6-tetrahydrothalidomide	48
−H	3,6-Dithia-3,4,5,6-tetrahydrophthalimide	48
−CH₃	N-Methyl-3,6-dithia-3,4,5,6-tetrahydrophthalimide	48
	Maleinimide	49
	3,4-Dichloromaleinimide	49
−CH₃	1-Methyl-3,4-dichloromaleinimide	49
−C₂H₅	1-Ethyl-3,4-dichloromaleinimide	49
	3,4-Dibromomaleinimide	49
−CH₃	1-Methyl-3,4-dibromo-maleinimide	49

isoglutamine and N-phthalyl-DL-glutamic acid, are among the twelve hydrolytic products of thalidomide [45]. Phthalimide is a hydrolytic product,
and phthalimide and maleinimide are fragments of the thalidomide molecule.
The other compounds are homologs based partly on substitution of C for N,
on N or S for C, reduction and on modifications of the maleinimide fragment.
The compounds were prepared to test the following hypotheses of thalidomide teratogenicity: (1) acylation of important macromolecules, (2) inter-
calation into the helices of DNA, (3) the importance of electrophilicity of
the molecule, and (4) trapping after crossing membranes. The molecular
mechanism is still not clear.

Alkylmercury

Toxic incidents due to methylmercury have occurred in Iraq, Japan and
the U.S., and human exposure, perhaps without symptoms, has been reported
in Sweden and Canada [50]. In all cases, the poisoning or increased blood
concentrations were due to eating contaminated foods.

In Iraq [51] grain that had been coated with alkylmercury as a fungicide
was used for the preparation of bread rather than for planting. There were
about 6000 hospital cases of poisoning and nearly 500 known deaths. A
study [52] of 29 children who were exposed in utero revealed some central
nervous system damage.

In Japan, methylmercury and inorganic mercury wastes were discharged
at Minimata Bay and at Niigata [53]. Methylmercury can also be biosynthe-
sized in bottom sediment from inorganic mercury by microbial reactions.
It then accumulates in fish and shellfish via their food chains. There were
more than 700 cases of poisoning at Minimata Bay and more than 500 at
Niigata. Forty infants were registered in Japan with fetal Minimata disease
up to 1976 [53].

In one U.S. incident, coated grain was fed to pigs, one of which was
sacrificed as meat for the family. Three family members were affected [54].
A child that had been in utero at the time of exposure developed myoclonic
convulsions in the first year. Although physical growth was normal in the
first year, he could not sit up or see [55]. His mother did not have clinical
symptoms, except for some slurring of speech during the same period of
time that the other family members were symptomatic.

In Sweden no symptoms were detected as a result of exposure to methylmercury compounds. In Canada symptoms were reported, but the findings
were contested on the basis that concomitant nutritional deficiencies and
consumption of alcohol could have confounded at least some of the
results [50].

The toxicity spectrum for organic mercurials covers a very wide range.

Of the aryl-, alkyl- and alkoxyalkyl compounds, the alkyl derivatives are by far the most toxic [56]. The effects of in utero methylmercury poisoning are generally not seen at birth. Some retardation in growth of the head may be the only morphologic malformation present, though most of the clinical symptoms result from diffuse cerebral damage. While the symptoms include those of cerebral palsy, there are effects on learning and behavior not generally present in cerebral palsy [57]. In Japan about one third of the affected children died within a few years after birth.

Other Chemicals

Table III lists other examples of reported chemically associated prenatal maldevelopment in humans, several with follow-up studies of structure-activity relationships in experimental animals. Only a few citations are given

Table III. Other Examples of Chemically Associated Prenatal Maldevelopment

Chemical or Pharmacologic Type	Reference
Vitamin A	58,59
Vitamin D	60,61
Folid Acid Antagonists	62-66
Anticonvulsant (antiepileptic) Drugs	67-73
Estrogens, Androgens and Progestogens	74-83
Ethanol	84-90
Cancer Chemotherapeutic Drugs	62,91

for each. The pharmacologic action indicated, of course, does not necessarily specify the reaction responsible for the maldevelopment. Other compounds not listed are suspect teratogens based on human and animal evidence. The *Handbook of Teratology* [92] is a good starting point for the consideration of other chemicals. Schumacher [28] also provides several references for structure-activity considerations with regard to 11 groups of chemical structures.

REFERENCES

1. Brent, R. L. "Litigation-Produced Pain, Disease and Suffering: An Experience with Congenital Malformation Lawsuits," *Teratology* 16(1):1-14 (1977).
2. Fabro, S. "Passage of Drugs and Other Chemicals into the Uterine Fluids and Preimplantation Blastocyst," in *Fetal Pharmacology*, L. Boreus, Ed. (New York: Raven Press, 1973), pp. 443-461.

3. Sieber, S. M., and S. Fabro. "Identification of Drugs in the Preimplantation Blastocyst and in the Plasma, Uterine Secretion and Urine of the Pregnant Rabbit," *J. Pharmacol. Exp. Ther.* 176(1):65-75 (1971).

4. Mirkin, B. L. "Drug Distribution in Pregnancy," in *Fetal Pharmacology*, L. Boreus, Ed. (New York: Raven Press, 1973), pp. 1-27.

5. Oh, Y., and B. L. Mirkin. "Transfer of Drugs into the Central Nervous System and Across the Placenta: A Comaprative Study Utilizing Aminopyrene (A), Diphenylhydantoin (D), Sodium Salicylate (S) and Mecamylamine (M)," *Fed. Proc.* 30:2034 (1971).

6. McNay, J. L., and P. G. Dayton. "Placental Transfer of a Substituted Pteridine from Fetus to Mother," *Science* 167(3920):988-990 (1970).

7. Dayton, P. G., A. W. Pruitt, J. L. McNay and J. Steinhorst. "Studies with Triamterene, a Substituted Pteridine: Unusual Brain to Plasma Ratio in Mammals," *Neuropharmacology* 11(5):435-446 (1972).

8. Wilson, J. G. "Environmental Chemicals," in *Handbook of Teratology*, Vol. 1, J. G. Wilson and F. C. Fraser, Eds. (New York: Plenum Press, 1977), pp. 357-385.

9. Warkany, J. "History of Teratology," in *Handbook of Teratology*, Vol. 1, J. G. Wilson and F. C. Fraser, Eds. (New York: Plenum Press, 1977), pp. 3-45.

10. Warkany, J. *Congenital Malformations, Notes and Comments* (Chicago: Year Book Medical Publishers, 1971).

11. Browne, D. "A Mechanistic Interpretation of Certain Malformations," in *Advances in Teratology, Vol. 2* D. H. M. Woolam, Ed. (New York: Academic Press, Inc., 1967), pp. 11-36.

12. Grabowski, C. T. "Altered Electrolytes and Fluid Balance," in *Handbook of Teratology, Vol. 2*, J. G. Wilson and F. C. Fraser, Eds. (New York: Plenum Press, 1977), pp. 153-170.

13. Kurent, J. E., and J. L. Sever. "Infectious Diseases," in *Handbook of Teratology, Vol. 1*, J. G. Wilson and F. C. Fraser, Eds. (New York: Plenum Press, 1977), pp. 225-259.

14. Gould, L. V., T. R. Bledsoe, C. E. Land and B. E. Oppenheim. "Genetic Damage from Diagnostic Radiation," *J. Am. Med. Assoc.* 238(10):1023-1025 (1977).

15. Swartz, H. M. "Hazards of Radiation Exposure for Pregnant Women," *J. Am. Med. Assoc.* 293(18):1907-1908 (1978).

16. Brent, R. L. "Radiations and Other Physical Agents," in *Handbook of Teratology, Vol. 1*, J. G. Wilson and F. C. Fraser, Eds. (New York: Plenum Press, 1977), pp. 153-223.

17. Dekaban, A. S. "Abnormalities in Children Exposed to X-Radiation During Various Stages of Gestation: Tentative Timetable of Radiation Injury to the Human Fetus, Part I," *J. Nucl. Med.* 9(9):471-477 (1968).

18. Bross, I. D. J., and N. Natarajan. "Risk of Leukemia in Susceptible Children Exposed to Preconception, *In Utero* and Postnatal Radiation," *Preventive Med.* 3(3):361-369 (1974).

19. Kalter, H., and J. Warkany. "Experimental Production of Congenital Malformations in Mammals by Metabolic Procedure," *Physiol. Rev.* 39(1):69-115 (1959).

20. Baker, J. B. E. "The Effects of Drugs on the Fetus," *Pharmacol. Rev.* 12(1):37-90 (1960).

21. Curran, W. J. "The Thalidomide Tragedy in Germany: The End of a Historic Medicolegal Trial," *N. Engl. J. Med.* 284(9):481-482 (1971).

22. Lenz, W. "Thalidomide and Congenital Anomalies," *Lancet* 1:45 (1962).

23. McBride, W. G. "Thalidomide and Congenital Abnormalities," *Lancet* 2:1358 (1961).

24. Smithells, R. W. "Defects and Disabilities of Thalidomide Children," *Brit. Med. J.* 1(5848):269-272 (1973).

25. Williams, R. T. "Thalidomide—A Study of Biochemical Teratology," *Arch. Environ. Health* 16(4):493-502 (1968).

26. McBride, W. G. "Thalidomide Embryopathy," *Teratology* 16(1):79-82 (1977).

27. Somers, G. F. "Thalidomide and Congenital Abnormalities," *Lancet* 1:912-913 (1962).

28. Schumacher, H. J. "Chemical Structure and Teratogenic Properties," in *Methods for Detection of Environmental Agents that Produce Congenital Defects*, T. H. Shepard, J. R. Miller and M. Marois, Eds. (Amsterdam: North Holland Publishing Co., 1975), pp. 65-77.

29. Jönsson, N. A. "Chemical Structure and Teratogenic Properties. III. A Review of Available Data on Structure-Activity Relationships and Mechanism of Action of Thalidomide Analogues," *Acta Pharmacol. Suecica* 9(6):521-542 (1972).

30. Scott, W. J., R. Fradkin and J. G. Wilson. "Non-Confirmation of Thalidomide-Induced Teratogenesis in Rats and Mice," *Teratology* 16(3):333-335 (1977).

31. Jackson, A. J., and H. J. Schumacher. "The Teratogenic Activity of a Thalidomide Analog EM_{12} in Rats on a Low Zinc Diet," *Teratology* 19(3):341-344 (1979).

32. Fabro, S., R. L. Smith and R. T. Williams. "Toxicity and Teratogenicity of Optical Isomers of Thalidomide," *Nature* 215(5098):296 (1967).

33. Wuest, H. M., E. B. Sigg and I. Fratta. "Pharmacological Properties and Teratogenic Action of 2-[Hexahydropthalimido]glutarimide and 2-Phthalimido-N-methylglutarimide," *Life Sci.* 3(7):721-724 (1964).

34. Gillette, J. R., and H. Schumacher. "Teratogenic Effects of Phthalimidophthalimide, An Analogue of Thalidomide," *Abstr. 3rd Intl. Pharmacol. Congr.* 50 (1966).

35. Schumacher, H., D. A. Blake and J. R. Gillette. "Acylation of Subcellular Components by Phthalimidophthalimide as a Possible Mode of Embryotoxic Action," *Fed. Proc.* 26(2):730 (1967).

36. Wuest, H. M., R. R. Fox and D. D. Crary. "Relationship Between Teratogenicity and Structure in the Thalidomide Field," *Experientia* 24(10):993-994 (1968).

37. Schumacher, H. J., J. Terapane, R. L. Jordan and J. G. Wilson. "The Teratogenic Activity of a Thalidomide Analogue, EM_{12} in Rabbits, Rats and Monkeys," *Teratology* 5(2):233-240 (1972).

38. Keberle, H., P. Loustalot, R. K. Maller, J. W. Faigle and K. Schmid. "Biochemical Effects of Drugs on the Mammalian Conceptus," *Ann. N.Y. Acad. Sci.* 123:252-262 (1965).

39. Fritz, H. "Failure of Thalidomide Metabolites to Produce Malformations in the Rabbit Embryo," *J. Reprod. Fertil.* 11:157-159 (1966).

40. Boylen, J. B., H. H. Horne and W. J. Johnson. "Teratogenic Effects of Thalidomide on the Developing Chick Embryo," *Can. J. Biochem.* 42(1):35-42 (1964).

41. Schumacher, H. J., R. L. Smith and R. T. Williams. "The Metabolism of Thalidomide: The Fate of Thalidomide and Some of Its Hydrolysis Products in Various Species," *Brit. J. Pharmacol.* 25(10):338-351 (1965).

42. Ménard, M., L. Erichomovitch, M., LaBrooy and F. L. Chubb. "Some Possible Metabolites of Thalidomide," *Can. J. Chem.* 41(7):1722-1775 (1963).

43. Schumacher, H. J. "Disposition of Thalidomide in Rabbits and Rats," *J. Pharmacol. Exp. Ther.* 160(1):201-211 (1968).

44. Köhler, F., and H. Koch. "Teratologic Investigation of the Thalidomide-like Compounds K-2004 and K-2604 in the Mouse and Rat," *Arzneim. Forsch.* 24(10):1616-1619 (1974).

45. Meise, W., H. Ockenfels and H. Köhler. "Teratologic Test of the Hydrolysis Products of Thalidomide," *Experientia* 29(4):423-424 (1973).

46. Fickentscher, K., E. Gunther and F. Köhler. "Teratogenicity and Embryotoxicity of Azaphthalimides," *Pharmazie* 31(3):172-174 (1976).

47. Köhler, F., K. Fickentscher, U. Halfmann and H. Koch. "Embryotoxicity and Teratogenicity of Derivatives of 1,3-indandione," *Arch. Toxicol.* 33(3):191-197 (1975).

48. Fickentscher, K., A. Kirfel, G. Will and F. Köhler. "Stereochemical Properties and Teratogenic Activity of Some Tetrahydrophthalimides," *Mol. Pharmacol.* 13(1):133-141 (1977).

49. Fickentscher, K., and F. Köhler. "Teratogenicity and Embryotoxicity of Some Maleinimides," *Arch. Toxicol.* 37(1):15-21 (1976).

50. "An Assessment of Mercury in the Environment," National Academy of Sciences (1978), pp. 88-105.

51. Amin-Zaki, L., M. A. Majeed, S. B. Elhassani, T. W. Clarkson, M. R. Greenwood and R. A. Doherty. "Prenatal Methylmercury Poisoning," *Amer. J. Dis. Child.* 133(2):172-177 (1979).

52. Marsh, D. O., G. Meyers, L. Clarkson, L. Amin-Zaki and S. T. Tikritio. "Fetal Methylmercury Poisoning: New Data on Clinical and Toxicological Aspects," *Trans. Amer. Neurol. Assoc.* 102:69-71 (1977).

53. Harada, M. "Congenital Minamata Disease: Intrauterine Methylmercury Poisoning," *Teratology* 18(2):285-288 (1978).

54. Pierce, P. E., J. F. Thompson, W. H. Likosky, L. N. Nickey, W. F. Barthel and A. R. Hinman. "Alkyl Mercury Poisoning in Humans: Report of an Outbreak," *J. Amer. Med. Assoc.* 220(11):1439-1442 (1972).

55. Snyder, R. D. "Congenital Mercury Poisoning," *New England J. Med.* 284(18):1014-1016 (1971).

56. Falchuk, K. H., L. J. Goldwater and B. L. Vallee. "The Biochemistry and Toxicology of Mercury," in *The Chemistry of Mercury*, C. A. McAuliffe, Ed. (London: The Macmillan Press Ltd., 1977), pp. 272-277.

57. Weiss, B., and R. A. Doherty. "Methylmercury Poisoning," *Teratology* 12(3):311-313 (1975).

58. Gal, I., I. M. Sharman and J. Pryse-Davies. "Vitamin A in Relation to Human Congenital Malformations," *Adv. Teratol.* 5:143-159 (1972).

59. Morris, G. M. "The Ultrastructural Effects of Excess Maternal Vitamin A on the Primitive Streak Stage Rat Embryo," *J. Embryol. Exp. Morphol.* 30(1):219-242 (1973).

60. Seelig, M. S. "Vitamin D and Cardiovascular, Renal and Brain Damage in Infancy and Childhood," *Ann. N.Y. Acad. Sci.* 147:537-582 (1969).

61. Palmisano, P. A. "Vitamin D: A Reawakening," *J. Am. Med. Assoc.* 224(11):1526-1527 (1973).

62. Nicholson, H. O. "Cytotoxic Drugs in Pregnancy: Review of Reported Cases," *J. Obstet. Gynaecol. Brit. Commonwealth* 75:307-312 (1968).

63. Netzloff, M. L., J. L. Frias and O. M. Rennert. "Maternal Aminopterin Ingestion," *Amer. J. Dis. Child.* 125:459-460 (1973).

64. Warkany, J. "Aminopterin and Methotrexate: Folic Acid Deficiency," *Teratology* 17(3):353-357 (1978).

65. "Folates and the Fetus," *Lancet* 1(8009):462 (1977).

66. Smithells, R. W., S. Sheppard and C. J. Schorah. "Folates and the Fetus," *Lancet* 1(8011):599 (1977).

67. Krall, R. L., J. K. Perry, H. J. Kupferberg and E. A. Swinyard. "Antiepileptic Drug Development: 1. History and a Program for Progress," *Epilepsia* 19:393-408 (1978).

68. Hanson, J. W., and D. W. Smith. "Reply," *J. Ped.* 90(4):674-675 (1977).

69. Goldman, A. S., and S. J. Yaffe. "Fetal Trimethadione Syndrome," *Teratology* 17(1):103-106 (1978).

70. Blattner, W. A., D. E. Henson, R. C. Young and J. F. Fraumeni. "Malignant Mesenchymoma and Birth Defects," *J. Am. Med. Assoc.* 238(4):334-335 (1977).

71. Smith, D. W. "Anticonvulsant Medication," *Am. J. Dis. Child.* 133(4):449-451 (1979).

72. Committee on Drugs, American Academy of Pediatrics, "Anticonvulsants and Pregnancy," *Pediatrics* 63(2):331-333 (1979).

73. Fabro, S., and N. A. Brown. "Teratogenic Potential of Anticonvulsants," *New England J. Med.* 300(22):1280-1281 (1979).

74. Saunders, F. J. "Effects of Sex Steroids and Related Compounds on Pregnancy and on Development of the Young," *Physiol. Rev.* 48(3): 601-643 (1968).

75. Manber, M. M. "Diethylstilbesterol," *Med. World News* (August 23, 1976), pp. 44-56.

76. "Offspring of Women Given DES Remain Under Study," *J. Am. Med. Assoc.* 238(9):932 (1977).

77. Clark, L. C., and K. M. Portier. "Diethylstilbesterol and the Risk of Cancer," *New England J. Med.* 300(5):263-264 (1979).

78. Bibbo, M., W. M. Haenszel, G. L. Wied, M. Hubby and A. L. Herbst. "Response to Clark and Portier," *New England J. Med.* 300(5):264 (1979).

79. Nora, J. J., A. H. Nora, J. Blu, J. Ingram, A. Fountain, M. Peterson, R. H. Lortscher and W. J. Kimberling. "Exogenous Progestogen and Estrogen Implicated in Birth Defects," *J. Am. Med. Assoc.* 240(9): 837-843 (1978).

80. Miller, J. R., and M. Yasuda. "Further Comments on Contraceptive Hormones and Congenital Heart Disease," *Teratology* 17(3):359-360 (1978).

81. McLachlan, J. A., and R. L. Dixon. "Transplacental Toxicity of Diethylstilbesterol: A Special Problem in Safety Evaluation," in *Advances in Modern Toxicology, Vol. 1*, M. A. Mehlman, R. E. Shapiro and H. Blumenthal, Eds. (New York: John Wiley & Sons, Inc., 1976) pp. 423-448.

82. Korach, K. S., M. Metzler and J. A. McLachlan. "Estrogenic Activity *In Vivo* and *In Vitro* of Some Diethylstilbesterol Metabolites and Analogs," *Proc. Nat. Acad. Sci.* 75(1):468-471 (1978).

83. Voorhess, M. L. "Masculinization of the Female Fetus Associated with Norethindrone Mestranol Therapy during Pregnancy," *J. Pediatrics* 71:128-131 (1967).

84. Jones, K. C., and D. W. Smith. "The Fetal Alcohol Syndrome," *Teratology* 12(1):1-10 (1975).

85. Lowry, R. B. "The Klippel-Feil Anomalad as Part of the Fetal Alcohol Syndrome," *Teratology* 16(1):53-56 (1977).

86. Hanson, J. W., K. L. Jones and D. W. Smith. "Fetal Alcohol Syndrome: Experience with 41 Patients," *J. Am. Med. Assoc.* 235(14):1458-1460 (1976).

87. Ouelette, E. M., H. L. Rosett, P. Rosman, L. Weiner. "Adverse Effects on Offspring of Maternal Alcohol Abuse During Pregnancy," *New England J. Med.* 297(10):528-530 (1977).

88. Collins, E., and G. Turner. "Six Children Affected by Maternal Alcoholism," *Med. J. Aust.* 2(14):606-608 (1978).

89. Weathersbee, P. S., and J. R. Lodge. "A Review of Ethanol's Effects on the Reproductive Process," *J. Reprod. Med.* 21(2):63-78 (1978).

90. Nora, A. H., J. J. Nora and J. Blu. "Limb Reduction Anomalies in Infants Born to Disulfiram-Treated Alcoholic Mothers," *Lancet* 2(8039):664 (1977).
91. Wilson, J. G. "Embryotoxicity of Drugs in Man," in *Handbook of Teratology, Vol. 1,* J. G. Wilson, and F. C. Fraser, Eds. (New York: Plenum Press, 1977), p. 323.
92. Wilson, J. G., and F. C. Fraser, Eds. *Handbook of Teratology* (New York: Plenum Publishing Corporation, 1977).

422,461,509,511,577,580,582
See also lab design, labeling,
    operation procedures, pack-
    aging, shipping, storage,
    transportation
hazardous materials laboratory
    See containment laboratory
hazardous materials (shipping)
    103-106
health physics   322,323
HEPA filters
    See filters
high hazard chemistry laboratory
    See containment laboratory
high hazard laboratory
    See containment laboratory
high performance liquid chroma-
    tography (HPLC)   12,13,16,
    18,75,77,212,226-231,236,
    443,636,639-641
hoods   6,7,12,16,17,19,35,36,40,
    53,56,59,60,64,67,73,74,84-
    91,94,96,136,145,147,157,
    158,160,511,512,579,580,
    618,620,621
    See also biological safety cabinets,
    glove boxes, ventilation
HPLC
    See high performance liquid
    chromatography
human biological monitoring   247-
    258
human genetic monitoring   247-258
human sperm cells   249,252,253,
    255
hydraazobenzene   132
hydrazine   39,132,165,166,292,
    510,514-517,520,527
N-hydroxy-2-acetylaminofluorene
    39
8-hydroxyquinoline   165
3-hydroxyxanthine   333

IARC
    See International Agency for
    Research on Cancer
IARC carcinogen monographs
    See carcinogen monographs,
    IARC
immunologic assessment   259-288

immunosurveillance   259-288
incineration   13,59,92,96,97,157-
    160,295,296,516,517,522,524,
    525,528,567,570,575,579,580,
    583-592,595,635,636
    See also chemical reactor, degrada-
    tion, disposal, waste products
information, chemical safety 3,4,9,
    11,49,62,70,75,86,96,123,124,
    133,138,144,148,295,296,299,
    302,303,307,310,319,320,386,
    411,513,519,526,527
information retrieval   299-311,320,
    323,385-392,394,396,407,411
infrared spectroscopy (IR)   172,
    194,597
Interagency Regulatory Liaison
    Group (IRLG)   320
International Agency for Research
    on Cancer (IARC)   305-307,
    418,513
intersociety cooperation   313-327
inventory   7,8,62,86,122,135,148
IRLG
    See interagency regulatory liaison
    group

K-region theory   444-448,455,494-
    498

labeling   13,63,68,70,73-75,101-
    127,144,146,148-150,154,577
    See also handling hazardous
    chemicals
laboratory design   1-47,49-77,79-
    99,139-166
    See also handling hazardous
    chemicals
landfill   12,295,516,528,548,579,
    580,637
    See also burial, degradation, dis-
    posal, waste products
laundering contaminated clothes
    85,93
L-region   494,495,497

management of hazardous materials
    1-47,49-77,79-99,129-152,